A HANDBOOK OF THE DRAGONFLIES OF NORTH AMERICA

By James G. Needham and Hortense Butler Heywood

ERRATA

p. 46. Paragraph 4, line 9, for *principle* read *principal*.

p. 68. Key, 2, for *anomalous* read *anomalus*. Key, 3, end, for *10* read *13*. Key, 5, end, for *8* read *11*.

p. 77. No. 21, line 1, for *stripes* read *striped*.

p. 84. Line 1, for *olivaceous* read *olivaceus*.

p. 87, 8. Line 4, for *lineatrifrons* read *lineatifrons*.

p. 116. Figure, names *furcifer* and *villosipes*, transposed.

p. 122. Line 1, for *below* read *above*.

p. 124. Key 8, at end add *more than one cell row*.

p. 135. Table, line 3, for *Ndm. '01, p. 470* read *Walk. '12, p. 181*. Table, *A. sitchensis* omitted.

p. 139. No. 92 for *caerulea* read *coerulea*.

p. 154. Key, 3, for *erroneous* read *erroneus*. Last line same.

p. 167. No. 122 for *allegheniensis* read *alleghaniensis*. 5 lines below for *8* read *7*, twice.

p. 174. Figure, for *yamaskarensis* read *yamaskanensis*. Expanse, for *6* read *64*.

p. 176. Key, line 3, for *one-half* read *one-third*.

p. 178. No. 30, line 5, for *separatiness* read *separateness*.

p. 183. No. 32, line 2, for *blue* read *brown*.

p. 184. Table, line 8, for *Ndm. '03, p. 269* read *Walk. '25, p. 95*.

p. 187. Line 4, for *charadriae* read *charadraea*.

pp. 195 and 196. Figures, names *whitehousei* and *septentrionalis* transposed.

p. 196. No. 163, for *whitehousi* read *whitehousei*.

p. 198. Paragraph 5, line 2, for *lepida* read *libera*.

p. 202. Key, 6, for Cu_2 read Cu_1.

p. 203. Key, 6, Inexact: for nymphs of Leucorrhinia see also table on p. 241.

p. 204. Key, 12, line 3, for *10* read *9-14*.

p. 205. Paragraph 3, line 3, for *Deptera* read *Diptera*.

p. 208. Key, 4, transpose lines 3 and 4.

p. 219. Table, for *quardrimaculata* read *quadrimaculata*.

p. 230. No. 208, line 4, delete ''as shown in accompanying figure.''

p. 231. Table, for *obstrusum* read *obtrusum*.

p. 232. Key, 8, line 1, after male insert *hamule*.

p. 234. Line 1, for *giluum* read *gilvum*.

p. 236. No. 217, after bibliography insert *syn: decisum* Hagen.

p. 237. No. 218, line 13, for *ganiums tems* read *ganium stems*.

p. 241. Paragraph 2, line 2, for *2* read *3*.

Table, the first figure in second column should be 3 throughout.

Table, line 5, for *¼ of 8* read *½ of 9* and for *p. 275* read *p. 375*.

Table, line 6, for *2-6* read *0* and for *½ of 9* read *½ of 8*.

p. 254. Key, 4, for *broader* read *narrower*. Omit No. 241; not regional. No. 242, line 9, delete *00*.

p. 257. Line 9, for *deeply cleft* read *variable*.

p. 264. No. 254, line 7, for *N.Am.* read *U.S.*

p. 277. No. 265, line 4, for *B.C.* read *Ont.*

p. 278. Figure, names *vidua* and *forcipatus* transposed.

p. 310. No. 71, paragraph 2, line 1, for *none* read *one*, delete *as yet* and add *(Walk. '14, p. 353, C. resolutum)*. No. 303, line 3, after *Sask.* add to *N.F.*

p. 314. Table, first two footnotes transposed.

p. 317. Key, 22, lines 3 and 4, includes *E. antennatum* by error.

p. 337. Fig. for *culicinum* read *culicinorum*.

p. 363. Walker 1913, for *45-6* read *45*.

Add the following extensions to distribution range: *Alta.* to the species numbered 16, 153, 154, 304; *B.C.* to 102, 127, 156, 162, 165, 226, 229, 266, 305, 309; *Calif.* to 222; *Colo.* to 222; *Ga.* to 149; *Ind.* to 147, 246, 347; *Labr.* to 156, 162, 165, 166; *Man.* to 8, 14, 33, 34, 48, 162, 229, 309, 333; *Me* to 162, 314; *Mich.* to 40; *Minn.* to 157; *N.F.* to 153, 166, 305, 333; *N.W.Terr.* to 152; *Ohio* to 49; *Okla.* to 350; *Ont.* to 9, 40, 42, 76, 119, 120, 152, 167, 170, 238, 260, 265, 298, 321, 322, 330, 331; *Que.* to 8, 12, 41, 50, 121, 284, 321, 322, 327, 330, 331; *Sask.* to 16, 46, 170.

A HANDBOOK
OF THE DRAGONFLIES
OF NORTH AMERICA

BY JAMES G. NEEDHAM

A HANDBOOK OF
THE DRAGONFLIES OF
NORTH AMERICA

BY

James G. Needham

PROFESSOR OF ENTOMOLOGY AND LIMNOLOGY
CORNELL UNIVERSITY, ITHACA

AND

Hortense Butler Heywood

ASSISTED BY SPECIALISTS IN CERTAIN GROUPS

1929

CHARLES C THOMAS · PUBLISHER

SPRINGFIELD, ILLINOIS
BALTIMORE, MARYLAND

The final preparation of the manuscript of this book was supported
by a grant from the Heckscher Foundation for the Advancement of
Research established by August Heckscher at Cornell University.

PREFACE

This is a book for collectors of dragonflies and for students of their natural history. It aims to furnish a ready means of finding the names of our North American species, and to report some observations on their habits. It contains keys, and descriptions and figures. The keys are guides: the descriptions and figures are together diagnostic. Both adult and immature stages, so far as known, are included.

Dragonflies are unique insects. They are very beautiful. They are wonderfully made. Their amazing shift from aquatic to aerial life at transformation is of absorbing interest. The completeness of their mastery of aerial navigation is a perpetual marvel. Surely these things are worthy of becoming a part of the common intelligence. We have sought to make them better known by providing the means for cultivating personal acquaintance with them.

This is a book for collectors: and we have tried to tell what the collector will want most to know, and there to stop. Data that belong to a treatise rather than to a guide we have omitted. There is elsewhere available (Tillyard's "Biology of Dragonflies") a treatise that deals with morphology, development and world fauna. Bibliography that is elsewhere available (Muttkowski's "Catalog of the Odonata of North America") we have for the most part omitted to save space. After a brief introduction the two things included are: (1) enough description to serve for the recognition of the species, and (2) the best knowledge that is available concerning the habits of the species.

Hence, conciseness and not completeness of description has been our object. Only the more salient diagnostic characters (usually color characters and venation) are stated. Our dragonflies all have a prothorax, though it is rarely mentioned in the description of this book. The ultimate criteria for species are oftenest found in the accessory genitalia, and these we hope we

v

have adequately illustrated. The information that the collector needs first—size and distributional range—is made prominent in our account of each species.

Owing to the insistence of other duties the completion of this book has been long delayed. Many of the pupils of the senior author have contributed materials for it. It is no longer possible to name them all, but the help of all is gratefully acknowledged. In the final putting together of these materials there are those who have aided so well and so generously as to deserve special mention. Mrs. H. E. Seemann assisted in the preparation of materials and drawings. Miss Elsie Broughton helped with the completion of both drawings and manuscript; and most of the drawings of genitalia were made by Mr. C. Francis Byers. Whole sections of the text have been written by the two last named. Dr. P. P. Calvert has very kindly read the galley proofs, and has helped with useful alterations and amendments. He has enabled us to eliminate some errors, but for such as may remain he is in no way responsible.

It is pleasant to be able to say at the end of this long-lagging task that we have met with only courtesy and help from all our scientific colleagues. During all these years peace and progress and good will have characterized the Odonatological Fraternity.

JAMES G. NEEDHAM
HORTENSE BUTLER HEYWOOD

CONTENTS

PART I—GENERAL

PART II—SYSTEMATIC

VIII CONTENTS—Continued

Part I
GENERAL

THE COMMON GREEN DARNER
(Anax junius),

Standing on the cast-off skin from which it has just emerged.

(Photo by H. H. Knight)

PART I. GENERAL

INTRODUCTION

RAGONFLIES are rapacious insects of large size, brilliant colors, and very striking form. They fly by day throughout the summer season about the borders of all ponds and streams and are well known to everyone; especially familiar are those forms that skim over the mirroring surface of still water in tireless flight. Their immature stages dwell in the water, where they are less easily observed. In all stages they are among the more important of nature's lesser carnivores.

The beauty of the dragonfly is that of the sleek, ferocious beast; its agility signifies prowess. There are other insects hardly more beautiful but of gentler habits, that have met with more popular interest and favor; but all naturalists speak with enthusiasm of the sure and graceful flight of dragonflies, and of their glittering metallic adornment. Dr. L. O. Howard in his *Insect Book* rates them next to butterflies as the most beautiful of insects.

Of course the poets have sensed both their beauty and their prowess. It was their color that appealed to Thomas Moore who spoke of them as "beautiful blue damselflies." Rossetti completed a picture of a warm sleepy summer noon with the lines:

> Deep in the sun searched depths the dragonfly
> Hangs like a blue thread loosened from the sky.

Their motions caught Riley's interest:

> And the dragonfly in light
> Burnished armor shining bright,
> Came tilting down the river
> In a wild bewildered flight.

Longfellow had a similar fancy of an armored knight, for he sings in "Fleur-de Lis":

> The burnished dragonfly is thine attendant.
> And tilts against the field,
> And down the listed sunbeam rides resplendent
> In steel blue mail and shield.

3

Their picturesque fitness in natural scenery has been appreciated by certain Japanese poets, as witness these lines gathered and translated by the late Lafcadio Hearn:

> Lonesomely clings the dragonfly
> To the underside of the leaf—
> Ah, the autumn rains.

> O the thin shadow of the dragonfly's wings
> In the light of sunset.

> Like a fleeting of crimson gossamer threads,
> The flashing of the dragonflies.

Amy Lowell celebrates their swiftness with the lines:

> Across the newly plastered wall
> The darting of red dragonflies
> Is like the shooting
> Of blood-tipped arrows.*

There are few more simple or satisfying word pictures than are contained in this couplet by Paul Heyse:

> Ich sitz am Bach, und sehe die Libellen
> Sich fliehen und jagen in der Sommerluft.

The poets of many nations have found inspiration in the life history of the dragonfly, which, grovelling for months in the mud and silt of some stagnant stream, finally, with mighty effort, casts off the nymphal skin to live thereafter as a lord of the upper air, ever on the wing in the golden sunlight.

To the dragonfly are attributed all sorts of malevolent powers. Some of the names in common use testify to this: as "devil's darning needles" they sew up the ears of the truant school boy; as "snake-feeders" and "snake-doctors" they minister to dreaded serpents; while the belief in their possession of a poisonous sting is so widespread that many ignorant persons avoid them as they would wasps or bees.

But there are other pleasanter popular names, such as "mosquito hawks," suggesting a service that they render us, and "damselflies" implying an attractive appearance and personality.

We find an interesting reflection of the popular attitude toward the dragonflies, and a recognition of their "murderous instincts" in the specific names which the older entomologists bestowed upon them. There is a whole series of names connecting the dragonfly with snakes,

* In **Time of War**, p. 17.

somewhat as does the popular nomenclature: *elaps, boa* and *viperinus,* etc. (signifying serpent). One of our common skimmers is *Libellula luctuosa,* the mournful one; another is *L. funerea,* of evil omen, and another is *L. saturata,* gorged (let us hope with mosquitoes). One Sympetrum is *S. rubicundulum,* blood red; one is *S. imbuta,* imbued with blood; one dainty little tropical ruby-spot has an apellation longer than its whole delicate self, of *Hetaerina cruentata,* dyed with blood; while another bears a name that in all ages and countries has been both feared and hated, *H. carnifex,* a hangman or executioner. But there are others with happier names: *Libellula pulchella,* the little beauty, and *L. auripennis,* with wings of gold.

Our knowledge of North American dragonflies has been long accumulating. Many species were described by the early European systematists, Linnaeus, Fabricius, Rambur, Burmeister, McLachlan and others. Earliest in this country was the "Father of American Entomology" Thomas Say, who described many species. Then came Baron Edmond de Selys Longschamps, who spent nearly all the spare moments of the long and busy life of a Belgian senator studying the dragonflies of the world. He laid the basis of our present system. Co-laborer with de Selys was Dr. Hermann Hagen of Königsberg, Prussia. He wrote the first general review of American dragonflies. It was included in his *Synopsis of the Neuroptera of North America* published by the Smithsonian Institution of Washington in 1861. This *Synopsis* came into the hands of Benjamin D. Walsh, an Englishman then residing at Rock Island, Illinois, inciting him to study and make known during the next two years a goodly number of local species.

When Dr. Hagen came to Harvard University he began to assemble in the Museum of Comparative Zoology what he called a "biological collection." This included immature stages, as well as adult dragonflies, and provided materials for studies in ecology and development. It meant that the study of dragonflies should be something more than merely learning the names of species. This gave a great impetus to the study of life histories in America.

After the publication of Dr. Hagen's *Synopsis* no other general work appeared until 1893. Then came P. P. Calvert's *Catalogue of the Odonata of the Vicinity of Philadelphia, with an Introduction to the Study of this Group of Insects.* To this excellent *Introduction* all students of American Odonata in the present generation acknowledge their great indebtedness.

That was followed by other local lists among which were five that were far more than mere catalogs of species with records of distribution: that of Kellicott for Ohio, that of Williamson for Indiana, that of Kennedy for the Pacific States, that of Garman for Connecticut, that of Mrs. Seemann for Southern California, and that of Howe for New England. There have been excellent monographs, also, of lesser groups, among which three are especially noteworthy: Garman's review of the Zygoptera of Illinois, and Walker's monographs of the two great northern genera Aeschna and Somatochlora. For monographic treatment of genera the two last named are models. Our bibliography will give testimony to the contributions of other recent workers.

There is much pioneer work still remaining to be done on the dragonflies of North America. Only one sex is known for a good many species, and there are doubtless new species yet to be described. Partial life histories have been traced for only about half the species, and full life histories for fewer than can be counted on the fingers of one hand. There is boundless opportunity for further study of habits and ecology and distribution. There is a good service to be rendered to education by developing methods for using dragonflies, and especially dragonfly nymphs, as nature study material.

1. THE LIFE OF A DRAGONFLY

The big green darner, *Anax junius* (see frontispiece), is one of our commonest and most widely distributed dragonflies. It is one of the earliest to appear in the spring and one of the last to disappear before the oncoming of the rigors of winter. It sweeps around the lake or pond of its nativity in great circles high above the water, spending in good weather practically all its daylight hours in tireless flight. Often it wanders far, over some country road or upland meadow, when the air of a summer afternoon is filled with flying insects. Its strongly braced and well balanced body, equipped with powerful muscles for operating its great wings is a perfect aeronautic machine, capable of swift, sustained and certain flight.

The warmer the day, the more untiring is its activity. When rain comes, it takes to shelter, usually suspending itself by its feet from the underside of a twig or leaf. After a storm it may sometimes be found clinging to a tree or house, buffeted by the elements, drenched and bedraggled, and for the time being, quite helpless.

It gets out early in the morning. It flies late at night and may be seen industriously gathering the early mosquito long after most other day-loving insects have gone to rest.

It is a handsomely colored insect. Its robust olive-green body has neat trimmings of blue and brown. Its gauzy wings gleam and scintillate in the sunlight. When it does stop to rest, it perches lightly on the top of a bush or twig on its six long, spiny, reddish legs, in an attitude of great alertness. It is easy to find, but not easy to capture, either perching or flying. The collector always knows when his stroke has been successful by the loud protesting rustle of its wings within the net.

The adult life of a dragonfly is short, perhaps a few weeks in duration. Growth having been completed it is mainly concerned with reproduction. Mating begins while the insects are on the wing. It is preceded by a wild nuptial flight, and is followed by the laying of eggs. The female Anax possesses an ovipositor. This instrument is adapted for cutting holes in the stems of aquatic plants. During the height of the season the eggs are usually laid in the stems of growing plants. Early in the spring they are deposited in masses of floating trash and in pieces of dead cat-tail leaves. Sometimes the male accompanies the female when she flies to the pond to deposit her eggs; sometimes

7

she is unaccompanied. Sometimes she inserts merely the tip of her abdomen beneath the surface of the water and sometimes she backs down the stalk which she has chosen, until she is completely submerged.

The eggs are about one twenty-fifth of an inch in length. A close examination of the stems of aquatic plants at the margin of a pond where Anax is abundant will often discover one that shows a double row of punctures, as even and regular as the stitching of a sewing machine. Within are the tiny, yellowish eggs, tucked carefully into the plant tissues.

This represents the only care which the mother gives her young. A very large number of eggs is laid by each female, so that a great many may be destroyed without reducing the standing of the species.

The development of the egg and the hatching of the nymph require about three weeks. When the nymph emerges from the egg it is a tiny, long-legged, spider-like object, scarcely a tenth of an inch in length. It moults many times before reaching maturity. After the third or fourth moult the wing covers appear and increase in size with each successive moult. The nymph grows rapidly, becoming ever more and more powerful and ferocious. It does not hesitate to attack creatures nearly as large as itself, and is a dangerous enemy indeed to the other little inhabitants of the water.

The body at first is pale green marked in a pattern of dark brown in longitudinal streaks. This is a scheme of protective coloration well adapted to conceal it among the stems of aquatic plants which form its chosen lurking place. The depth of coloring varies with environment and age. Directly after a moult the coloring is much paler; at this time, too, the skin is soft and tender, and the nymph is more likely to fall a victim, then, to some one of his relentless enemies. The body of the nymph is smooth and slender; the legs, as befit the climbing habit, are long and fitted with strong tarsal claws.

The lower lip or labium, by means of which the nymph secures its food, quickly, quietly, and cleverly, is a wonderfully fine grasping mechanism. It may be extended with wonderful quickness to a length that is nearly a fourth of that of the entire body. At the tip it bears two lobes that are armed with powerful hooks. When a victim is seized, the lobes shut down upon the body of the captive, and the labium is closed, thus bringing the prey into a position where it is easily torn by the powerful jaws. If the insect thus captured be a large one, the grip of the labium is usually shifted as much as is necessary to enable the nymph to begin his meal at the tail end; slender, soft bodied creatures, such as damselfly or mayfly nymphs are stuffed in just as they happen to be seized—head first, tail first, or even sometimes doubled in the middle. One may often see a damselfly nymph, the major portion of whose body has already been benevolently assimilated by an Anax, while his head and legs, protruding from the jaws of his captor, wave a sad farewell to the watery world of which he has so recently been a free inhabitant.

The appetite of an Anax nymph is well nigh insatiable. It is not dainty in its choice of food; it requires only that the prey be living and moving, and apparently any living thing that it is capable of handling will be devoured. If a number of dragonfly nymphs of various sizes and species be placed in water in a jar or bottle, the smaller ones will gradually disappear, until but one Anax is left.

The Anax nymph is an extremely clever hunter. Its sly, stealthy ways are much like those of a cat. It clings to the stems of aquatic plants, preferably hanging head downward, and conceals itself as much as possible. If some hapless damselfly or mayfly nymph comes near Anax regards it with that air of unconcern with which a cat watches a mouse hole. It does not stir, but watches immovably until the prey comes within reach, then a swift stroke of the labium like the stroke of the cat's paw captures it. Even the alert water boatman may not long escape this sly hunter.

The duration of the nymphal life of Anax has been determined by Dr. Calvert as eleven months. During that time Anax lives contentedly in the pond, eating voraciously, when the food supply is abundant, and fasting expectantly when it is scanty. When the winter and spring have passed and the water is warm under the growing influence of the sun, the time comes at last when the span of the nymphal life is ended and the marvelous change is at hand, which completely alters every circumstance of the dragonfly's life. From an inhabitant of the water it becomes a denizen of the air; from a quiescent creature, clinging for hours quietly to the stem of a water plant, it becomes an aerial sprite, winging its way untiringly through space; from a lover of water and coolness, it becomes a veritable embodiment of light and sunshine. In one respect only, it remains unchanged; its voracity is unaltered, and, as in the water it was the scourge of all living things smaller than itself, so in the air it is no less the dread and terror of the flies and mosquitoes.

The spectacle of the transformation of a dragonfly nymph is wonderful, but though common enough, it is seldom seen. This is because most species transform at night or very early in the morning; and for this somewhat disobliging habit there is a most excellent reason. Fleet and strong as the dragonfly is, just at the moment of emergence from the nymphal skin it is at the mercy of its enemies. Its body, just released, has not yet become hardened and toughened. Its wings, which have been closely folded in the wing cases of the nymph, are tender and easily torn; they are moreover too damp and crumpled to sustain the body of the dragonfly in flight. Consequently it is well that transformation occurs at that period of the day when there is least chance of discovery by enemies.

For some days before the time of transformation the nymph takes no food, but remains quietly clinging to its support, until some mysterious impulse causes it to leave the water and crawl up on a reed or the strong stem of some other plant. It grasps the reed firmly with its sharp tarsal claws; for a fall after the transformation had begun might mean death. When it has established itself firmly on the reed, it remains for some time motionless; after a time slight movements of the head and wings are noticed and then a split appears in the nymphal skin just behind the head. The back of the emerging adult is first drawn through the opening, then the head, the legs and wings and lastly the long abdomen. Even when it is thus quite free from the old skin the insect is extremely soft and helpless, so it remains for a long time clinging to the cast skin, while its wings and body become drier and stiffer. After an hour or so the wings are quite dry and completely expanded and the dragonfly flies away.

It is now a full grown insect and has completed the interesting cycle of its life, but it still has the pale coloring that characterizes the newly emerged insect. Not until somewhat later in adult life does the body assume its maturer tints.

It is now an adult insect and has completed the cycle of its life, but it is still teneral, that is, it still has the pale coloring that characterizes the newly emerged insect. Not until somewhat later in adult life does the body assume its maturer tints, and the chitinous armor harden to its full strength. It must fly and forage and feed before its pigmentation fully develops. Then if it escapes casualties and enemies and lives out the full measure of its days the surface of its armor will grow *pruinose*, developing a whitish bloom: it will become hoary with age.

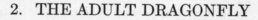

2. THE ADULT DRAGONFLY

FOR the beginner there is no difficulty about recognizing the two principal groups of dragonflies that make up the insect order **Odonata.** These are

Dragonflies proper: Suborder **Anisoptera**
Damselflies: Suborder **Zygoptera**

These are easily distinguished. The Anisoptera are stout bodied and have the hind wings broader at the base than the fore wings. The Zygoptera are slender and have fore and hind wings similar in form. When at rest the dragonflies hold their wings extended horizontally; the damselflies hold them laid together above the back, or at least (in Lestes) lifted obliquely upward. In their immature stages, also, the two groups are equally easy to distinguish as will be seen in the next chapter. We will first discuss some of the characters they all have in common, and then proceed to the consideration of their differences.

STRUCTURES

Body Plan.—The body of a dragonfly is built upon the common insect plan, and its external, armor-like skeleton is composed of the same plates as in other insects. These parts are named in the accompanying diagrams. The most peculiar features of its organization are (1) The head, largely overspread by the enormous compound eyes, and freely movable upon a neck-like projection of the thorax as on a pivot. (2) The large syn-thorax (fused meso- and metathorax), with side plates greatly elongated, slanted forward below and backward above. (3) The wings, of aeroplane aspect, strongly and peculiarly veined and highly efficient. (4) The legs, set well forward and adapted for perching, and not for walking. And (5) The long abdomen, with accessory genitalia in the male developed on the under side of its basal segments.

The head has for its framework a strong chitinous capsule, which is hollowed in the rear for the insertion of the neck, bulged at the front for the bench-like protuberance of the face, and expanded at the sides where covered by the huge eyes. It bears three ocelli and a pair of slender bristle-like antennae in front and the usual mouth parts beneath. Of these the upper and lower lips (*labrum* and *labium* respectively) are exposed to view, and only these will be further noticed in the descriptions of this book. The two pairs of included jaws (*mandibles* and *maxillae*) which show only their toothed tips between

11

the lips (Fig. 1) are of a strictly flesh-eating type. Above the upper lip (*labrum*) the clypeus (in two pieces *ante-* and *post clypeus*) covers the flat central portion of the face. The front rises above it in a more or less shelf-like or angulate prominence. The vertex, bearing the ocelli, and elevated, often into a high prominence at the front, extends backward between the compound eyes; and at the rear the angulate hind margin of the head is formed by the occiput.

The prothorax is small, more or less deeply divided by transverse furrows on the dorsal side into a succession of lobes, the hindmost of which is often hair-fringed or sculptured. The synthorax is large and quite remarkable for the great development of its side plates. By their expansion the tergum and wings are pushed far upward and

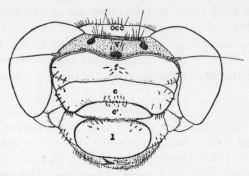

FIG. 1. Face view of the head of the club-tail *Gomphus graslinellus*. *occ*, occiput; *v*, vertex; *f*, frons; *c*, postclypeus; *c'*, anteclypeus; *l*, labrum.

backward, and the sternum and legs, far downward and forward; the episterna meet on the middle line at the front above; and the epimera meet at the back below. By this arrangement the very large muscles of flight are accommodated within. Their pull is vertical, and to withstand it, strong braces are developed along the edges of these chitinous plates: at the lateral sutures infolded edges form internal ridges (not externally visible); and at the front the episterna meet on the median line in a strong and conspicuous ridge that is called the *middorsal thoracic carina*. It ends below in a transverse ridge called the *collar*, and above in a forking ridge, that runs out around the wing roots, called the *crest* (see fig. 27). These are landmarks much used in descriptions.

The backward slant of the side pieces of the synthorax is one of the striking peculiarities of the structure of dragonflies. This slant has been measured in a series of forms (Needham and Anthony, '03) and found to increase progressively throughout the order, as shown by the following figures:

Families	Angle of humeral suture*			Angle of tilt of wing bases**		
	Min.	Max.	Ave.	Min.	Max.	Ave.
Aeschnidae	21	50	38	22	35	26
Libellulidae	29	52	40	18	38	26
Agrionidae	43	64	56	35	61	39
Caenagrionidae	59	72	64	38	62	51

* This is the angle that the humeral suture (the foremost of the three lateral sutures), viewed from the side, makes with the perpendicular.

** This is the angle that a line drawn through the wing bases makes with the axis of the body.

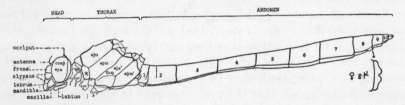

FIG. 2. Side view of the club tail *Gomphus cavillaris*; *sp, sp*, spiracles of thorax; *cox* 1, 2 and 3, basal segments of the three pairs of legs; *eps* and *epm*, episternum and epimeron of mesothorax; *eps'* and *epm'*, same of metathorax; *g pl*, genital plate; *x*, mesinfraepisternum.

The primitive position of thoracic segments was doubtless at right angles to the axis of the body, and, indeed, this condition is still found in the early developmental stages of dragonflies. With the development of large wings and greatly increased wing muscles, these segments are slanted backwards in such a way as to throw the wings far back (in the Agrioninae, indeed, the front pair of wings is placed directly above the hind legs), while the legs are somewhat in front of their normal position. When we consider the resting habits of dragonflies, their momentary pauses and sudden flights, we appreciate the advantage of this adaptation. The legs are thrown forward where they readily reach and grasp the vertical stem and the wings are shifted backward, and tilted, so that their cutting edges are directed obliquely upward, in which position a simple sculling action lifts the body instantly from its support. The dragonfly can thus launch itself all in an instant from a position of rest.

The legs are composed, as in other insects, of two short basal joints (*coxa* and *trochanter*), that make the upward turn from beneath the body; two long joints (*femur* and *tibia*), that meet at the knees; and three short joints and a pair of claws that together form the foot (*tarsus*). In dragonfly legs there is great variation in size, length and development of the spines. Generally speaking, each femur and each tibia has a double row of spines, one on the anterior and one on the posterior aspect, beneath. The spines increase in size and number from the front to the hind legs, and are inclined toward the tarsi. These spines, which at first glance might appear to be intended as weapons, seem to have developed for employment of the legs as a food trap. It is perfectly easy to understand how the "leg basket" operates, but extremely difficult actually to observe the process, because of the lightning-like swiftness of the dragonfly's movements. Kellogg ('05) says of it: "When the prey is come up with, however, it is caught, not by the mouth but by the 'leg basket.' The thorax is so modified and the insertion of the legs is such, that all the legs are brought close together and far forward so that they can be clasped together like six slender, spiny, grasping arms just below the head. Although the catching and eating is all done in the air and very quickly, observers have been able to see that the prey is caught in this 'leg basket' and then held in the fore legs while being bitten and devoured."

The spines on the anterior sides of the fore tibia show an interesting modification which is doubtless for holding the food. Instead of a regular series of long spines such as are found upon the tibiae of the second and third pair of legs, the inferior third of the first tibia bears a series of small spines very numerous and closely set, so as to form a sort of comb. This comb no doubt enables the dragonfly to hold very firmly the small insects which compose his bill-of-fare.

Venation.—The wings are always well developed. Certain wing structures demand particular attention.

Nothing will be more useful to one who is trying to learn the dragonflies than a little knowledge of the venation. Vein characters are very definite. They are plain as the printed page. Nearly all the genera may be recognized from the venation of their wings alone. If at the first glance their rich network appears complicated, half an hour's study of the following diagrams and comparison of them with real wings should enable one to master details sufficient for all purposes of this book.

The principal veins are the same as in other insects. In our figures they bear the following names and designations:

C. Costa	M. Media
Sc. Subcosta	Cu. Cubitus
R. Radius	A. Anal vein

The costa (*C*) is marginal, and coincides with the front border of the wing. It is notched in the middle at the nodus (*n*).

The subcosta (*Sc*) ends at the nodus, and is a concave vein.

The Radius (*R*) is a strong vein that parallels the two preceding, and appears simple; but at its base it is fused with the media as far as the arculus (*ar*), and at the nodus it gives off a strong branch to rearward called the radial sector (*Rs*).* This branch descends by way

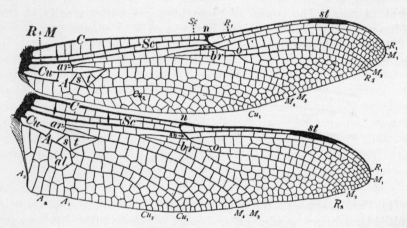

FIG. 3. Wings of *Cordulegaster sayi*.

of *subnodus* (*sn*) and oblique vein (*o*) to its definitive position behind the first two branches of the median vein, and at the point where it bends outward it is connected proximally by a brace, called the bridge (*br*), that appears like its true base, and that joins it again to the median vein.

The media (*M*) is a four-branched vein. At its base it is fused with the Radius as just stated. The fusion is not quite complete. It has been compared to the union of the barrels of a double barreled gun. At the arculus (*ar*) the media descends to meet a crossvein, and then bends sharply outward again toward the wing margin. It gives off to rearward a strong branch (M_1) at its departure from the arculus, and another (M_3) just beyond, and these two branches run parallel to the wing margin. At the subnodus (*sn*) it forks, one branch (M_2) running

* Called *median sector* (Ms) by Tillyard: later, labelled 1R3.

parallel to the radial sector, and the other (M_1) parallel to the main radial stem (R_1).

The cubitus (Cu) is a two-branched vein. Like the median vein, it is strongly zig-zagged. Its base is free and straight to the arculus or beyond. Then it bends sharply to rearward, forming the inner (proximal) side of the triangle (*t*). At the hind angle of the triangle it forks, and its branches arch outward running more or less parallel to reach the hind margin.

The anal vein (*A*) is here treated as a single vein though its branches are perhaps the equivalent of the separate anal veins of other orders of insects. It is convenient to designate them as A_1, A_2, A_3, etc., from front to rear. The course of these branches varies greatly in the different groups, and sometimes in fore and hind wings.

There are three principal transverse joinings of veins together in the dragonfly wing:

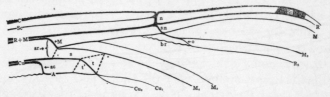

Fɪɢ. 4. Diagram illustrating principal veins and their connections.

(1) The outermost is the stigma (*st*). Two veins (*C* and *R*) are here united by a heavy quadrangular deposit of chitin, that adds strength and weight at the point of greatest impact of the wing against the air.

(2) The middle conjunction is at the nodus, where the subcosta ends in a transverse ridge and a furrow. The ridge adds strength to basal part of the wing, and the furrow gives pliancy to the wingtip, improving its sculling action. The nodus joins two veins (*C* and *Sc*) strongly to R_1 at the front; and subnodus (*sn*), oblique vein (*o*) and bridge (*br*) together join three principal branches (M_1, M_2, and Rs) more flexibly to it at the rear.

(3) The basal cross connection is the most extensive one. It is effected by the bending to rearward of median and cubital veins at arculus and triangle, as already noted, and adjustment of crossveins to meet and support the bends. The triangle is composed of a portion of the cubital vein (the inner side) and two crossveins approximated at their front ends. Then at the hind angle of the triangle the cubitus is strongly joined to the anal vein. Thus strong basal braces are formed involving all the principal veins.

This may seem a bit puzzling at first glance. It long was so to entomologists. The puzzle was solved by studying vein origin. Wing veins develop about the air tubes or tracheae that traverse the wing buds of the dragonfly nymph. Chitin is deposited about these tracheae forming the stiff, rod-like but hollow supporting veins, while the areas between expand and become thin membrane. Crossveins develop late; so that if one examine with a microscope the wing pad of a well

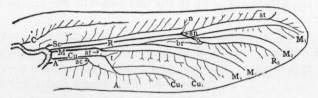

Fɪɢ. 5. Tracheation of nymphal wing of Gomphus.

grown (but not full grown) dragonfly nymph he may see the course of the antecedent tracheae very clearly. The accompanying sketch shows clearly the tracheae of the six principal veins. It shows also how the three cross connections at stigma, nodus and triangle are formed. The stigma is merely a thickening—an area of heavy chitin deposition. The subnodus (*sn*), oblique vein (*o*) and bridge (*br*) are all formed about the base of the radial sector. Arculus (*ar*) and triangle (*t*) are initiated by basal bends in media and cubitus respectively. These bends are very gentle at first and become sharply angulated only in the adult wing.*

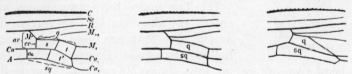

Fɪɢ. 6. Region of arculus and triangle in Zygopterous wings.

Such is the plan of the venation of the dragonflies (suborder *Anisoptera*): that of the damselflies (suborder Zygoptera) differs only in small particulars. The most marked difference is in the cubital vein, which does not bend sharply backward to form a triangle but runs directly outward to its place of forking. There its posterior branch (Cu_2) is offset to the rear and angulated at its junction with the tip of the anal vein. There is no "triangle" in the damselfly wing. Instead

* This matter was discussed and illustrated more adequately by the senior author in Proc. U. S. Natl. Mus. 26: 703–764, 1903.

there is a quadrangle (*q*); and it is the equivalent of both triangle (*t*) and supertriangle (*s*) of the dragonfly wing, as a comparison of the accompanying figures will show clearly. There is also a subquadrangle; and these same figures will show that it is the equivalent of both subtriangle (*t'*) of the dragonflies and the space before that cell extending baseward to the anal crossing (*Ac*).

Such are the principal features of dragonfly wing venation. The lesser details will be taken up in the discussion of the groups to which they pertain.

Genitalia.—The abdomen of a dragonfly is composed of ten distinct segments and a rudiment of an eleventh that is combined with the terminal appendages. The first and tenth segments are shorter than the others. The second and third are swollen to form a more or less spindle-shaped enlargement of the base of the abdomen. In the male dragonfly they bear on the ventral side the unique copulatory organs that are a distinguishing characteristic of this order.

Since the ultimate criteria of species are often to be found in the form of the accessory genital apparatus, it is important to know these parts. They differ so much in the two groups that the suborders are better considered separately; but there are these things in common:

(1) The males have appendages at the end of the abdomen that are forceps-like in action, and that are used for seizing and holding the female. He grasps her by the top of the head (Anisoptera) or pro- thorax (Zygoptera) and leads her about in flight. The two thus speed about together in tandem, or settle together, still in tandem on a stem.

Fig. 7. Diagram of copulatory position, *Aeschna constricta.*(After Calvert).

(2) The males have, also, in a cleft on the ventral side of the swollen second abdominal segment, paired hamules for grasping, and a penis for sperm transference. Previous to copulation the sperm must be transferred from the spermaries, whose ducts open on the ventral side of the ninth segment to a cavity in the tip of the penis. This is done by bending the abdomen downward and forward, bringing the two orifices into apposition.

(3) The female is not so different from females of other orders. She has a genital opening at the apex of the eighth abdominal segment

on the ventral side. In copulation she is swung beneath the suspended body of the male into an inverted position, the reverse of his own, his caudal appendages still holding her in front. Her genital segments are grasped and held by the hamules of the male during the transfer of the sperm.

The form of hamules and caudal appendages in the male, and of the plate that covers the genital opening of the female is shown in many figures on succeeding pages of the book.

In the Anisoptera the caudal appendages of the male are three; a pair of decurved superiors (*cerci*), and a single median upcurved

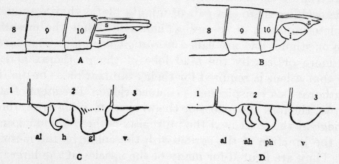

Fig. 8. Diagrams illustrating principal types of male genitalia. *A* and *B*, end of abdomen; *A* in Zygoptera, *B* in Anisoptera; *s*, superior, *i*, inferior appendages.

C and *D*, genitalia of second segment; *C* in Libellulidae, *D* in Gomphinae; *al*, anterior lamina; *h*, *ah* and *ph*, hamules (anterior and posterior); *gl*, genital lobe; *v*, vesicle.

inferior appendage. Between these the top of the head of the female is grasped preparatory to a mating flight. On the second abdominal segment the genital cleft is guarded in front by an *anterior lamina*, and contains one or two pairs of hamules. Folded compactly between the hamules is a triple-jointed penis that belongs to the third segment, and is attached to a rather conspicuous *vesicle* at the front end of the sternum of that segment.

In the Zygoptera the caudal appendages of the male are two pairs: a pair of superiors (*cerci*) as before, and a pair of upcurving inferiors, developed lower down and not homologous with the single inferior of the other suborder. That appendage is represented in this suborder by a low rudimentary protuberance between the bases of the superiors. The genitalia of the basal segments in the male differ chiefly in that the penis belongs to the sternum of the second abdominal segment, and is not an appendage of the vesicle of the third segment: it stands in the place of the penis sheath of the Anisoptera.

Such of these parts as are used in diagnosis of species in this book are illustrated in figure 8.

In all Zygoptera and in many Anisoptera there is an ovipositor developed at the genital opening of the female; and when this is developed, the anterior lamina of the male is cleft to accommodate it in copulation. Females that possess an ovipositor make punctures with it for the reception of their eggs, either in green stems, or in logs or bottom mud.

At the front of the mesothorax in the females of the bluets and other small damselflies there is a pair of minute plates that are much used in the determination of species. These rise beside the mesothoracic spiracle or stigma and are called *mesostigmal plates*. They are overlapped more or less by the hind lobe of the prothorax and are so minute that a lens is required for their examination. On the front of the synthorax is a conspicuous Y-shaped ridge. The stem of the Y is the *carina;* the fork above, beside the wing roots, is the *crest;* the transverse ridge at the front next the prothorax is the *collar;* and on either side at the junction of the carina with the collar lie the mesostigmal plates. They are figured for many of the species of the larger genera of Coenagrioninae in the following pages.

HABITS†

ORE than any other creatures, dragonflies are dependent on their wings for meeting the ends of existence. They not only hunt on the wing, but many of them also eat and mate on the wing, and some of them lay their eggs while flying. The larger and stronger species are among the fleetest of living creatures. Most of their time is spent in pursuit of food or of mates.

In powers of flight they differ, however, enormously. This is most easily seen on a hot summer day at the side of a pond where many kinds of dragonflies and damselflies are flying together. They fly at different levels, somewhat as indicated in the diagram; the big darners highest, the little bluets lowest, the others each habitually and generally at a rather constant level in between. Many of the damselflies move along so close to the surface that it is hard to take them in a net without dipping the water. That it is also harder for big dragonflies and for birds to take them at the lower levels is doubtless the explanation of the habit. Powers of flight in this order of insects seem to vary rather directly with size and strength of wing.

Their "hawking" operations could not escape the notice of that good naturalist, Henry D. Thoreau, and there are frequent brief entries like this one in his Notebook:

Large devil's needles are buzzing back and forth. They skim along the edge of the blue flags, apparently quite around this cove and further, like hen harriers beating the bush for game.*

The game they seek is other flying insects. The most direct service rendered to man by the dragonfly is doubtless in the destruction of many annoying little flies and mosquitoes, some of which, on account

† Other observations will be found under the account of the genera and species in Part II, especially under the following: *on manner of flight,* species numbers 2, 12, 16, 34, 44, 50, 53, 55, 66, 78. 93, 95, 100, 116, 121, 136, 137, 148, 154, 159, 160, 166, 171, 172, 173, 186, 187, 198, 199, 207, 230, 231. 234, 236, 242, 251; *on oviposition,* species numbers 2, 18, 34, 36, 55, 93, 98, 104, 116, 127, 171, 201, 211, 217, 225, 230, 242, 251, 254, 258, 261, 358; *on feeding,* species numbers 7, 116, 277; *on transformation,* species numbers 2, 48, 173, 190, 220, 358.

* Collected Writings: entry for June 10, 1857

of the role which they play in the transmission of disease, are not only annoying but even positively dangerous.   Dr. Robert H. Lamborn thought their destruction of mosquitoes of such value that he offered prizes for the best essays on the artificial rearing of dragonflies as a means of exterminating the mosquito.   The testimony of the prize essays, published in 1890 shows the suggestion to be impractical, although there is no doubt that dragonflies do destroy myriads of the pest.   Kellogg ('05)‡ testifies that

in Samoa and in Hawaii, where the dragonflies are conspicuous by their abundance and variety, they do much to keep in check the quickly breeding mosquitoes.

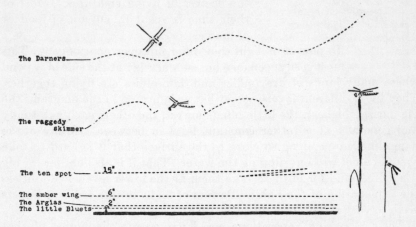

FIG. 9. Diagram illustrating flight levels over a pond.

Apparently, dragonflies are in places used for food of man, for Carveth Wells says (*Six Years in the Malay Jungle*, p. 17):

Once I saw a little Malay boy running about with a long stick, chasing a big dragonfly! I thought he was crazy; but he managed to touch the fly with the end of the stick and catch it.   The stick was covered with sticky stuff like fly paper.   He pulled the wings off the big fly and popped it into a box with a lot more; that night he went home and fried them in oil, and served them for his dinner smothered with onions and shrimps.

The most direct and obvious injury wrought by dragonflies is that of killing honey bees.   In the southeastern United States they cause very serious losses.   They have made queen rearing impractical, because unprofitable, in Florida.   The damage is due to one or two

‡ Numbers thus placed in parenthesis indicate works that are listed chronologically under authors' names in the Bibliography beginning on page 366.

large species that become very abundant. Sometime the air of the bee yard is filled with them, darting about capturing worker bees as they slowly wing their way, heavily laden with nectar, back to the hive. They crunch and dismember the bees body as they fly, dropping detached legs and wings until the ground is sprinkled with bee fragments. Sometimes, when they fly low in the late afternoon, the exasperated bee man lashes them to the earth with willow boughs.*

The chief enemies of adult dragonflies are birds and frogs. Both destroy many at the time of transformation. The destruction of teneral imagoes that may occur at this time is well shown by the observations of Mary Lyon ('15, p. 57) at Ithaca:

. . . . The unusual number of birds along the banks attracted my attention as I came into the meadow. When I walked over to look I saw a great many Gomphine exuviae, and closer examination showed many glistening wings among them. Along the banks of the stream and pond as far as six feet away from the water the ground was strewn with them. In a typical spot I counted twenty-seven cast skins in a space only two feet square. Not a Gomphus was seen on the wing nor were any observed for several days afterward. The sandpipers, bronzed grackles, red-winged blackbirds, sparrows and probably other birds had enjoyed a sumptuous feast as this was evidently the one morning of the season which hundreds of Gomphines had chosen for their emergence.

This is the work of the early bird. Frogs do not remove the wings, but fold them up, wings, legs and body together, and swallow them whole. V. R. Haber, in a study of the food of the Carolina tree-frog (*Hyla cinerea*) found that the blue pirate (*Pachydiplax longipennis*) had been eaten by six out of one hundred frogs examined, and that one frog had eaten two.‡ Ovipositing females must often risk capture by frogs, fishes and watersnakes, when they hover over the water or descend into it for the purpose of laying their eggs.

The birds that most habitually eat Odonata and that capture them in flight are the swifts and swallows. They eat mainly the smaller damselflies. They sweep the tops of the marshes and the edges of the ponds, and gather them in their wide gapes along with mayflies and midges. The bird that is most often seen deliberately selecting individual dragonflies for capture is the kingbird. Perched upon a stake by the waterside, he watches the dragonflies disporting themselves in chase or courtship, and pounces down upon one when he sees a

* Mr. H. D. Grinslade of Wewahitchka, Fla., has furnished specimens enabling us to certainly identify the "bee-butcher." It is *Coryphaeschna ingens.* One big male sent us had his mouth filled with bee fragments, a worker wing protruding from his jaws. The case is not yet proven against any other species.

‡ Journal Comparative Psychology, 6: 206, 1926.

good chance of capture. If successful he may be seen to return to his perch and to strip off its wings before breaking and swallowing it. The smaller hawks, shrikes, cuckoos and flycatchers also eat dragonflies, only less openly.

The bee-eater, *Merops persicus*, is said to capture dragonflies with the sole purpose of using the wings as a lining for his nest.

Spiders capture dragonflies in their webs. Oftenest the litle bluets (Enallagma) are found enshrouded in their silk; but even the big darners are ensnared by some of the orb weavers. The senior author found *Aeschna multicolor* not infrequently in webs of *Argiope trifasciata* in Southern California. Large dragonflies also eat the small ones.

Casualties, also, befall dragonflies. Some get accidentally drowned. Some (oftenest the bluets) fall afoul of the leaves of sundew (Drosera), and are there engulfed and digested. The speeding automobile captures some in the front of its radiator. At times they are destroyed in large numbers by storms and high winds. A wholesale calamity of this sort was once reported by the senior author ('00). Two days after a violent storm from the northwest on Lake Michigan, a change of wind swept back to the west shore vast numbers of insects which had been blown out and had drifted widely on the surface of the lake. The dragonflies averaged 49 to each linear meter of the drift line. They were chiefly the large strong flying darners (Anax and Aeschna), with a few of the skimmers (*Libellula pulchella*) and a very few of the damselflies. While some of the other species of insects survived the calamity and reached shore living, although sadly battered, the dragonflies without exception had succumbed to the buffeting of wind and wave.

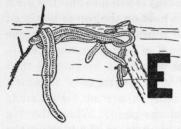

EACH species of dragonfly has its own way of laying its eggs, and what that may be can be learned only by observation, but there are general habits that are shared by groups of species. As already noted the gift of an ovipositor enables some to place their eggs in punctures of plant tissues, while others, lacking it, scatter their eggs through the water strewing them over the bottom. In either case the male may or may not remain with the female after copulation, assisting in the placement of the eggs.

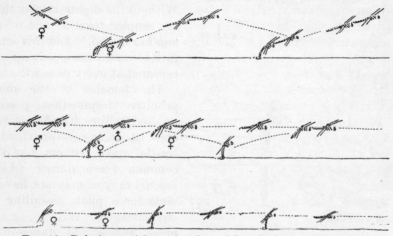

FIG. 10. Relative positions of male and female during oviposition. Above, Celithemis; middle, Tramea; below, Pachydiplax.

The female oviposits alone in the majority of species that lack an ovipositor. This is the rule with the clubtails (Gomphinae). She dashes across the stream, sweeping hither and yon, touching the surface of the water now and then and releasing at each descent a cluster of eggs. Our diagram (fig. 10) illustrates some of the diversity of habit that is found among the skimmers (Libellulinae). The female blue pirate (*Pachydiplax longipennis*) is unattended by the male. She flies along at a constant level, the length of her abdomen above the water, and now and then swings the tip of it down against the surface to wash off her eggs.

The Eponina skimmer (*Celithemis eponina*) is attended by the male throughout the egg laying. He retains his hold on the top of her head for a long time. He seems to direct the course and to assist in the flight as they wing up and down in long sweeping sinuous curves between distant places of contact with the water.

The prettiest performance of all is that of the raggedy skimmer, *Tramea onusta*. After copulation the pair, in a wild flight, come dashing downward toward the surface of the pond. When about a foot above the surface the male releases his hold on the head of the female and moves forward a little at that level, marking time, while the female descends and touches the water with the tip of her abdomen. As she rises, without a sign of effort he seizes her again. Her head seems to slip between his claspers with wonderful precision. Without the slightest delay they are coupled together and off on another bound.* And this separation and recouplement is repeated at every descent.

Fig. 11. *Cordulegaster dorsalis. A,* Nymph with protective coat of algae. *B,* Cast skin. *C.* Female ovipositing. (After Kennedy).

The females of the more primitive forms that possess an ovipositor (Cordulegaster, etc.) lay their eggs unattended by the male. Others, like the common green darner (*Anax junius*) may or may not have a male for a pilot, according to circumstances. But among the more specialized damselflies (Coenagrioninae) the female seems to have been granted by nature a proprietary right to her spouse. When he proposes and she accepts him, and he, rashly or otherwise, clasps her by the thorax placing the tips of his superior appendages in the paired cup-like depressions between her pro- and synthorax, then she draws these parts together, gripping his appendages as in a vise. Then she has him, for life, or at least during satisfactory behavior. He cannot get away.

* The limitations of space do not permit us to indicate in our diagram the high leaps that are made by the pair between tappings of the water surface.

Females of Enallagma and of Argia (especially of *A. apicalis*) are not infrequently found with only the abdomen of a male attached to the thorax. Has the remainder been snapped up by some bird or frog? Did the body break before the grasp of the female would let go?

Some curious egg laying attitudes result when the superior appendages of the male become very short. The senior author once ('03, p. 243) reported this for *Argia violacea* as follows:

This species, like the preceding, oviposits commonly in mats of algae lying at the edge of the water, or covering floating vegetation. On such mats I have frequently seen many females at work side by side, each with a male clasping her prothorax with his forceps, his body sticking up straight in the air, his legs and wings placidly folded. This curious position—standing, as it were, on the tip of the abdomen—is assumed, I think, on account of the greater ease of maintaining the position. The inferior appendages of the male are so much longer than the superiors that were the male to remain with his feet on the ground, when the female depresses her abdomen in ovipositing, the flexion of his body would be extreme, and perhaps uncomfortable. At any rate, he takes the elevated position very philosophically, folds his legs and waits till his spouse gets ready to let him down; and, when she wants to move from place to place, he uses his wings to help her.

The females of Lestes and Archilestes habitually place their eggs in stems above the water, the former in herbaceous stems of iris and bur-

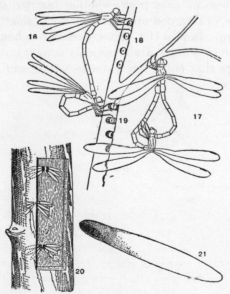

Fig. 12. *Archilestes californica.* *16*, Ovipositing. *17*, In copulation. *18*, scars from oviposition one year old. *19*, Scars 2 years old. *20*, Bark cut away showing eggs in cambium. *21*, Egg. (from Kennedy).

reed (Needham, Amer. Nat. 34: 375, 1900), the latter in the woody stems of willow. Kennedy (15, p. 267 has described the process in Archilestes as follows:

The male holds the female during oviposition. The female draws the tip of her abdomen up until her body forms a loop with the ovipositor between her legs, when she makes in the willow branch a downward thrust. On examination of twigs it was found that no egg is laid in this first downward thrust. Next she partly withdraws the ovipositor, making a lateral thrust on the right side. This for the first egg. A third thrust is made in the same side by partially withdrawing the ovipositor first and aiming it forward of the second. A fourth thrust is made forward of the third for the third egg. Then she twists the tip of the abdomen around, making three thrusts on the left side, the lower thrust first, the upper thrust last. In each of the six lateral thrusts an egg has been laid with the small dark end at the point of insertion. (See figs. 20 and 21.) After such a series of eggs has been laid the female withdraws her ovipositor and the pair back down the branch about one-fourth of an inch and repeat the process. One pair was watched for an hour, at the end of which time the female took longer rests between thrusts and finally ceased ovipositing.

The eggs probably pass the winter in the live cambium tissue of the twigs, for in a twig I kept alive until January 1, 1914, the eggs were still unhatched.

Both dragonfly and damselfly eggs, when laid above the surface of the water, are subject to parasitism. Minute hymenopterous egg parasites find them an easy prey, whether inserted into the stems of iris, as in Lestes, or dropped upon the surface of floating mats of algae as in Sympetrum. Indeed the eggs of Ischnura when placed in stems beneath the water's surface are commonly sought out and parasitized by minute wasps that enter the water as adults and swim through it with their wings.

THE chief instrument for collecting dragonflies is an insect net: and the requirements are, that it should be large and light and strong; large in diameter, so as to sweep a big section of the atmosphere; light in weight, so that it may be swung quickly; and strong, so that it will not break or tear. In this chase, a net is certain to receive hard usage. The complement of the net is, of course, the killing bottle; cyanide, or whatever preferred.

The beginner will soon learn that main strength will avail little in the capture of the big dragonflies. They can fly faster than he can run; they can dodge quicker than he can turn; and they can go where he cannot follow. He must study their habits, and adapt his methods and his strategy to them.

He will probably soon learn by observation that many of the large ones tend to follow a regular beat in their flight, and then he will station himself where they will fly past, and he will wait. He will learn by experience that they dodge best when approached from the front; and then he will keep his net down out of sight until they are passing and sweep them into it by a stroke from the rear. Even then he will sweep the vacant air many, many times; and some of the finest dragonflies will hover about him most tantalizingly without ever coming within reach of his net.

That there is an element of sport in dragonfly chasing is nowhere better brought out than in Kennedy's account ('17, p. 551) of his first capture of a male of *Gomphus intricatus* on the Humboldt River in Nevada.

Until late in the afternoon I saw only two of this small species, and these females, both of which were wild and unapproachable. But about four o'clock in the afternoon I flushed a male from a clump of rose bushes; and with that suspense, which comes to a collector perhaps once a season as he sees a prize of prizes flying away, waited several very long moments, while he decided whether to alight or to fly across the river out of my reach. Indifferent to danger he lit on my side of the river but in the safest place possible, as he chose a bare patch of ground in the midst of a broad area of salt grass. As salt grass at its best is only six inches high there was no cover whatever to aid in stalking him. Resorting to the only antics available, I very slowly approached him on my hands and knees and was greatly relieved when I got close enough to see that he

29

still unmindful of his danger, was busily engaged in scratching his head with his foot. I was more relieved when a moment later I had the net over him, but the suspense was not entirely relieved until I had him in a cyanide bottle, and the cork in tight.

Bits of odd behavior—species idiosyncracies—will be met with afield, while collecting. Here is one, related by E. B. Williamson ('07) from his collecting of *Boyeria vinosa* in upper Ontario. It is

A common species along the streams where its tendency to examine critically every object projecting above the water often makes its capture an embarrassing matter to the collector. More than once as I waited for an approaching male this insect suddenly left the line of flight I had mapped out for it, flew to within an inch of my legs, circled around one leg a time or two, then around the other, then about both, and then quietly resumed its flight along the stream, oblivious to the net which had been frantically fanned all around it.

There are more prosaic ways of getting dragonflies. The high flyers may be brought down with a gun; and if the finest shot be used to load the gun, a fair proportion of usable specimens will be obtained so. Small dragonflies and damselflies that sit on the low grass by the waterside or on the ground may be captured more easily and quickly with a fly-swatter than with a net. This calls for a big swatter on a long, light handle. A light stroke beats them down and stuns them, and they are then picked up, usually uninjured, before recovering.

The foresighted collector will take advantage of times and places of abundance and get plenty of specimens when the getting is good. Easy picking for dragonflies rarely occurs; but sometimes numbers of them can be picked by hand from their roosting places, and sometimes a storm will toss good specimens upon the driftline of a beach.

Specimens may be preserved either dry or in alcohol. If dry—the usual way—they may be either pinned or papered; and the methods in either case are those that are so familiar to entomologists generally that we will not take space to describe them here.*

It is important that specimens be dried quickly before moulds grow and ruin them. No extra precautions are necessary in a dry place; but when the atmosphere is very humid some application of artificial heat may be needed.

* For these methods, see Needham's *Elementary Lessons on Insects*, or any of the larger textbooks of entomology, or better still, consult Williamson's *Directions for Collecting and Preserving Dragonflies for Museum Purposes*, Univ. of Mich. Museum of Zoology, Misc. Publications No. 1, 1916. This embodies the best results of the long experience of a very successful dragonfly collector.

3. THE IMMATURE STAGES

ENERALLY speaking, dragonflies in their immature stages fall into three more or less distinct behavior groups: climbers, sprawlers and burrowers. They are very different in appearance from the adults, and altogether different in manner of life. They have but one habit in common with the adults; they are all carnivorous.

The more active ones climb about in the submerged weed beds or cling to the stems of reeds or to roots. The nymphs of the darners (Aeschninae) and of the damselflies (Zygoptera) are of this habit. These very slowly and stealthily steal, cat-like, upon their prey, with head poised low, and when it is within reach, catch it with a flash. Some of these climbing forms are rather prettily colored in patterns of green and brown.

The more sluggish sprawlers lie flat upon the bottom amid the silt with legs outspread. Protected by their coloration and often by a coat of adherent silt that hides them perfectly, they wait in ambush until their prey wanders within reach. Here in the accompanying figure is shown a nymph which lay still so long that a rapidly growing spray of Plumatella attached itself to the back of the nymph, anchoring it in place. Would a nymph so anchored, when grown, have been able to transform? Some of the most sluggish of the sprawlers such as the nymphs of the belted skimmers (Macromiinae), are among the most fleet and wide ranging of adult dragon flies.

Fig. 13. A nymph of Epicordulia overgrown with Bryozoans.

The burrowers are the nymphs of the club-tails (Gomphinae). They live shallowly buried in the silt and sand of the bottom, with the upturned tip of the abdomen reaching up to the water for respiration. They lie so near the surface that the footfalls of their prey walking overhead, or the wriggling as of blood worms in their tubes, may

31

invite seizure. They have more or less wedgeshaped heads, short thick close-laid antennae, and flattened scraper-like front tibiae. These are all adaptations for getting through the bottom silt.

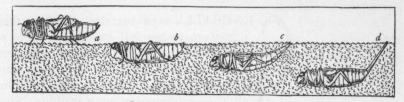

FIG. 14. Sprawlers and burrowers. *a*, Libellula; *b*, Cordulegaster; *c*, Gomphus; *d*, an unknown Gomphine. Drawn by Olive Tuttle (Mrs. J. T. Lloyd).

Some habits intermediate between those of sprawlers and burrowers will be discussed under the subfamilies Petalurinae and Cordulegasterinae.

STRUCTURES

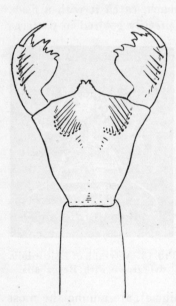

FIG. 15. Labium of *Cordulegaster diastatops*.

Perhaps the most remarkable feature of nymphal anatomy is the labium or lower lip. It is very much elongated, folded upon itself like a hinge at the base of the mentum and then folded backward beneath the head and thorax, the middle hinge resting between the legs. At the front end of the mentum it bears a pair of strong grasping lateral lobes that are variously armed with teeth hooks and spines. It is a grasping organ of altogether unique design. When extended, its full length is almost that of the fore leg. It is thrown out and retracted again with such swiftness that the eye cannot follow it. With it the nymph reaches for a victim, clutches it between the armed lateral lobes, and draws it backward right into the jaws. The hooks and spines hold; the jaws devour; and if fragments are let fall, they are retained on the mentum as on a tray. The labium is finally thrust forward a little and even these fragments are gathered up. This combination of hands, carving tools and serving table is highly efficient.

Two pairs of muscles each side operate the labium; one pair, projector and retractor, lying in the submentum, operates the middle hinge; another smaller pair, extensor and flexor lying in the mentum, swings the lateral lobe.

The jaws are of a distinctly flesh-eating pattern. The mandibles with their Z-shaped sharp chitinous ridges cut the victim to pieces, while the maxillae, shaped like meat forks, turn it conveniently for cutting. So it is made up into pellets and swallowed. These pellets stop for a time in the proventriculus or crop whose walls are lined with chitinous teeth and prickles. This is a chewing stomach where further comminution of the food takes place before it is passed on into the true stomach for digestion.

The structures so far mentioned all nymphs of Odonata have in common, but in the breathing organs we come upon structures in which dragonflies differ markedly from damselflies. Both breathe by means of tracheal gills, but in the dragonflies the gills are numerous and are located inside the body, and in damselflies they are but three vertical gill plates attached at the tip of the abdomen like tails.

The dragonfly gill chamber is a modified portion of the hinder (rectal) part of the alimentary canal. It is set off by a constriction from the part in front that has to do with nutrition, and is enlarged into an oval chamber that half fills the abdomen; the gills hang from the inner walls of this chamber in longitudinal rows. They are minute, thin walled, and very numerous. They are filled with fine air tubes (tracheoles) that are connected with four big air trunks running lengthwise of the body. The walls of the gill chamber are provided with muscles for changing its shape. When it expands, water is drawn in from the rear, bringing fresh oxygen. When it contracts, the water is expelled. The posterior (anal) opening is guarded by the cluster of five spinous caudal appendages which terminate the abdomen. Between these are three little valves that guard the immediate opening. They serve as strainers, partly closing the opening while water is flowing in; they fly open like shutters when the water is squirted out.

The regular expanding and contracting of the abdomen is readily seen in a living dragonfly nymph. The water currents may be watched also if a bit of colored fluid be placed at the end of the abdomen.*

The gills of the damselflies are three flat plates placed edge upward

* As by holding a copying "indelible" pencil there a moment, until the color dissolves. See Needham's *Guide to the Study of Freshwater Biology* for directions for the dissection of the dragonfly gill chamber.

at the end of the abdomen, one median and two lateral. They are generally thin, as befits the respiratory function, but sometimes (Agrioninae) they are thick and ridged lengthwise, and they are very variable in shape and coloration. They develop during early nymphal life, and if broken off before the nymph is grown they are regenerated; wherefore a nymph is often found bearing one or more smaller (regenerating) gills.

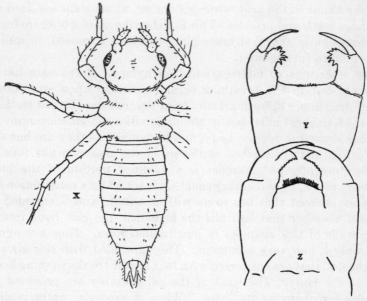

FIG. 16. *Gomphus graslinellus.* *X*, new hatched nymph; *Y*, its labium; *Z*, labium of an old nymph.

DRAGONFLY nymphs emerge from the egg in a form that is retained with but little alteration until they are grown and ready to transform. There are, of course, no wings, nor even wing buds present at hatching. The lateral abdominal appendages (cerci), also, are wanting. The labium, though already developed and ready for business, is often quite different in the details of its armature, as shown in the accompanying figures. There are some characters such as the head tubercles of the new hatched green jacket nymph (fig. 17) (marks of past Macromian ancestral history?) that will be lost with the earliest moultings. The definitive nymph form is assumed after a few moults and while the nymph is still very small.

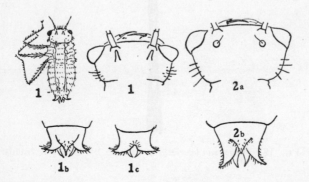

FIG. 17. Nymph of the green jacket, *Mesothemis simplicicollis. 1*, new hatched; *1a*, head enlarged, *1b*, dorsal, *1c*, ventral view of adbominal appendages; *2*, second instar nymph of same.

A detailed study of the form changes, moult by moult, in the nymph of *Pantala flavescens* through the first ten instars has been made by Miss Laura Lamb ('25, pp. 285–312). She has subsequently determined

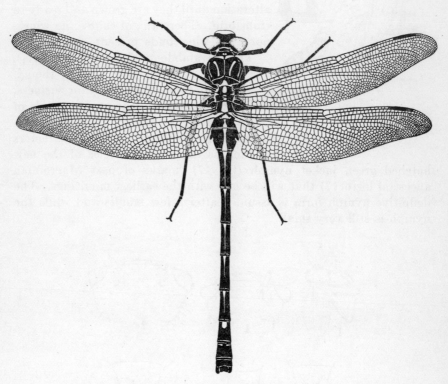

FIG. 18. *Hagenius brevistylus* (drawn by C. H. Kennedy).

that there are two additional instars, twelve in all. From her account we abstract and tabulate the data covering ten points.

Instars	1	2	3	4	5	6	7	8	9	10
Days duration	6	6	6	7	7	7	7	9	11	14
Ant. joints	4	4	5	5	5	6	7	7	7	7
Trs. joints	1	1	1	1	1	2	2	3	3	3
Wings	0	0	0	0	r	i	i	i	i	i
Lat. abd. app.	0	0	0	0	r	i	i	i	i	i
Lat. sp. of 8	0	0	0	0	r	i	i	i	i	i
" " " 9	0	0	r	i	i	i	i	i	i	i
Ment. setae*	0	2	4	6–7	8–9	10–11	10–11	12	13	14–15
Lat. setae*	0–1	0–1	4	5	6	8	8–9	9–10	11	11–12
Length (mm.)	1.4	1.8	2.2	2.8	3.9	4.9	7.3	8.2	10.7	14.0

* On labium. *r*, rudiments. *i*, increasing in size.

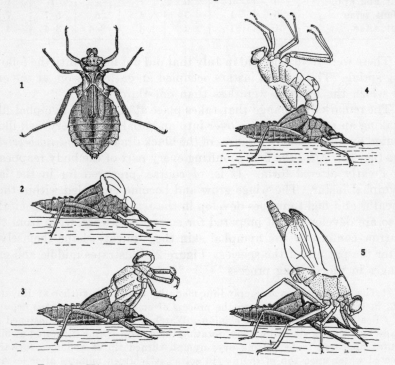

Fig. 19. Hagenius transforming (drawn by C. H. Kennedy).

From this it appears that the wing buds and the lateral abdominal appendages arrive together at the 5th instar: that the full number of segments is attained by the antennae in the 7th, and by the tarsi in the 8th instars: and that the lateral spines appear earlier on the 9th than on the 8th abdominal segment. During the first four instars the nymphs are practically colorless and very small, and after that the definitive characters of nymphal form are rapidly assumed.

Walker has reported ('25, p. 28) the rearing of nymphs of *Somatochlora kennedyi* through seven instars with somewhat similar results, as shown in the following table:

Instars	1	2	3	4	5	6	7
Length (ave.)	1.7	2.2	2.7	3–2	4.2	?	?
Ant. joints	3	3	5	5	6	6	6
Trs. joints	1	1	2	2	2	2	
Wings	0	0.	0	r	i	i	i
Lat. abd. app.	0	0	0	r	i	i	i
Ment. setae	0	1	3	4	5	5–7	7
Lat. setae	1	1	2	3	3–4	3–4	4

These were from eggs laid in July that did not hatch until the following spring. These seven instars occupied an entire season, at the end of which the nymphs were less than one-third grown.

The remarkable change that takes place at the end of nymphal life, making an aquatic creature over into an aerial one, is very well illustrated by Dr. Kennedy's figures of the black dragon, *Hagenius brevistylus* (fig. 19). After the final moulting every part of the body reappears in greatly altered form. It is, of course, prepared for in the last nymphal instar. The wings grow and become crumpled within their sheaths and flight muscles develop in the tense thorax. The genitalia also are developed and prepared for emergence; when freed from the narrow confines of the nymphal skin they quickly shape themselves after the pattern of the species. Figure 20 illustrates middle and end stages in the shaping process.*

* The following is a memorandum made by the senior author at Havana, Ill., in 1896, of observations on the process of emergence in *Gomphus notatus*:

"Boathouse, 5:30 P.M.; sun shining. Watched one emerge. It fastened its claws by swinging its entire body, rotating them, as if boring in; rested awhile; thorax appeared to be getting dry; nymph turned tip of abdomen forward; ejected water upon top of thorax (to soften it?) fifteen minutes after leaving water. Emergence began with a split of the skin which started between the wing pads and extended to head and across between eyes. Head freed first, mouthparts hanging limp; then legs and wings were withdrawn, together with entire thorax; body thus lifted at nearly right angles to the abdomen; held this position 15 minutes, resting. Then it turned forward, fastened its feet, and withdrew its abdomen. Rested until wings were fully expanded; half an hour expanding its wings. Time from leaving water until wings were fully expanded (but not dry), one hour. Water was squirted on top of thorax three or four times at intervals of several minutes before the skin broke open."

The cast skins left behind at transformation are called *exuviae*. Though rent down the back and gaping they preserve perfectly the form of the nymph, and are very satisfactory material for the study of chitinous nymphal structures. Labia and other parts when detached, outspread and mounted, show skeletal structures most clearly. In all life history work the skins should therefore be carefully preserved and labelled to correspond with the individuals that come out of them.

The exuvia are left at transformation somewhere near the edge of the water. The smaller damselflies clamber up the slender stems of emergent water weeds, usually about an inch above the water surface. The club-tail nymphs (Gomphinae), with legs set wide apart, require broad surfaces on which to ascend, such as trees or logs, or more often they transform while lying flat on the sand or mud within a few inches of the margin of the water. The belted skimmers (Macromiinae) go farthest afield to transform, often climbing up tree trunks and fences some meters distant from the shore.

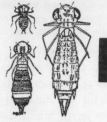

I N COLLECTING dragonfly nymphs the best single tool is a sieve-net which scrapes up the bottom sediment and sifts it at a single operation. Thus it gathers bottom sprawlers and burrowers. Being stoutly built it may be used, also, to sweep standing vegetation, to dislodge and gather up the climbing forms. A good sieve-net costs several dollars.

Lacking a sieve-net, a common garden rake may be used. When there is a sloping shore, and the bottom is strewn with fallen trash (as is usually the case), the rake will draw ashore the mixed mud and trash and nymphs. When drawn out of the water the nymphs begin kicking and squirming, and may readily be found by picking over the rakings.

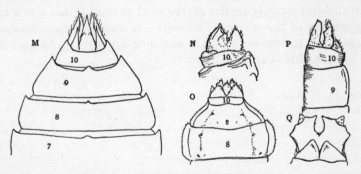

FIG. 20. The reshaping of the end of the abdomen during the process of transformation in *Ophiogomphus carolus*. *M*, nymph; *N* and *O*, adult just emerged; *P* and *Q*, mature adult.

The nymphs move shoreward and climb higher as the time of their transformation approaches; and forms that ordinarily live as sprawlers on the bottom, may at such times be found abundantly in mats of floating pond scum. A dip net of some sort will then be useful. A stout dip net is best for collecting from green, growing aquatic plants.

For rearing the nymphs the best kind of a cage is the "pillow cage" (so called, from its shape) shown in figure 21. It is also the simplest. We have used very many kinds of rearing cages, and have discarded all the others for this one. It is made out of a square of ordinary window-screen wire-cloth. The tools needed are a tinner's shears

(to cut the cloth) and folding tongs (to close the seams). A suitable
size is eighteen inches square, and a square yard cuts four cages. To
make a cage, opposite edges of the cloth are laid flat and
twice folded together (making a tinker's "hem"). This
(opened out) makes a wirecloth cylinder. Then the ends
are cross-folded in a similar manner to close the cage.
One of these endfolds may be opened and closed by hand
for introduction or removal of specimens. The woven
edge should be at the top to prevent pricking fingers on
wire ends. Anyone can make a cage of this sort with his
own hands, in a few minutes.

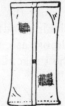

FIG. 21. A
pillow cage.

Such a cage half immersed in the water gives a good
foothold and plenty of room for transformation. If placed a little
aslant, any adults that flutter and fall into the water can crawl up and
out of it again.

There are mishaps in plenty that may happen to rearing cages when
placed out in the field. We believe we have encountered them all.
A few precautionary measures will save valuable specimens. Losses
from sudden changes of water level may be avoided by attachment
of cages to a float. When set in a stream, losses of cages from being
swept away by flood waters may be prevented by anchoring them
with a wire to the shore. Losses from vandals and ignorant meddlers
are most frequent and hardest to control; but we have found that a
very dirty (paint smeared) piece of cloth spread over the cages, hiding
them, will often keep the meddler's hands off them. It is in the field
where conditions are quite natural, and where nymphs can be caged
as soon as captured, that the most successful rearing work can be done.

It can, however, be done indoors. A row of pillow cages may be
set in an aquarium, or in a deep pan of water in a sink, and a trickle
of fresh water from the tap allowed to flow through. Grown nymphs
if introduced uninjured will usually transform under these conditions.

Rearing cages should be visited every morning and the adults that
have appeared should be placed singly with their cast skins in paper
bags (small grocer's bags are excellent), and left there until their color
are well developed and their chitin is hard; else pale and shrivelled
specimens will result.

Most of the larger dragonflies transform very early in the morning.
By searching the shores at daybreak, many of them may be taken in
transformation. Teneral adults and the skins from which they have
just emerged may be found together. Sufficient material for identify-
ing nymph and imago may thus be obtained very easily. Each limp

creature should be bagged with its own cast skin and kept alive to color and harden.   The two should then be pinned or papered together.

Only the early-rising entomologist may avail himself of such easy picking, but there is another way, sometimes very successful and almost as easy, and more congenial to sleepy-heads—a way in which the dragonflies may be induced to cage themselves, cast skins and all.

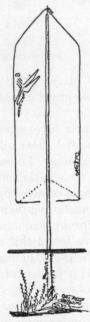

At the height of the season of transformation, every dragonfly collector has seen some bed of water weeds teeming with dragonfly and damselfly nymphs with only here and there a stem projecting above the water surface, and every emergent stem piled high with cast skins. When the nymphs are all moving towards these vantage points for transformation, if the projecting stems be all cut off below the surface and removed, then they will go to any other projecting thing that offers. If a stick be thrust in the bottom, they will climb up the projecting end of that. And if a trap like the one shown in figure 22 be placed on the top of the stick, they will enter it on transformation and there await the arrival of the collector.

This cage is merely the pillow cage described above, with one end left open. The lower end, instead of being closed is slit lengthwise in half a dozen segments an inch or more deep and the segments are bent inward horizontally to form a shelf around the lower border. This shelf is to keep a fluttering imago from falling out after transformation. If it falls, it will alight on this shelf and climb up again. Between the inner edge of the shelf

FIG. 22.
Automatic
rearing cage.

and the stick there must be left enough room for the ascending nymph to climb into the trap. The wire brace from stick to cage is to prevent dislodgement of the latter by wind. The upward inclination at the middle avoids interference with the ascent of the nymphs. A pin in the top end of the stick keeps the top of the cage in position. Such a cage was used very successfully by the senior author at Laguna Beach, California.

4. THE EGGS

The eggs of dragonflies are very numerous, especially those of dragonflies that drop their eggs at random in the water. The senior author once obtained 5200 eggs from an ovipositing female of *Gomphus externus* that had already deposited a part of her stock. They are less numerous when carefully bestowed in punctures of plant stems, where they are less liable to be smothered by silt. They differ in shape also according to the manner of oviposition. Eggs dropped free are in general oblong oval; eggs inserted into plant stems are much more slender and elongate.

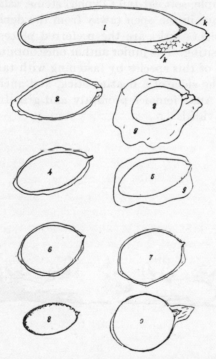

Fig. 23. Eggs. *1. Anax junius* (line *k. k.* indicates depth of insertion into cat tail. *2. Hagenius brevistylus. 3. Gomphus descriptus. 4. Cordulia shurtleffi. 5. Plathemis lydia. 6. Leucorhinia glacialis. 7. Celithemis eponina. 8. Perithemis domitia. 9. Tramea lacerata.* (*g.* indicates gelatinous envelope).

It is the Clubtails (Gomphinae) and the Skimmers (Libellulidae) that scatter their eggs; and it is easy to get the eggs of these if one can

43

capture a female while ovipositing. If she is held by the tips of her
closed fore wings, leaving the hind wings free to flap, and the tip of
her abdomen dipped repeatedly in the surface of a tumbler full of
water, she will usually freely liberate her eggs. She will drop them a
dozen or so at a time and they will at once descend through the water,
tending apart as they go, to scatter over the bottom. They are white
at first, but they quickly gather a covering of adherent silt, and become
quite undiscoverable in a pond.

The eggs of other groups are best obtained by collecting the stems
and leaves in which they have been thrust by the ovipositor of the
female. It is possible to have fresh eggs "laid to order" by supplying
ovipositing females with their favorite places and positions for egg
laying. For example, soft cat-tail (Typha) stems, aslant at the surface
and placed well out in the open (away from the denser growth of the
shores where dangers lurk) are the preferred places of *Anax junius*
females for ovipositing. The junior author once obtained an abundance
of fresh-laid eggs of this species by fastening with tacks a few cat-tail
stems aslant to the sides of a floating stick, and anchoring it well out
in a pond. The Anax females promptly and gratefully accepted the
conveniences provided.

5. DRAGONFLIES AND FISH CULTURE

The nymphs of Odonata are strictly carnivorous. This means that, directly or indirectly, they are competitors with the fishes for the common food supply of the water. They belong to the consuming class. They are not primary producers of flesh. They are themselves eaten by fishes, to be sure, and under certain conditions of abundance they may be important in the food supply*; but their production involves an additional turnover of the flesh that herbivores create, and from the economic point of view, this is wasteful. Whether the waste is justifiable in practice remains to be demonstrated.

That the larger dragonfly nymphs habitually eat very young fishes is well known to fish culturists. The following letter communicated by Professor Cockerell (*Ent. News*, 30: '19) furnishes good evidence. It was written by Mr. Frank Springer from the Abbott Ranch, Rito de los Frijoles, N. Mex., and concerns the nymphs of the Western Biddy, *Cordulegaster dorsalis*:

I am sending you some beasties, that I should like to know more about. They are highly predacious devils, and I first discovered them in the act of seizing some of a lot of young trout which I was placing in the brook here. The bug lies buried in mud or sand, and in shallow parts of the stream where the current is not very swift, with only his eyes projecting. When a little fish (about an inch long) comes wiggling along close enough over the bug, he snaps, projecting his formidable mandibles and the shovel-like part below them for quite a distance to the front, and catches the fish by his wiggling tail. By simulating the wiggling motion of a fish with a knife blade, I could induce the bug to snap at it, and thus saw the motion several times. . . . . I found the creatures quite numerous in the shallow, quieter waters where I was planting the young fry, and apparently they constitute a rather serious menace to the stocking of the stream, as they infest the shallow places, while the deeper water is dangerous on account of the older fish. I found that the trout eat these bugs to some extent as in several instances they were contained in the stomach; and they are readily taken when offered as bait.

We have as yet no measure of the losses thus occasioned, but where large dragonfly nymphs become abundant these are doubtless considerable.*

* Wilson ('20) has made the best possible argument for their economic value.
* Here are some extemporaneous remarks by the Fish Warden of Kansas, quoted in the *Trans. Amer. Fisheries Soc.*, 56: 62, 1926:
"The dragonfly has an apparatus that he shoots out ahead of his body, like a snapping turtle; he grabs the young fish right in the stomach, and the result is that the fish dies. We have had large numbers of fry killed by the larvae of dragonflies, which, as you know, attain a considerable size in our country. The dragonfly may be classed among the vermin of the ponds, and he certainly wrecks havoc among the fry when there is nothing to protect them."

NOTES INTRODUCTORY AND EXPLANATORY TO PART II

The remainder of this book is a condensed account of the North American species of Odonata, with brief diagnostic descriptions and figures, and with all that is known about their habits. Here we offer a few suggestions that are intended to aid the beginner in its use.

Confusion of names:—The reader who would make use of the literature cited in this book (if unacquainted with the intricacies of zoological nomenclature) will need to know two things:

1. That the older authors used fewer and more inclusive group names. The tendency has been and is to multiply subdivisions, creating new families, subfamilies and genera, and to name them all.

2. That the Law of Priority adopted by the international zoological congress required the restitution to present day use of older names, even to the displacement of many that had obtained general currency. This law was first applied to the whole order by W. F. Kirby in his Catalogue of the Neuroptera-Odonata in 1890. Its application wrought great confusion in our literature through the transfer of names from one group to another. For example, the family name Agrionidae was long applied to a different family from that which the Law of Priority demands that it shall designate. The principle sources of such confusion are the following:

Names used by the older authors and by non-conformists		Names used by others since Kirby
Calopteryx, which equals		Agrion, whence
Calopteryginae	"	Agrioninae, and
Calopterygidae	"	Agrionidae.
Agrion, which	"	Caenagrion, whence
Agrioninae	"	Caenagrioninae, and
Agrionidae	"	Caenagrionidae.
Diplax	"	Sympetrum
Aeschna*	"	Aeshna
Progomphus*	"	Gomphoides
Gomphoides*	"	Negomphoides
Herpetogomphus	"	Erpetogomphus
Hoplonaeschna	"	Oplonaeschna

* We follow the older usage here.

46

Citations of species.—Under each species we cite:

(1) The original description.

(2) The page in Muttkowski's *Catalogue of the Odonata of North America** (Milwaukee, 1910) whereon other citations may be found.

(3) Descriptions and additions to knowledge made since the publication of that Catalogue.

(4) Omissions from that Catalogue, and amendments.

All these citations are by the numbers corresponding to the years of publication as indicated in the list of papers beginning on page 359.

Genera and species have been numbered, and all these numerals have been assembled on a single page at the end, to serve the collector as a concise checking and exchange list (p. 366).

For the convenience of the user, size and distribution are condensed to a single line at the head of each description, and both are stated broadly. Color is used for easy marks of guidance, venation for positive recognition of the groups, and figures of genitalia are given where needed, for criteria of species. Only experience will enable one to judge how much latitude must be allowed for variability in all these, especially in color and size. Colors fade with age, greens becoming yellow, and blues discoloring to black; they also vary in extent according to the age and condition of the specimen, and descriptions must be interpreted with some judgment and some discernment as to the trend of patterns.

Binomials only.—A name is merely a name and not a treatise on relationships: hence our decision that, if a group of individuals is distinct enough to bear a name, that name shall be a binomial.

ABBREVIATIONS

Beauv., Beauvais	*McL.*, MacLachlan
Brim., C. S. Brimley	*Mrtn.*, R. Martin
Brtn., Elsie Broughton	*Mtk.*, R. A. Muttkowski
Burm., H. Burmeister	*Ndm.*, J. G. Needham
Calv., P. P. Calvert	*Prov.*, Provancher
Charp., Charpentier	*Ramb.*, P. Rambur
Ckll., T. D. A. Cockerell	*Scud.*, S. H. Scudder
Dav., W. T. Davis	*Selys*, Baron de Selys
Fabr., J. C. Fabricius	*Smn.*, Marian Seeman
Garm., P. Garman	*Walk.*, E. M. Walker
Hag., H. A. Hagen	*Whed.*, A. D. Whedon
Hrvy., F. L. Harvey	*Whts.*, F. C. Whitehouse
Holl, Holland	*Wils.*, C. B. Wilson
Klct., D. S. Kellicott	*Wmsn.*, E. B. Williamson
Kndy., C. H. Kennedy	*Wstwd.*, Westwood

* For sale by Milwaukee Public Museum: price $1.25 postpaid.

PART II.
SYSTEMATIC

PART II. SYSTEMATIC

The two suborders of Odonata have already been distinguished on page 11. We now proceed with their further analysis.

1. SUBORDER ANISOPTERA

Dragonflies

Insects of rather robust stature. Eyes convergent or touching on the top of the compact head. Wings held horizontally in repose. Hind wings broader at base than are the fore wings. Triangle and supratriangle and membranule present. Males with a single median inferior appendage at end of abdomen. Females with or without an ovipositor.

KEY TO THE FAMILIES

Adults

1 Triangles about equally distant from the arculus in fore and hind *(See fig. 5, p. 17)* wing and similarly shaped.................**Aeschnidae**, p. 53
   Triangles nearer the arculus in the hind than in the fore wing and of different shape...................**Libellulidae**, p. 161

Nymphs*

1 Labium flat, or nearly so, without raptorial setae (except in Cordulegaster, fig. 15)....................**Aeschnidae**, p. 53
   Labium mask shaped or spoon shaped; when closed covering the face up to the base of the antennae; armed within with raptorial setae.................................**Libellulidae**, p. 161

* Some additional data on the nymphs of the eastern species will be found in Garman's ('27) paper on the dragonflies of Connecticut, which came to hand after our tables for nymphs had been set. That paper is cited under each of the species that Garman treated.

There are seven principal groups of North American dragonflies, whose most available diagnostic characters are set forth comparatively in the following table:

Diagnostic Characters of the Subfamilies of Anisoptera

Name	Eyes above	Tri- angles[1]	of H.W.[3]	Brace vein to stigma	Bisector of anal loop	Lat. car. abd.[4]	Auricles.[5]
AESCHNIDAE							
Petalurinae	well apart	alike[2]	far out	present	absent	variable	present
Gomphinae	well apart	alike[2]	far out	present	absent	absent	present
Aeschninae	meeting	alike	far out	present	absent	present	present
Cordulegast- erinae	touch- ing[2]	alike	far out	absent	absent	absent	present
LIBELLULIDAE							
Macromiinae	meeting	different	nearer	absent	absent	present	present
Corduliinae	meeting	different	opposite	absent	present	present	present
Libellulinae	meeting	different	opposite	absent	present	present	absent

[1] Of fore and hind wings.
[2] Or nearly so.
[3] In relation to arculus.
[4] Lateral carinae on abdomen.
[5] On side of second abdominal segment of male; notching of inner margin of wings goes with presence of auricles.

Diagnostic Characters of Dragonfly Nymphs

Groups	trs. j.	ant. j.	labium	m. lobe	lat. set.	ovp. ♀
Petalurinae	3–3–3	7[6]	flat	entire	absent	absent
Gomphinae	2–2–3	4[6]	flat	entire	absent	absent
Aeschninae	3–3–3	7[7]	flat	cleft	absent[8]	present
Cordulegasterinae	3–3–3	7[7]	mask	cleft	present	present
Libellulidae	3–3–3	7[7]	mask	entire	present	absent

The successive columns show the number of tarsal joints on fore, middle and hind tarsi, and of antennal joints; the shape of the labium, whether flat or mask shaped, covering most of the face, and whether cleft at the apex of the median lobe or not; also, whether there is a row of definite raptorial setae upon the upper edge of the lateral labial lobe; and finally, whether there is an ovipositor developed underneath the apical abdominal segments of the female nymphs.

[6] Terminal joints broad.
[7] Terminal joints slender, setaceous.
[8] Except in Gynacantha.

FAMILY AESCHNIDAE

KEY* TO THE SUBFAMILIES

Adults

1 Stigma with a brace vein at its inner end.....................2.
  Stigma without brace vein at inner end..**Cordulegasterinae,** p. 152
2 Fore wing, anal vein apparently forked before the triangle......
  ....**Petalurinae,** p. 53
  Fore wing, anal vein extends direct to hind angle of triangle......3.
3 Eyes widely separated on top of head. ....**Gomphinae,** p. 58
  Eyes meeting on top of head...............**Aeschninae,** p. 123

Nymphs

  Labium flat, or nearly so...................................2.
  Labium spoon shaped...............**Cordulegasterinae,** p. 152
2 Tarsi 2-2-3 jointed; antennae 4 jointed; burrowing nymphs
  ....**Gomphinae,** p. 59
  Tarsi 3-3-3 jointed; antennae 7 jointed......................3.
3 Antennae thick...........................**Petalurinae,** p. 54
  Antennae setaceous........................**Aeschninae,** p. 123

* It is assumed that the user of this Handbook has some elementary knowledge of insects; but if not, the parts are named (so far as needed) on the figures of the preceding pages; terms not so named will be found in any good English dictionary. He should know that insects, like other animals, are grouped successively into Orders, Families, Genera, and Species; that by common consent Family names end in *idae* and subfamily names in *inae*; and that in order to use a "key" for determining specimens he has only to choose between the alternatives offered and follow the numerals in the margin to the destination indicated.

SUBFAMILY PETALURINAE

These are large, hairy dragonflies of obscure grayish coloration. The eyes are widely separated on the top of the head. The labium is divided at the tip by a median cleft. The triangles of fore and hind wings are similar in form and nearly equilateral. In the fore wing the anal vein appears as if forked before the triangle. The stigma is long and narrow, with a well developed brace vein at its inner end.

The nymphs, so far as known, are rough, angular, thick-set, hairy creatures that live in the mud of bogs.

53

KEY TO THE GENERA

Adults

1   Vein M 1–3 (upper sector of the arculus) springs from the slanting upper end of the arculus; triangle of the hind wing not divided by a cross-vein: no intercalary sectors running down to the wing margin in the two areas between veins M2, M3 and M4. Thorax black spotted with yellow..............**Tanypteryx.**

Vein M 1–3 springs from near the middle of a perpendicular arculus; triangle of the hind wing traversed by a cross-vein. There are well developed intercalary sectors in the marginal spaced between veins M2, M3, and M4; thorax yellow, striped with black...................................**Tachopteryx.**

The nymph is known for but one of our species, *Tachopteryx thoreyi*; it is figured on page 60.

The group is represented in our fauna by but two genera, each with a single species, one Eastern, one Western. It is much more abundantly represented in antipodean regions (Chile and Australia) and it was a dominant group in past geological times, as evidenced by abundant fossils.

1. TANYPTERYX Kennedy

Includes the following species, and another, *T. preyeri*, in Japan.

1. Tanypteryx hageni Selys

The Western Grayback

Selys '79, p. 68: Mtk. Cat. p. 74: Ndm. '03, p. 739 (fig.): Kndy. '17, p. 508.

Length 55 mm. Expanse 74 mm.   **Nev. Wash. Calif.**

This is a large blackish species, rather conspicuously spotted with yellow. Face and occiput brown.   Front of thorax black, with two upward-pointing yellow triangles just above the collar, and two smaller subtriangular spots just below the crest. Sides of thorax black with two pairs of rather large ovoid spots, the first pair behind the humeral suture, the second smaller pair behind. Legs black. Wings hyaline but with a slightly brownish tinge. Abdomen black with paired submedian dorsal yellowish spots on segments 2 to 7, slender and sinuous on 2, broader, but diminishing in size on 3 to 7. Segments 8 and 9 black. Appendages black, with a pale spot on the sides of the superiors of the male at base.

Nymph unknown.

2. TACHOPTERYX Selys

These are big, gray dragonflies of rather local distribution.   The triangle of the fore wings is nearly equilateral, that of the hind wings has its outer side longest and angulated at a point whence springs a trigonal supplement. There are a number of supernumerary sectors springing from vein Rs and M4, and running rearward to the wing margin.

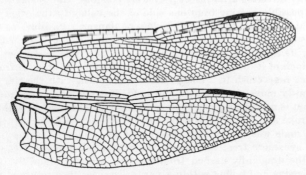

FIG. 24. Wings of *Tanypteryx hageni*.

2. **Tachopteryx thoreyi** Hagen

The Eastern Grayback

Hag. '57, p. 373: Mtk. Cat. p. 75: Davis '13, p. 18: Kndy. '17, p. 190 (Figs): Howe '17, p. 24: Howe '23, p. 126.

Length 78 mm. Expanse 106 mm.   Eastern U. S.

This white-nosed, gray, archaic-looking dragonfly, has a hairy thorax that is striped, and an abdomen that is ringed with black. The carina is solid black but has no closely bordering stripes. A diffuse black stripe overlies the humeral suture and turns up at its lower end to rearward, ending just before the spiracle. Another similar stripe covers the third lateral suture, likewise turned rearward at its lower end in a long subparallel blackish mark that reaches to the base of the abdomen. The legs are black. The wings are hyaline, with black stigma. The abdomen is mostly yellow on the basal segment, mostly yellow above and black on the lateral margin on 2 to 7, with a small spot on the anterior half and a large quadrate one on the posteri or half of each of these segments and with both broadly on successive segments, connecting laterally with the black of the side margins on 6 and 7. Pale areas reduced to small basal spots on 8 and 9, and 10 and appendages wholly black.

Davis ('13, p. 18) says of this dragonfly that it is often found resting on the trunks of trees where, owing to its gray color it can hardly be detected.

Williamson ('00, p. 398) thus describes the habitat and habits of this species, as found by him in a swampy tract, an acre or two in extent, in a small valley in western Pennsylvania:

In this valley a mile in length, closed in by its wooded sides and cut by the small stream which wanders through it, *Tachopteryx* seemed to be at home. Oftenest we found them resting on the rail and board fences which separated the woodland from the open fields. Sometimes they were on logs or trees or clinging to a twig; always in the sunshine and in an open place, where sudden dashes in any direction after insect prey were possible. Rarely one was seen over the fields, possibly passing from one side of the valley to the other with swift, strong flight. At rest, they seem careless of danger. Possibly, as undisputed insect lords of the valley, they have grown to fear nothing. One will hang on a fence post, its abdomen pressed against the wood. The insect net is brought within an inch of it, but it never moves. To attempt to brush it from the post into the net may crush it. You touch the abdomen with the rim of the net. The dragon-fly moves impatiently and holds its abdomen away from the post. Then the net is moved up along the post till the abdomen hangs within the ring. A quick stroke and the thing is done.

Once a male was seen within two feet of the ground, clinging to the trunk of a small sycamore tree; the writer was within half a dozen feet of the tree. Suddenly the dragon-fly dashed from the tree, seized a crane fly (numbers of these were rising and falling within a yards distance) then returned to the tree, alighting a little higher than its former resting place. This was repeated several times, till the dragon-fly was resting ten or twelve feet from the ground. Each trip was made with great swiftness and vigor.

The nymph of *T. thoreyi* was described by E. B. Williamson ('01), from whose plate our figure is taken. It has a length of 38 mm. It will be readily recognized and distinguished from all other nymphs in our fauna by the breadth of the segments of the 7-jointed antennae. The shape of the labium and of its median cleft, and by the angularity of the abdominal segments.

The nymph was found by Mr. D. A. Atkinson in a boggy spot in a small tributary to the Allegheny River. He saw the nymph clinging to the trunk of a tree, about two feet above the mud from which it had recently crawled. The mud which covered it was not yet dry. This was about 10 A.M. Placed in a box the nymph climbed up one side to a height of about eighteen inches, and the imago emerged at 5 P.M. In the boggy spot where the nymph was collected, at that time the only surface water was that which was retained in small depressions, such as the tracks of cattle, among the roots of the sedges and grasses. On July 15, 1900, Mr. J. L. Graf observed another female ovipositing in this same swale. She alighted among the dense grasses and placed the eggs among the roots or in wet decaying vegetable matter above the surface of the water. She would raise and lower her abdomen eight or ten times in one place, then fly to another spot. The time was between 10 and 11 A.M. On June 23, 1900, at Ohio Pyle, Mr. Graf discovered still a third female of this species ovipositing. A mere thread of water flowed along the railroad track from several small springs. The bed of this small stream was composed of cinders and sand. The dragonfly alighted in the grass near this stream and placed her eggs in a small depression in the cinders. This depression contained not more than a tablespoonful of water.

This species appears among the earliest dragonflies of the season in the South. It was found by the Senior author in early April at Rock Bluff on the Appalachicola River in West Florida. The place was near the Torreya Field Station of the University of Florida. Adults were resting on the trunks of the trees, or making short foraging sallies across the sunny openings between the trees, in a little nook at the mouth of a rill where it joins the great muddy river. A number of specimens were taken, but no egg laying was observed. Probably this species flies and forages a long time before the eggs are matured.

Subfamily GOMPHINAE

The Club-tails

Large dragonflies of low-perching habits and rather bright coloration, usually in a pattern of alternating blackish and greenish* stripes. Eyes widely separated on top of head. Tip of labium entire. Stigma broad, and with a brace vein at its proximal end. Females with no ovipositor, but with a small subgenital plate.

In the descriptions which follow the blackish stripes of the thorax will be designated by the numbers that they bear in figure 27.

This is a large group of mainly stream-inhabiting forms. The adults fly about the shores in sallies from one resting place to another. They

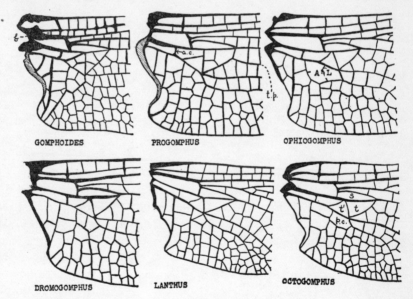

GOMPHOIDES   PROGOMPHUS   OPHIOGOMPHUS

DROMOGOMPHUS   LANTHUS   OCTOGOMPHUS

FIG. 25. Wing bases. *a.l.*, anal loop; *t.p.*, trigonal planate; *b*, basal subcostal cross vein; *ac*, anal crossing; *t*, triangle; *t'*, subtriangle; *s*, supratriangle; *p.c.*, first post anal cell.

squat oftenest flat upon the bare ground, or on some rock projecting from the water. The males fly more constantly than the females, coursing the banks in search of food and mates. The females in their

* The greens fade to yellow in old museum specimens.

egg laying are unattended by the males. They move slowly above the water, descending to strike the surface at irregular intervals, liberating a score or more of eggs at every stroke. In copulation the pairs seek the shelter of shore vegetation. Some of the larger forms hang up in the tree tops.

The nymphs of this group are burrowers in bottom mud, sand and sediment. They are at once distinguishable by the wedge-shaped form of the head, the thick four-jointed antennae and the two-jointed front tarsi. The tips of the front tibiae are more or less flattened and hooked for burrowing. Their legs being scarcely opposable, they do not climb up slender stems at time of transformation, but lie flat upon the sand of the shore or sprawl over mats of grass or climb a little way up on broad rough surfaces, such as tree trunks.

KEY TO THE GENERA

Adults

1 Fore wing, nodus beyond the middle of the wing and basal subcostal cross vein generally present........................2.

Fore wing, nodus at the middle of the wing and basal subcostal cross vein absent..5.

2 Anal loop present...3.

Anal loop wanting.......................................4.

3 Triangle short, outer side nearly straight, not at all sigmoid ....**Cyclophylla,** p. 65

Triangle long, outer side with sigmoid curvature..............
....**Gomphoides,** p. 63

4 Hind wing triangle with outer side nearly straight; trigonal planate weak...............................**Aphylla,** p. 64

Hind wing triangle with outer side angulate; trigonal planate well developed...........................**Progomphus,** p. 62

5 Triangles with a cross vein; anal loop of four cells **Hagenius,** p.65

Triangles open; anal loop of fewer cells or wanting.............6.

6 Anal loop semicircular, of three cells......**Ophiogomphus,** p. 67

Anal loop indistinct, or wanting.............................7.

7 Hind wing with anal crossing distant from second cubito-anal cross vein by less than its own length......................8.

Hind wing with anal crossing distant from second cubito-anal cross vein by more than its own length....................10.

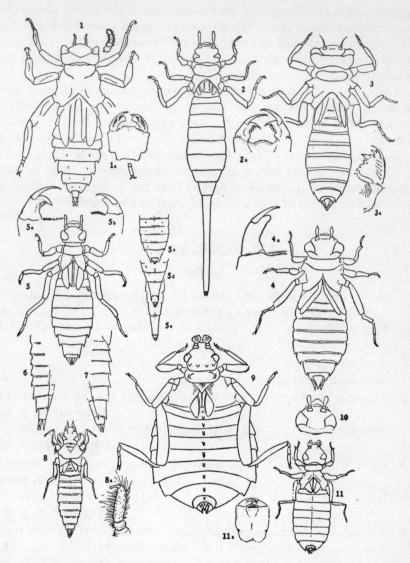

FIG. 26. Nymphs. *1*, Tachopteryx; *2*, Unknown Gomphine from Florida; *3*, Cordulegaster; *4*, Ophiogomphus; *5*, Gomphus; *6*, Gomphoides; *7*, Dromogomphus; *8*, Progomphus; *9*, Hagenius; *10*, Octogomphus; *11*, Lanthus. Parts of antenna and labium are shown more enlarged; also for 5, variants in form of abdomen within the genus. (From Needham's *Guide to the Study of Freshwater Biology*.)

8 Stigma very broad, doubling width of space between bordering longitudinal veins................... **Erpetogomphus,** p. 78

Stigma normal, widening this space by not more than half......9.

9 Hind femora armed with many short spines..... **Gomphus,** p. 81

Hind femora armed with 5–7 long strong spines..............
..................................**Dromogomphus,** p. 117

10 First post anal cell little wider than long. Eastern. **Lanthus,** p. 119

First post anal cell twice as wide as long. Western...........
...................................**Octogomphus,** p. 121

Nymphs

1 Abdomen circular; third antennal segment circular; legs not fossorial...............................**Hagenius,** p. 66

Abdomen much longer than wide; third antennal segment elongate; legs fossorial...................................2.

2 Tenth abdominal segment longer than all the others together
...................................**Genus?,** p. 60

Tenth abdominal segment not longer than other single segments....................................3.

3 Wings cases divergent.................................4.

Wing cases not divergent.................................5.

4 Fourth antennal segment cylindric.......... **Progomphus,** p. 62

Fourth antennal segment a spherical rudiment **Ophiogomphus** p. 67
....................and **Erpetogomphus,** p. 79

5 Third antennal segment thin, flat, oval....................6.

Third antennal segment elongate or linear..................7.

6 Far eastern...........................**Lanthus,** p. 119

Far western..........................**Octogomphus,** p. 121

7 Segment 9 with a sharp middorsal ridge ending in a straight apical spine.......................................8.

Segment 9 not so..........................**Gomphus,** p. 81

8 Lateral abdominal appendages as long as the inferiors..........
...................................**Gomphoides,** p. 63

Lateral abdominal appendages shorter than the inferiors.......
...................................**Dromogomphus,** p. 117

3. Progomphus Selys

This genus, as at present constituted, is a rather heterogeneous lot of about a dozen tropical American species, and the one widely ranging and very variable North American species described below. This species has the nodus situated a little beyond the middle of the fore wing. In both wings the triangle is broad, and its outside is angulated at the point of origin of the trigonal planate. In the fore wing it is usually divided into 3 cells and in the hind wing into 2. The inferior abdominal appendage of the male is rather long and very deeply divided.

Fig. 27. Progomphus nymph.

The nymph (Cabot, '72, p. 6- Hagen, '80, p. 247; and Ndm. and Hart, '01, p. 55) is readily recognized by the cylindric and upturned fourth segment of the antennae and by the indrawn bases of the middle legs. It is a superb burrower and lives in the sandy beds of both lakes and streams.

3. Progomphus obscurus Rambur

Rmbr. '42, p. 170: Mtk. Cat. p. 79 (as *Gomphoides obscura*): Howe '18, p. 27: Kndy. '21, p. 596: Davis '13, p. 19: Wlsn. '12, p. 190: Wmsn. '20, p. 100: Howe '23, p. 127: Smn. '26, p. 19.

Syn: borealis McL.†

Length 60 mm. Expanse 75 mm.   **U. S. generally.**

This is a handsome greenish gray species, striped with brown, and with yellow knee caps. Face and occiput greenish. Thoracic stripes of the first pair narrowly separated at the pale carina, widened strongly forward and abbreviated at the collar, confluent above with stripe 2. Stripes 2 and 3 of nearly equal width confluent above, then separated by a small triangular spot, then fused again, and then separated by a narrow yellow line below. Stripe 4 obsolete, or an exceedingly faint trace in the bottom of a crooked suture. Stripe 5 complete. Wings hyaline, brownish at base, as far out as basal crossveins, Costa yellow, Stigma brown. Legs yellowish basally almost to the knees, brown beyond. There is a distinct yellow kneecap covering the base of the tibia externally. The middorsal row of abdominal pale markings begins on segment 2, and continues as somewhat abbreviated triangles on 3 to 7, on 7 being half as long as the segment. Segments 8 to 10 are blackish above. The yellow of the little expanded side margins is full length on 7, divided into basal and apical spots on 8, and smaller apical spots only on 9 and 10. The superior appendages of the male are yellowish.

† Perhaps the west coast G. **borealis** of McLachlan should rank as a distinct species. Kennedy thought so, and gave some good reasons ('17, p. 527).

The senior author found nymphs of this species exceedingly abundant in the sandy bed of the Santa Ana River below Riverside California in April. A dozen or more of them could be taken at each sweep of the sieve net on the bottom. In May the adults were seen along the upper reaches of the Santa Margarita River further southward They flew swiftly from one resting place on the bare sand to another, and were very inconspicuous when at rest. They were not especially difficult to approach by stalking, or to capture when at rest.

Davis ('13, p. 19) found them on several occasions in May and June flying up and down a shaded ditch by the side of the railroad track at Lakehurst, N. J.

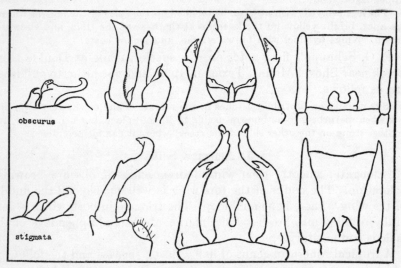

4. GOMPHOIDES Selys

This is another tropical American genus of about a dozen species, of which a single one enters our limits on the Mexican border. That one is a big yellowish clear-winged species. Its triangles are all unusually broad and divided by cross veins into several cells. Its anal loop of several cells is well delimited in the rear by the converging branches of the anal veins. Its stigma is large and heavily pigmented. Texas.

The nymph is a burrower in muddy stream beds. It is recognizable by the sharp middorsal ridge ending in a straight spine on the tapering abdominal segments, and when grown, by the length of the lateral appendages, these then being about as long as the other appendages.

4. Gomphoides stigmata Say

Say '39, p. 17: Mtk. Cat. p. 81 (as Negomphoides).

Length 60 mm. Expanse 75 mm.   **Tex.**

A large yellowish species, broadly striped with brown, and with yellow-tipped abdomen. Face and occiput yellow. Thoracic stripes of the first pair well separated by the yellow of the carina, strongly widened and abbreviated at the collar, confluent with 2 at the crest. Stripes 2 and 3 of about equal width, confluent along the crest, but well separated below by a rather broad yellow line. Stripes 4 and 5 rather broad, coytinuous, well defined. Stripe 4 is connected with 3 below and with 5 at its upper end. The mid dorsal yellow triangles of the abdomen run down at the sides on segments 2 to 7, giving a ringed appearance to the abdomen and they overspread almost the whole of segments 8 to10. Appendages yellow.

The legs are yellowish at base, black lined on the sides of the femora toward the apex, bright yellow on the kneecap at the base of the tibia, and elsewhere brown. Wings hyaline, with brown stigma, and yellow costa.

F. G. Schaupp's field notes on this species, made at Double Horn Creek near Shovel Mount, Texas, in 1907, and not hitherto published are as follows:

Sits usually on protruding stones in the middle of the creek; very shy; flies low when disturbed, sometimes returning to the old place, but usually selecting another stone on the other side of the creek. where it cannot be crossed.

5. Aphylla Selys

Elongate, smooth, clear-winged dragonflies of obscure brownish coloration. The nodus of the fore wing is well out beyond the middle of the wing. There is no anal loop. The triangle in both wings is generally divided into 3 cells. The inferior abdominal appendage of the male is rudimentary.

A tropical American genus of half a dozen species, and the following which just enters our southeastern limits. Habits unrecorded.

5. Aphylla producta Selys

Selys '54, p. 79: Mtk. Cat. p. 80.

Length 42 mm. Expanse 68 mm.   **Fla.**

An elongated brownish species, very obscurely striped on the thorax and with abdomen almost unmarked. Face brown, with a greenish anteclypeus. Occiput pale, with a rather wide black border. Thoracic stripes of the first two pairs very broad and broadly confluent at the ends, covering the front of the thorax except for two wholly inclosed linear-oblong pale lines. Stripes 2 and 3 are confluent at the ends but well separated between by a pale line, Stripes 4 and 5 diffuse but entire, obscure. The legs are brown with the femora somewhat paler. The wings are subhyaline, with brown veins and tawny stigma; costa brown. The usual mid-dorsal line on the abdomen is obsolete except for triangular spots on the two basal segments. Segments 8, 9, 10 and appendages somewhat rufous.

The nymph is unknown.

6. Cyclophylla Selys

Elongate, brownish, clear-winged dragonflies of moderate or rather large size. The triangle of the forewing points outward, the angulation of the cubital vein being moderate. In both wings the triangle is divided by one to three cross veins. There is an anal loop of two or three cells. (For an exotic nymph see Ndm. '11, p. 394.)

This is another tropical American genus of about a dozen species, one of which just enters our limits on the Mexican border.

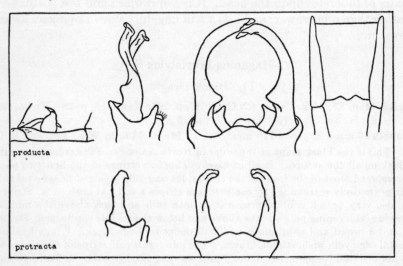

6. Cyclophylla protracta Selys

Selys '59, p. 546: Mtk. Cat. p. 80.

Length 68 mm. Expanse 86 mm.   **Tex.**

This is a fine brown species with a long slender abdomen. Face yellowish, cross striped with pale brown; labrum bordered and crossed with reddish brown. Thorax brown striped with bright yellow. Brown stripes of the first pair confluent with each other and with 2, around the narrow, isolated, yellow stripes upon the front. Stripes 2 and 3 confluent at ends; separated between by a narrow yellow line. Stripes 4 and 5 complete, confluent above; 4 broader than 5. Abdomen yellowish above, brown at sides and across apices of segments 2–9; more brown posteriorly. 10 yellow. Appendages brown.

7. Hagenius Selys

These are big black stout-bodied, long-legged dragonflies. The wings are long and powerful, with a rather narrow but well-braced stigma. The triangles are elongated, and angulated on the outer side, with a well developed trigonal supplement springing from the angle. The anal loop is 4 celled and a little broader in the female than in the male. The male abdominal appendages are short and blunt.

This genus, properly delimited, includes only the single widely distributed North American species, described below. The nearest allies are in Japan and India.

The nymph is of most extraordinary form, the abdomen being flat and nearly circular, with a row of blunt dorsal hooks down the middle. The enlarged third joint of the antenna also is flat, and their are two pairs of tubercles upon the head. It is a sprawler amid the bottom silt rather than a burrower; and it is a stiff ungainly slow-moving awkward creature.

7. Hagenius brevistylus Selys

The Black Dragon

Selys '54, p. 82: Mtk. Cat. p. 82: Calv. '17, p. 205: Howe '18, p. 28: Wmsn. '20, p. 81; Howe '23, p. 130: Garm. '27, p. 12.

Length 80 mm. Expanse 110 mm. **Me. to Md., to Wis., Tex. and B. C.**

This is the black giant of the order in North America. Face cross-lined with black on all the sutures. Occiput black. Thoracic stripes of the first two pairs overspread most of the front of the thorax, leaving only a pair of linear-oval pale stripes entirely surrounded by confluence of stripes 1 and 2 at both ends. Stripe 3 is also very broad, confluent with 2 at both ends and just above the middle, leaving intervening pale streaks above and below the middle confluence. Stripes 4 and 5 broad and continuous and well defined. Legs black. Wings hyaline, costal edge yellowish, stigma brown. The middorsal pale stripe of the abdomen is abbreviated on segments 6 and 7 and wanting farther back, 8, 9 and 10 and appendages being wholly black. (Figs. 18 and 19 on pages 36 and 37)

This is a wide ranging species with a long season of flight. It flies from June to September. It frequents clear woodland streams and is not at all rare. It flies swiftly from one resting-place to another. When at rest on a rail or on the ground it is approachable by careful stalking, and is not at all impossible to capture with a net. The female drops her eggs during flight, unattended by the male. She strikes the water surface at points wide apart, liberating 10 to 20 eggs each descent. Thus they are well distributed. The senior author saw Hagenius capture a big Gomphus in flight, carry it up to a high bough on a tree, strip off its wings and send them fluttering down, as it began its repast. Davis ('13, p. 19) records having seen Hagenius on Jefferson Mountain near New Foundland, N. J., chasing butterflies, though he saw none of the latter captured. Williamson ('20, p. 81) records the capture of a female Hagenius in the center of the business part of the city of Bluffton, Ind.

The nymphs frequent trashy shores, preferably in running water. Several different sizes of nymphs are usually found together, indicating that a number of years are probably required for development. The grotesque cast skins left behind at transformation, sticking to logs and trash, are usually within a foot of the water's edge.

8. OPHIOGOMPHUS Selys

These are stream-haunting dragonflies of moderate size and of greenish or gray-green coloration. The inferior appendage of the male is large and four-lobed, and the occiput of the female usually bears sharp thorn-like horns.* The triangles are all free from cross veins. The anal loop is semicircular and well defined posteriorly by convergence of veins A_1 and A_2 and a connecting cross vein. Usually it is divided into three cells.

This is a holarctic genus with a score or more of species, most of which are North American. The adults are often locally abundant, but they are of elusive habits and are not commonly collected. They are singularly difficult to see as they flit about the rapids that are their breeding places.

Kennedy carefully studied this genus in the mountains of the Pacific slope. He says of it ('17, p. 529):

The imagoes of the various species spend the greater part of their time seated on gravel bars from which they fly up at intervals to catch insects or to intercept individuals of their own kind. They are rarely found far from running water.

Copulation is a lengthy affair. The male usually captures the female as she flies along the water's edge on her business of oviposition, when he grasps her head with his feet and then, bending his abdomen forward, grasps her occiput with his claspers while freeing his feet. She in the meantime bends her abdomen forward and copulates. After a short nuptial flight the pair settles on some bush and remains in copulation many minutes. In ovipositing the female deposits the eggs in swift water, usually on rapids, where she flies back and forth dipping

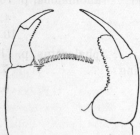

the tip of her abdomen in the stream. Though the eggs are laid on the shallow rapids, the nymphs during the latter part of their life live in the muddier bottom of the quieter water, for the exuviae are usually found along the edges of the deeper pools.

The nymphs of Ophiogomphus are shallow burrowers in the sandy or gravelly beds of clear flowing streams and lakes. They are always silt covered and inconspicuous. They agree in having a rather short stocky body with divergent wing cases, and abruptly

FIG. 28. Tip of labium of Ophiogomphus, with its lateral lobe more enlarged.

* Whence such specific names as *O. bison* and *O. spinicorne.*

pointed abdomen.   The labium is short, the mentum little longer than
wide, parallel sided. The median lobe is convexly rounded, its edge
is beset with minute quadrate denticles (a score or more of them) at
the base of the fringe of scale-like hairs. The lateral lobe is rounded
on the end, there being no end hook, and the inner margin is beset with
very numerous minute teeth.

As nymphs the species are not sharply defined. Such characters as
have hitherto (1927) been found for distinguishing the known forms are
given in the following table:

The Known Nymphs

Species	Length	Teeth on lat. lobe	Lat. spines on	Dorsal hooks	Described by
aspersus	27	12–15	7–9	2–9	Ndm. 01, p. 438
bison	29	14	6–9	2–9	Kndy. '17, p. 547
carolinus	26		7–9	2–9	Hag. '85, p. 258
carolus	26	14	7–9	7–9	Ndm. '01, p. 439
colubrinus	23		7–9	2, 7–9	Hag. '85, p. 257
morrisoni	28	12–15	7–9	2–9	Kndy, '17, p. 548
occidentis	28		6–9	2–9	Hag. '85, p. 259
severus	28	14	7–9	2–9	Hag. '85, p. 259
rupinsulensis	25		6–9	2–9	Ndm. & Hart. '01, p. 60

KEY TO THE SPECIES

Adults

1 Face cross striped with black...............................2.
   Face not cross striped with black..........................3.

2 Expanse 64 mm.; clypeal stripe entire.........**colubrinus**, p. 70
   Expanse 48 mm.; clypeal stripe interrupted....**anomalous**, p. 70

3 Tibiae yellow externally...................................4.
   Tibiae black..10.

4 Stripe 2 sinuous on the front margin...........**phaleratus**, p. 71
   Stripe 2 straight or gently curved or wanting................5.

5 Stripes 4 and 5 wanting....................................6.
   Stripes 4 and 5 present....................................8.

6 Stripe 1 present...7.
   Stripe 1 absent..9.

7 Hair of thorax above hind coxae white.........**occidentis**, p. 71
   Hair of thorax above hind coxae brown......................8.

8   Male, superior appendages in dorsal view acutely pointed; female, with two thorn-like spines on head before occipital ridge

aspersus, p. 71

Male, superior appendages in dorsal view obliquely truncated; female with no spines on head before occipital ridge

carolinus, p. 72

9   Stripe 2 wanting, or almost so..........................10.
Stripe 2 almost entire....................**rupinsulensis, p. 73**

10   Stripe 2 a small round spot; inferior appendages half as long as superior...................................**arizonicus, p. 73**
Stripe 2 vestigial or wanting; inferior appendages nearly as long as the superiors...............................**severus, p. 74**

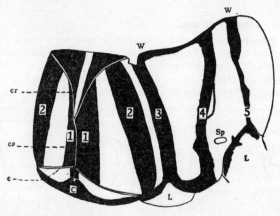

FIG. 29.   Diagram of color pattern of *Gomphus graslinellis*.   *cr*, crest; *ca*, carina; *c*, collar; *W*, wing bases; *L*, leg bases; *Sp*, spiracle; *C*, collar band; *1*, median dorsal stripes; *2*, antehumeral stripe; *3*, humeral stripe; *4* and *5*, lateral stripes.

11   Tarsi yellow dorsally........................**montanus, p. 75**
Tarsi blackish or brown................................12.

12   Stripe 1, 2 and 3 broad.......................**aspersus, p. 71**
Stripe 1, 2 and 3 very narrow.................**morrisoni, p. 75**

13   Stripe 2 free above.....................................14.
Stripe 2 fused to 3 above...............................15.

14   Stripes 1 broad and conjoined...............**howel, p. 76**
Stripes 1 narrow and separate....................**carolus, p. 77**

15   Expanse 66 mm.; stripe 1 broad...................**bison, p. 77**
Expanse 55 mm.; stripe 1 narrow............**mainensis, p. 78**

8. Ophiogomphus colubrinus Selys

Selys '54, p. 40: Mtk. Cat. p. 84: Howe '18, p. 29: '23, p. 128: Garm. '27, p. 133.

Length 51 mm. Expanse 64 mm.   **Me., N. F.**

A greenish species rather heavily marked with black. Face greenish cross lined with black on all the sutures and around the free border of the labrum. Occiput greenish. Thoracic stripes of the first pair confluent, rather narrower than the bordering pale stripes, and slightly widened forward. Stripes 2 and 3 well developed, separated by a narrow green line, 4 and 5 obsolete. Legs blackish except at extreme base. Wings hyaline with yellow stigma. Abdomen with the usual maculose middorsal line. Appendages yellowish, the inferior blackish on its edges.

9. Ophiogomphus anomalus Harvey

Hrvy. '98, p. 60 (fig.): Calv. '01, p. 241: Mtk. Cat. p. 83: Howe '18, p. 28: Garm. '27, p. 133.

Length 47 mm. Expanse 58 mm.   **Me.**

A slender greenish species rather heavily striped with black. Face greenish cross-striped with black on both the frontal and labral and on the middle of the clypeal sutures, and around the front border of the labrum. Occiput greenish with blackish on outermost angles that are continued in a black ridge behind the eye. Thoracic stripes of the first pair confluent and slightly widened forward

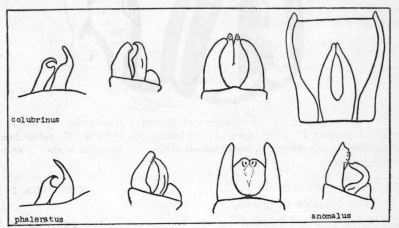

to the collar. Stripe 2 presents a free angle above and then is fused with 3 for a space, then separated by a greenish line for most of its length, and then fused with 3 again below. Stripe 4 is obsolete above the spiracle; from that level a blackish bar runs backward and downward to join the lower end of stripe 5, making a black N. Stripe 5 complete continuous. Wings hyaline; stigma brown. Legs black. Abdomen black with middorsal and lateral yellow stripes the whole length; reduced basal spots on the middle segments; on 8 clubshaped; on 9 square; on 10 round, pointed behind. Side margins of 9 and 10 entirely yellow; on 9 a C-shaped mark. Appendages black.

10. Ophiogomphus phaleratus Needham

Ndm. '02, p. 277; Mtk. Cat. p. 85: Kndy '17, p. 543 (as *occidentis*).

Length 50 mm.   Expanse 62 mm.   **Ore., Calif.**

A handsome yellowish species striped with brown and with a brown abdomen that is half ringed and tipped with yellow. Face and occiput yellow. Thoracic stripes of the first pair divergent at the lower end of the carina, widened downward. Stripe 2 complete, widest in the middle and with bowed anterior border, confluent above with 3 and with the brown of the crest, separated from 3 below by a narrow pale line. Stripe 4 obsolete except for a dash at the extreme ends. Stripe 5 an obscure and narrow line in the bottom of the suture. An inverted U-shaped mark joins the lower ends of 4 and 5. Legs brown, yellow at base and on the outer side of the tibiae. The middorsal line of pale spots on the abdomen is abbreviated on the middle segments, where the bright yellow is surrounded by black U-marks opening forward; 9 is mostly and 10 wholly yellow. The moderately expanded side margins of segments 7 to 10 are yellow bounded by brown externally on 7 and 8. Appendages yellow.

Kennedy ('17, p. 543) records finding this species emerging in abundance from the Columbia River at Umatilla, oregon on July 13, 1913.

11. Ophiogomphus occidentis Hagen

Hag. '82, p. 173: Ndm. '99, p. 238.

Length 53 mm.   Expanse 68 mm.   **B. C., Wash., Utah**

This species is barely distinct from *O. severus*, but has a little better development of thoracic stripe 1; the black of the abdomen is darker and there is less yellow toward the tip; the superior appendage of the male is less pointed, and the notch in the anterior genital hamule more square.

12. Ophiogomphus aspersus Morse

Morse '95, p. 209: Mtk. Cat. p. 83: Howe '23, p. 129: Garm. '27, p. 132.

Length 48 mm.   Expanse 60 mm.   **N. Y., Mass.**

A greenish species with narrow stripings of brown on the thorax and with black feet. Face and occiput greenish. Thoracic stripes of the first pair present or absent; when present narrow, separate, abbreviated in front, convex exteriorly, being narrowed to both ends, conjoined with the brown of the crest above but isolated below. Stripe 2 isolated at both ends well separated from 3, which is broader and arches forward to join the crest above the free end of 2. Stripe 4 is wanting above the spiracle, and of 5 there is hardly a trace. Legs pale to near the knees, then brown, the tibiae yellow externally, and the tarsi black. Wings hyaline; costa yellow; stigma tawny.

Abdomen brown, with the usual middorsal line of yellow spots that are triangular on segments 3 to 5, subquadrate on the basal third of 9, and full length lanceolate on 10. Appendages black.

The senior author observed this species at Saranac Inn, N. Y., where it was common. Many imagos of both sexes were observed flying over Little Clear Creek in the places where the shallow current rippled over sand. The males would fly back and forth a few times and then rest for a time on some prominent twig near shore, generally on a higher bank. They were not difficult to approach or to capture when at rest. Except when ovipositing, the females seeemed to remain less in the vicinity of the water. The female makes a succession of sweeps back and forth near the head of some little riffle striking the water, after short flights, again and again near the same place, leaving her eggs in it.

Imagos, living and mature, are of a rich deep green color with the usual oblique stripes of blackish brown. Unfortunately the color fades readily, even whey daylight is excluded.

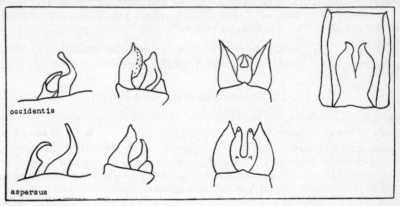

The nymphs were very common in the sandy bed of the creek. The cast skins were abundant along the banks through the months of June and July, sticking to whatever support offered, within a foot of the edge of the water.

The nymph is a rapid burrower, trailing along at a slight depth through nearly clean sand under the currents, often leaving a faint line behind showing where the tip of the abdomen, upturned for respiration, has pushed the sand grains aside.

13. Ophiogomphus carolinus Hagen

Hag. '85, p. 259 (nymph): Ndm. '99, p. 238: Mtk. Cat. p. 83.

Length 48 mm. Expanse 60 mm.   N. C.

Similar in coloration to *O. aspersus*. Stripe 1 of the thorax is more distinct; 4 and 5 are absent. There is no pale median spot on the middle of the posterior part of frons (not always present in *aspersus*); the pale line on exterior of tibiae is narrower. The real distinction between the two species is that of genitalia as stated in our key.

14. Ophiogomphus rupinsulensis Walsh

Walsh '62, p. 388: Mtk. Cat. p. 85: Howe '18, p. 29: '23, p. 129, Garm. '27, p. 138.
Syn: pictus Ndm.

Length 50 mm. Expanse 62 mm. **Me. to Pa., to Wis., to Kan.**

A fine greenish species with brown shoulder stripes, and a rusty tipped abdomen. Face and occiput yellow. The blunt and wrinkled occipital horns of the female are situated behind the eyes and their tips are directed toward the median line. Thoracic stripes of the first pair wanting. Stripe 2 abbreviated above, not reaching the crest, widely separated from 3 by a greenish line better

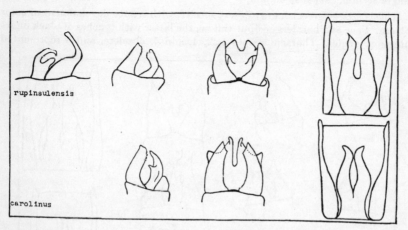

defined on rear margin than on the front. Stripe 3 continuous, widest toward the upper end. Stripes 4 and 5 obsolete. Legs brown, pale to near the knees and on the outside of the tibiae. Wings hyaline costa yellow, stigma rufous. The middorsal pale line of the abdomen is continuous on the basal segments and becomes diffuse and obscure on 5 and 6, and has a russet tinge on the remaining segments. Segments 7 to 9 are black above in the apical half, narrowly divided by rufous on the middle line in the male. Appendages pale or rufous.

Muttkowski ('08) reports this species as occurring about moist Woods and marshes from May to July.

15. Ophiogomphus arizonicus Kennedy

Kndy. '17, p. 538 (figs.).

Length 54 mm. Expanse 72 mm. **Ariz.**

This is a pale yellowish desert species, with stripes of thorax reduced to a minimum. Face and occiput yellow. Female with one pair of occipital horns. Thoracic stripes 1 and 4 are wanting; 2 is represented by a roundish spot midway the space that stripe usually occupies; 3, a narrow but complete line, and 5, a point of brown in the lower end of its suture. Legs black with yellow bases; the tibiae are pale externally. Feet black. Wings hyaline, stigma tawny. The usual middorsal pale stripe on the abdomen is invaded at the sides by brown and bilobed on segments 1 to 3 and to a less extent on 4 to 8 where becoming abbreviated, reduced on 9 to a small round spot, and outspread again to cover 10. Segments 7 to 9 are broadly yellow on the moderately dilated side margins.

16. Ophiogomphus severus Hagen

Hag. '74, p. 591: Mtk. Cat. p. 85: Kndy. '15, p. 341 and '17, p. 531 (figs.). Whitehouse '17, p. 99.

Length 53 mm. Expanse 68 mm.   **Colo., Wyo., N. M.**

This is a large greenish gray desert species, with scanty development of color pattern. Face and hornless occiput yellow, the latter with touches of black on its outermost angles. Thoracic stripes 1, 2, 4, and 5, obsolete, and 3 represented

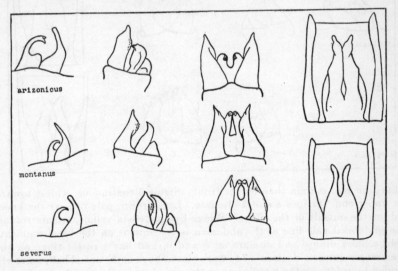

by a very narrow and obscure pale brownish line. Legs blackish, yellow before the knee, on the outer face of tibiae and tarsal segments. Wings hyaline, costa yellow, stigma tawny. The usual pale color of the dorsum of the abdomen overspreads the sides of the basal segments but is delimited in the rear by blackish V-marks on segments 2 to 9; 10 obscure. Appendages yellow.

Whitehouse ('17, p. 99) says that this species frequents sandy roads near the river and rests on the soil frequently. Kennedy ('15, p. 341) observed that

On Satus Creek south of Alfalfa (Washington) the emergence commenced the second week in June and lasted until the first week in July. It occurred from 9 o'clock in the morning until 4 o'clock in the afternoon, the nymph seldom crawling more than six inches from the water. Oviposition was most common on about August 1 and the last specimens were seen August 24. Oviposition occurred almost altogether on the riffles, but emergence was almost altogether along the deeper mud-bottomed pools. In copulation the male sought the female while she rested on a stone. Copulation occurred immediately after the male grasped the female. The latter would rest on a stone in a riffle and every few seconds make a short flight, striking the tip of her abdomen on the surface of the water just once, when she would rest for a few seconds on a stone and repeat the process. These short flights were repeated five or six times in succession. By August 1 many individuals showed age in the frayed wings, the olive coloration, and in their difficulty in standing. Frequently when one would attempt to alight on a stone it would fall over on its side or tumble on its head. During the first part of their season they were most abundant on the gravel bars, but during the oviposition period they were most abundant about the riffles.

17. Ophiogomphus montanus Selys

Selys '78, p. 430: Mtk. Cat. p. 84.

Length 54 mm. Expanse 64 mm. **Mont.**

A greyish green western species, faintly striped with brown. Face and occiput greenish, the latter without horns and with a touch of black on its outermost angles. Thoracic stripes of the first pair narrow, parallel sides, separated by the pale carina. Stripe 2 broader and well separated from 3, which is of equal breadth, but tapers downward. Stripe 4 obsolete above the spiracle, cross connected at the spiracle with the lower end of 5 by two narrow curved lines; 5 continuous but narrow. Legs brown, pale on base of femora, and outer side of tibiae. Wings hyaline, stigma tawny. The pale middorsal line on the abdomen is reduced to elongate triangular spots on the middle segments, and to small round spots on 7 and 8 and 9; 10 wholly pale. The slightly dilated side margins of segments 6 to 9 are yellow; 6 and 7 black margined. Appendages yellow.

18. Ophiogomphus morrisoni Selys

Selys '79, p. 65: Mtk. Cat. p. 84: Kndy. '17, p. 534: '15, p. 336.

Var: nevadensis Kndy.

Length 50 mm. Expanse 68 mm. **Nev., Calif.**

This is a large grayish green species obscurely striped with brown, having the legs brown and yellow and the abdomen chrome yellow ringed with black.

Face and hornless occiput yellow, the latter touched with black on its outermost angles. Thoracic stripes of the first pair narrow, barely reaching the collar below; stripe 2 broad, abbreviated and isolated above and mostly separated from 3 except at lower end; stripe 3 widened above, confluent with 5 above and 4 below; stripe 4 present only below level of spiracle; stripe 5 narrow, complete. Legs yellow at base, on femora beneath and toward base and on tibiae; elsewhere black. Abdomen yellow with middorsal and lateral rows of broad yellow spots, the dorsal row club-shaped on 2–9 and narrowing to rearward, the lateral spots linear, marginal, and notched by a black spot at the hind angle on 3–8; 9 is all yellow at the side and the side spot of 10 is confluent with the dorsal spot around the hind margin.

Kennedy found this species abundant at Donner Lake, Oregon, where he says ('17, p. 535) it is found on the gravel beaches.

The males rest on the cobblestones scattered over the gravel or pursue each other in zig-zag flights along the lake shore. The females are not as numerous and are usually found seated on stones very close to the edge of the water. Here the males find them and take them back among the bushes in copulation. In

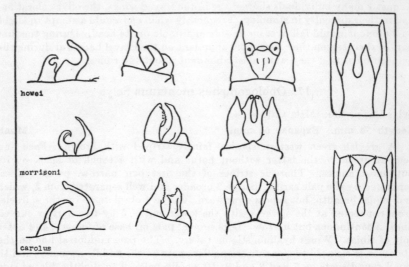

ovipositing the female poises just over the water and as the wave passes beneath her drops the tip of her abdomen into the water raising it again as soon as the wave has passed. Emergence occurred between 10 in the morning and 4 in the afternoon. Usually the nymph crawled just above the wash of the waves. Robins caught many of the tenerals among the rocks.

Kennedy has described ('17, p. 536) as *O. morrisoni nevadensis* a paler, desert inhabiting variety, in which the yellow dorsal and lateral spots are confluent at the base of the middle abdominal segments.

19. Ophiogomphus howei Bromley

Brom. '24, p. 343: Calv. '24, p. 345: Garm. '27, p. 135.

Length 33 mm. Expanse 43 mm.   **Me., Pa.**

A short stocky greenish species striped with brown. Face and occiput yellow. Thoracic stripes of the first pair confluent dilated toward the crest and narrowed forward. Stripe 2 free above and rather widely separated from 3, which is of equal width. Stripe 4 wanting above the spiracle, and forked below. Stripe 5 complete, narrow, and with an inverted U before its lower end. Hind wings flavescent on the midst of their basal half, strongly in the female, faintly in the male, legs blackish, yellowish at base. The yellowish line of middorsal spots is wide on segment 2, abbreviated on the middle segments disappearing on 8 or 9.

The moderately dilated side margins of segments 7 to 9 are yellow, bordered with black distally and externally. Appendages brown.

20. Ophiogomphus carolus Needham

Ndm. '97, p. 183: Mtk. Cat. p. 83: Howe '18, p. 29: '23, p. 129: Garm. '27, p. 134.
Length 46 mm. Expanse 56 mm.   **N. Y.**

A rather small greenish species, smartly striped with brown. Face and occiput yellow, the latter with or without horns. When horns are present they are small, a single pair, close together situated just in front of the hind (occipital) margin. Thoracic stripes of the first pair narrow, separate, parallel-sided, complete; together, narrower than the stripe of yellow at either side. Stripe 2 abbreviated at both ends and separated from 3 by a rather wide green stripe. Stripe 3 wider, especially near its upper end. Stripe 4 obsolete except for a dash below the spiracle, and stripe 5 complete. Legs brown, the femora paler. Wings hyaline, costa blackish, stigma cinereous. The middorsal line of pale markings on the abdomen is broadest and completest on 2, bilobed and narrowed on 3 to 7 reduced to a small round spot on 8 and 9; 10 and appendages pale. The side margins of the moderately expanded segments 7 to 10 are yellowish within a narrow brown outer marginal line. Appendages pale.

The nymphs may be collected by hundreds in Ithaca, N. Y. in April, and in May the banks of the stream are fairly covered with cast skins, but the adults are rarely seen.

21. Ophiogomphus bison Selys

Selys '73, p. 496: Mtk. Cat. p. 83: Butler '14, p. 346: Kndy. '17, p. 540 (figs.).
Syn: sequoiarum Butler
Length 50 mm. Expanse 66 mm.   **Calif., Nev.**

Our largest species and a very handsome one; olive green stripes with brown, with half-ringed black and yellow abdomen. Face and occiput yellow, the latter with a pair of slender horns placed close together. Thoracic stripes of the first pair rather narrow, parallel-sided, constricted before the collar to a narrow line which crosses it. The upper angle is prolonged at the crest to join stripe 2, which is fused with stripe 3 in its upper third and then separated by a narrow greenish line below. These two stripes are rather broad and heavily colored. Stripes 4 and 5 almost obsolete, the former practically wanting, the latter a mere black line in the bottom of its suture. Legs brown, paler basally. Wings hyaline with black stigma. The middorsal pale stripe of abdomen is a well marked row of abbreviated spots surrounded and invaded at the sides by brown on the middle segments, broadened on 9 and wholly overspreading 10. The side margins of the somewhat dilated segments 7 to 9 are yellow surrounded distally with black. Appendages yellow, tipped with blackish.

Kennedy ('17, p. 541) says that

"This species occurs on the smaller perennial streams emptying into San Francisco Bay and Monterey Bay, also on the smaller tributaries of the Sacramento River. On the Sacramento itself and its larger tributaries it appears to be displaced by *Ophiogomphus occidentis*. I have not found it on streams which carry much snow water. It is found on the same streams that are occupied by *Octogomphus*, but the latter stays on the torrential headwaters while *bison* occupies the lowland sluggish portion of the stream.

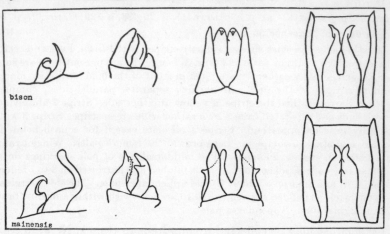

"It is usually found on gravel bars bordering a riffle and seldom more than five or six are found at one place. The females oviposit where the water is swiftest.'

22. Ophiogomphus mainensis Packard

Pkrd. '63, p. 255: Mtk. Cat. p. 84: Ndm. '97, p. 182: Harv. '01, p. 209: Woodruff '14, p. 61: Howe '18, p. 29: '23, p. 128: Garm. '27, p. 137.

Syn: johannus Ndm.

Length 42 mm. Expanse 55 mm.   **Me., N. Y., Pa.**

A small yellowish green species, striped with brown. Head and thorax clothed with brownish hairs. Face and occiput yellow. The occipital border is cleft and produced into a pair of long sharp horns that are directed forward. Thoracic stripes of the first pair narrowly linear, slightly separated by the pale carina, complete from crest to collar, much narrower than the pale area alongside. Stripe 2 free at upper end, then fused a little with 3, then separated by a pale line below, hardly as wide as 3. Stripe 4 almost obsolete, reduced to two dashes at the ends. Stripe 5 continuous, narrowly linear. Legs brownish, pale on under side of femora. Wings hyaline costa scarcely yellow, stigma pale. Middorsal line of pale markings on abdomen reduced to abbreviated triangles on the middle segments, absent on 7 and 8 reappearing on 9; 10 pale. The lateral margins of the slightly dilated 7 to 9th segments yellow, with a brown border about the postero lateral margins of the segments. Appendages brown.

9. ERPETOGOMPHUS Selys

These are clear-winged dragonflies of elongate form and rather striking coloration. Patterns in black and yellow with much repetition on the segments of the long body have suggested a lot of snaky names for the species, as well as the one for the genus. In both wings triangles are rather long and free from cross veins, and there is no development of the anal loop. The long bifurcated inferior abdominal appendage of the male is sharply upcurved in its apical half. The female lacks occiptal horns.

The nymphs of this genus are so like those of Ophiogomphus that up to the present time (1928) no means has been found for distinguishing them. One species has been reared *E. designatus* (Hagen, '85, p. 255), and another, referred by supposition *E. compositus*, has been described (Cabot, '72, p. 4).

This is a North American genus, with several species in Mexico and Central America, (one doubtfully reported from Brazil), but with most of the species occurring within our range. The adults may be distinguished as follows:

KEY TO THE SPECIES
Adults

1   Face striped with black....................................2.
    Face not striped with black.............................3.
2   Thoracic stripe 1 widest in middle...........**diadophis**, p. 79
    Thoracic stripe 1 not widest in middle.......**lampropeltis**, p. 79
3   Stripe 2 free above.........................**designatus**, p. 80
    Stripe 2 fused with crest above...............**compositus**, p. 80

23. Erpetogomphus diadophis Calvert
Calv. '05, p. 167; Mtk. Cat. p. 87.

Length 48 mm. Expanse 58 mm.   **Tex**

Head and thorax yellowish green. Face greenish yellow with cross stripes of brown. Vertex and occiput brown. Thoracic stripes of the first pair separate, not reaching collar, wider in the middle; stripe 2 broad, isolated above, tapering downward; 3 narrow complete, narrowly confluent with 1 on crest; 4 and 5 very narrow, complete, 4 subobsolete. Legs blackish except for base of femora. Wings hyaline, more or less yellowish at base, especially in front; costa lined with yellow; stigma brown with black bordering veins. Abdominal segment 1 yellow; 2 with a middorsal full length narrow yellow line; 3 and 4 with abbreviated middorsal line conjoined with a transverse yellow one, the latter repeated on 5, 6 and 7, interrupted in middle on 7. Round lateral spots on 3 to 7. 8 to 10 obscure brownish, paler on sides. Appendages brown. Male unknown.

24. Erpetogomphus lampropeltis Kennedy
Kndy. '18, p. 297.

Length 45 mm. Expanse 56 mm.   **Calif.**

Face grayish, cross lined with brown. Vertex brown. Thorax brownish in front with stripes 1 and 2 separated by isolated pale lines that diverge forward;

2 and 3 by a pale hair line (widened above to a triangular spot); stripes 4 and 5 complete, 4 very irregular and conjoined to 5 above. Legs black beyond the knees and on dorsal side of femora; grayish at base. Wings hyaline; stigma black. Abdomen blackish in middle, whitish toward the base, orange brown toward the

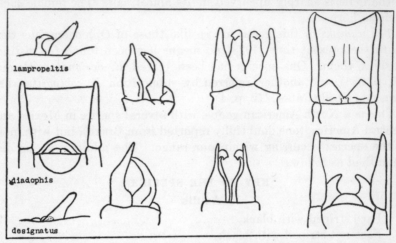

tip. Segments 1 and 2 with middorsal pale stripe which on 3 becomes a triangle, and on 4, 5 and 6 a lanceolate spot; 2–7 with basal pale rings. Very broad on 7; 7–9 with narrow apical rings. 10 and appendages wholly pale.

25. Erpetogomphus designatus Hagen

Hag. '58, p. 401: Mtk. Cat. p. 86.

Length 50 mm. Expanse 70 mm.   **Kan. and Ohio to Tex.**

Face yellow; labrum margined with brown anteriorly. Thorax yellow; stripes of the first pair broad, separate, widened forward almost reaching the collar; stripe 2 isolated above and below; stripe 3 complete and straight; stripe 4 interrupted in the middle; stripe 5 complete. Legs blackish on superior surface and tarsi, paler basally. Wings hyaline; costa and area near triangles yellowish; veins brown; stigma black. Abdomen yellowish becoming reddish on terminal segments. Middle segments ringed with blackish at the joints, yellowish at sides and with the usual middorsal yellow spots, pointed to rearward, confluent basally with the yellow of the sides. Appendages yellow.

26. Erpetogomphus compositus Hagen

Hag. '58, p. 400: Mtk. Cat. p. 86: Smn. '26, p. 22.

Syn: viperinus Hag.

Length 49 mm. Expanse 64 mm.   Ore., Wyo. and Ariz. to Tex. and Calif·

A greenish gray species striped with brown and with brownish abdomen. Face and occiput greenish. Thoracic stripes of the first pair narrow, confluent across the carina, parallel sided and isolated at ends. Stripe 2 narrower and well isolated from 3 by a broad yellow stripe; 3, 4 and 5 wider, entire. Legs blackish, greenish at base. Wings hyaline; stigma black. Abdomen with the usual line of middorsal yellow triangles narrowing apically and disappearing on segment 9; on 2 a rather broad trilobed band covers the dorsum, separated by black lines from the yellow of the sides. Appendages yellow.

10. Gomphus Leach

The Common Club-tails

These are clear-winged dragonflies of moderate or large size with greenish bodies broadly striped with black or brown (the darker color sometimes prevailing over the green). The triangles are free from cross veins. There is no anal loop. There is a well developed brace vein behind the stigma. The inferior abdominal appendage of the male is broadly furcate. The side margins of the sub-terminal abdominal segments are often broadly dilated, forming the club shaped abdomen to which the generic name alludes, (Gomphus, a club).

Fig. 30. Color pattern of front of thorax in Gomphus. Left to right: *scudderi, plagiatus, amnicola, brevis*, and *villosipes*.

This is the largest genus in our fauna. It is distributed around the northern hemisphere but the eastern United States is the center of its abundance. It is not reported from below the Mexican border.

The task of determining species in this genus is somewhat difficult. The ultimate criteria are found in the accessory genitalia in both sexes. The figures of these parts should therefore be carefully compared with the specimens collected before names are applied.

ARTIFICIAL KEY TO THE SPECIES
Adults

1 Face cross lined with black or brown (faintly so in *brimleyi, cavillaris* and *abditus*)..................................2.
  Face not cross lined with black or brown...................15.
2 Tibiae paler externally......................**brimleyi**, p. 106
  Tibiae not paler externally................................3.

3   Abdominal segment 9 shorter than 8; expanse less than 60. . . .4.
    Abdominal segment 9 as long as 8. . . . . .7.

4   Thoracic stripes of the first pair widened forward to form a tri-
    angle that is broader than the bordering pale color. . . . . .5.
    These stripes little widened forward, narrower than the bordering
    pale color. . . . . .6.

5   Stripes 4 and 5 narrow. . . . .**parvidens**, p. 89
    Stripes 4 and 5 broad. . . . .**alleni**, p. 89

6   Labrum with a median cross stripe; femora not pale beneath
                                                        brevis, p. 88
    Labrum with black border but no median cross stripe; femora
    pale beneath. . . . .**viridifrons**, p. 89

7   With a single pale brown stripe across top of frons
                                                      cavillaris, p. 105
    With black stripes on sutures of face. . . . . .8.

8   Expanse more than 80. . . . ,. . . . . .9.
    Expanse less than 75. . . . . .10.

9   Stripe 4 continuous; sides of stripe one diverging; fronto-clypeal
    stripe a broad band. . . . .**dilatatus**, p. 97
    Stripe 4 interrupted; sides of stripe one parallel sided; fronto-
    clypeal stripe a narrow line. . . . .**lineatifrons**, p. 98

10 Stripes 4 and 5 coalescent; base of femora yellow. .**abditus**, p. 110
    Stripes 4 and 5 separate; base of femora blackish. . . . . .11.

11 Labrum bordered with black and with a transverse black stripe.12.
    Labrum bordered with black but with no transverse black stripe
    . . . . .13.

12 Occiput bordered with black; 10 black below. . . . .**adelphus**, p. 94
    Occiput not bordered with black; 10 yellow below. . .**vastus**, p. 95

13 Stripes one and two conjoined above collar; carina black
    . . . . **scudderi**, p. 95
    Stripes one and two separate above collar; carina more or less pale
    . . . . .14.

14 Side (anterior face) of hind femora yellow. . . . . . .**amnicola**, p. 95
    Side of hind femora black. . . . .**consanguis**, p. 94

15 Stripes of pair one short and more or less indistinct (Arigomphus)
    . . . . .16.
    Stripes of pair one longer and better defined. . . . . .23.

16 Occiput bordered with black. . . . . **villosipes**, p. 116
    Occiput not bordered with black. . . . . .17.

17 Abdominal appendages black..............................18.
    Abdominal appendages not black.........................19.

18 Superior appendages of male forked and with a long external tooth
    .... **cornutus**, p. 115
    Superior appendages of male merely angulate externally
    .... **whedoni**, p. 115

19 Stripe 5 complete............................**lentulus**, p. 113
    Stripe 5 obsolete or wanting.............................20.

20 Stripes 2 and 3 conjoined above................**furcifer**, p. 115
    Stripes 2 and 3 not conjoined above......................21.

21 Femora and tibiae uniformly pale.............**pallidus**, p. 114
    Femora and tibiae partly black..........................22.

22 Stripes 2 and 3 subequal....................**subapicalis**, p. 114
    Stripes 2 and 3 reduced to a line..........**submedianus**, p. 113

23 Stripes of pair one triangularly widened to collar............24·
    Stripes of pair one less widened to collar..................25·

24 Stripes 4 and 5 fused........................**spiniceps**, p. 101
    Stripes 4 and 5 obsolete......................**notatus**, p. 99
    Stripes 4 and 5 complete and separate; 1 and 2 conjoined below
    ....**plagiatus**, p. 101

25 Tibiae yellow externally..................................26.
    Tibiae black externally..................................32.

26 Stripe not connected with collar; legs more or less yellow
    .... **intricatus**, p. 99
    Stripe 2 connected with collar...........................27.

27 Abdominal appendages yellow ....**militaris**, p. 104
    Abdominal appendages brown or black......................28.

28 Stripes 1 and 2 conjoined above the collar; 4 and 5 coalescent
    ....**exilis**, p. 108
    Stripes 1 and 2 not conjoined above the collar; 4 and 5 not co-
    alescent...29.

29 Stripe 2 not connected with 1 and 3.......................30.
    Stripe 2 connected with 1 and 3..........................31.

30 Length more than 50.........................**externus**, p. 90
    Length less than 50..........................**minutus**, p. 107

31 Stripes 4 and 5 subequal; yellow on 9 and 10
    .... **graslinellus** and **williamsoni**, p. 107
    Stripe 4 wider than 5; brown on 9 and 10........**lividus**, p. 104

32 Stripes 4 and 5 entirely wanting; expanse 72...**olivaceous**, p. 100
    Stripes 4 and 5 present, at least in part; expanse less than 70..33.

33 Stripe 5 better developed than 4..........................34.
    Stripe 5 not better developed than 4......................38.

34 Expanse 52.................................**abbreviatus**, p. 89
    Expanse more than 60.................................35.

35 Stripe 4 wanting.....................................36.
    Stripe 4 partially present................................37.

36 Stripes 2 and 3 separate; abdominal segment 9 partly yellow
    ....**confraternus**, p. 92
    Stripes 2 and 3 fused; 9 above wholly black.......**donneri**, p. 94

37 Femora of male partly yellow...................**crassus**, p. 92
    Femora of male black........................**fraternus**, p. 90

38 Stripes 4 and 5 about equally developed..................39.
    Stripe 4 better developed than 5.......................41.

39 Expanse more than 60.................................40.
    Expanse 54............................**quadricolor**, p. 111

40 Legs all black; black points on occiput........**descriptus**, p. 109
    Base of femora yellow; occiput yellow...........**borealis**, p. 110

41 Stripe 4 well developed................................42.
    Stripe 4 incomplete....................................44.

42 Stripes 1 and 2 fused above collar..............**spicatus**, p. 108
    Stripes 1 and 2 not fused above collar....................43.

43 Expanse 48.................................**cavillaris**, p. 105
    Expanse 65..................................**australis**, p. 109

44 Base of femora black..........................**hybridus**, p. 90
    Base of femora yellow.......................**ventricosus**, p. 97

Adults

Name	H. fem.[1]	Hamules[2]	Abd. 8[3]	Club of abdomen
Gomphurus	alike	variable	variable	mostly wide
Gomphus	alike	erect	square cut	moderate
Stylurus	alike	aslant forward	square cut	narrow
Arigomphus	unlike	aslant backward	oblique	moderate

[1] Hind femora of male and female.
[2] Slant of posterior hamules of male.
[3] Apical margin of eighth abdominal segment.

Four fairly well defined subgenera are recognizable in our fauna, and, to further facilitate identification, these groups will be characterized, and supplemental keys supplied, for the species of each group. The known nymphs will be tabulated also under the four subgenera to which they seem to belong.

Nymphs

Name	Labium			Abdomen			
	m. lobe[1]	lat. lobe[2]	teeth[3]	width[4]	lat. sp.[5]	groove[6]	9:8[7]
Gomphurus	convex	variable	4–11	wider	6–9	long	equal
Gomphus	convex	pointed	4–10	wider	6 or 7 to 9	variable	equal
Stylurus	straight	hooked	3–4	not wider	6–9	long	greater
Arigomphus	very convex, with med. tooth	pointed	6–7	wider	7 or 8 to 9	wanting	greater

[1] Front border of median lobe.
[2] End of lateral lobe.
[3] Teeth on inner margin of lateral lobe.
[4] Width of abdomen as compared with width of head.
[5] Lateral spines on abdominal segments.
[6] Middorsal groove or impressed line on abdomen.
[7] Length of ninth as compared with eighth abdominal segment.

Subgenus GOMPHURUS Needham

Here belong some large species with a very broadly expanded and and club-shaped abdomen, and some smaller stocky species that are little expanded; but all are characterized by thick heavy bodies, and (except in the first five species) squarely cut terminal abdominal segments. The hamules of the male stand perpendicular to the axis of the abdomen or nearly so, and the subgenital plate of the female is rather large.

The nymphs of the group are broader and flatter of abdomen and more blunt at the apex than any others of the genus Gomphus. The lateral spines are rather long, especially those of the ninth segment. The tenth segment is short, annular and included. The following tabular statement of the characters of the nymphs of those species that have hitherto (1928) been reared will help in their recognition.

The Known Nymphs

Species	Length	Med. lobe	Teeth	Dorsal hooks	Relative lengths				Lateral spines‡	Described by
					8	9	10	app		
adelphus	29	convex	7–11	8–9	9	10	3	8	6–9	Hag. '85, p. 262
amnicola		straight	5	0					6–9	Ndm. & Hart '01, p. 83†
confraternus	28	slightly convex	6–9	4–9					6–9 = ½×10	Ndm. '04, p. 291
crassus	34	straight	8–9	8–9	8	10	3	6	6–9 1½×10	Brtn. '28, p. 32
dilatatus	42	straight- ish	5–6	8–9	8	10	4	6	6–9 2×10	Ndm. '03, p. 266
externus	32	slightly convex	5–10	8–9	8	10	2	9	6–9 2×10	Ndm. '01, p. 451
fraternus	31	convex	7–11	8–9	9	10	3	8	6–9	Ndm. '03, p. 264
hybridus	28	slightly convex	8–9	8–9	8	10	3	5	6–9 2×10	Brtn. '28, p. 32
scudderi	38	slightly convex	3–6	0	8	10	3	4	6–9 = ½×10	Ndm. '01, p. 457†
vastus	31	concave	4–5	8–9	8	10	3	5	6–9	Cabot. '72, p. 3*

‡ Lateral spines on segments 6 to 9, on 9 equalling.
† Also in Walk. '28, p. 55 and 87.   * Also by Hag. '85, p. 265.

This table includes only known nymphs of the larger wide-clubbed species (Gomphurus proper). Nymphs of two species of the smaller group are known (Needham '01, pp. 448 and 449): *G. abbreviatus* (length 24 mm.) and *G. brevis* (length 26 mm.). These two are alike in all the characters named in the table, having the median lobe of the labium convex, the lateral lobe armed with 8 to 9 teeth, very rudimentary dorsal hooks on abdominal segments 8 and 9, the relative length of segments 8, 9, 10, and appendages as 9:10:4:8, and lateral spines on segments 6 to 9. Those of 9 being as long as the tenth segment. The real difference between these two species is found in the length of the foremost lateral spines, those of the 6th segment in *G. abbreviatus* being less than half, and in *G. brevis* more than half the length of the spines of the 7th segment. In form of the flat blunt-tipped body these nymphs resemble those of Gomphurus proper.

KEY TO THE SPECIES
G. consanguis (p. 94) omitted: see key on p. 82

Adults

1   Short, stocky species (ex. 50–60 mm.) with little widening of the
    club (segments 7 to 9) of the abdomen....................2.
    Larger forms (ex. 60–95 mm.) with a great widening of the club
    of the abdomen...6.

2   Face yellow including the labrum............**abbreviatus**, p. 89
    Face cross striped with black.............................3.

3   Thoracic stripes of the first pair widened forward, together forming a broad triangle..4.

      Thoracic stripes of the first pair parallel sided...............5.

4   Stripes 4 and 5 narrow.....................**parvidens,** p. 89

      Stripes 4 and 5 broad.........................**alleni,** p. 89

5   Labrum with a median longitudinal black line......**brevis,** p. 88

      Labrum with no median longitudinal black line..**viridifrons,** p. 89

6   Face cross lined with black.................................7.

      Face not cross lined with black...........................12.

7   Expanse more than 80 mm.................................8.

      Expanse less than 75 mm.................................9.

8   Stripe 4 continuous; sides of stripe 1 diverging; frontal stripe a broad band...............................**dilatatus,** p. 97

      Stripe 4 interrupted; sides of stripe 1 parallel sided; frontal stripe a narrow line............................**lineatrifrons,** p. 98

9   Stripes 1 and 2 confluent at lower end; no median stripe present on labrum...10.

      Stripes 1 and 2 not confluent at lower end; median stripe present on labrum...11.

10   Clypeus black; stripe 2 and 3 conjoined; stripe 5 present
      ....**scudderi,** p. 95

      Clypeus yellow; stripe 2 and 3 free; stripe 5 wanting
      ....**amnicola,** p. 95

11   Stripes 2 and 3 separate below...................**vastus,** p. 95

      Stripes 2 and 3 conjoined below...............**adelphus,** p. 94

12   Dilatation at end of abdomen wider than thorax; stripe 5 wanting
      ....**ventricosus,** p. 97

      Dilatation not wider than thorax; stripe 5 more or less present 13

13   Stripe 4 wanting; club narrow............................14.

      Stripe 4 more or less present; club broad..................15.

14   Stripes 2 and 3 separate; abdominal segment 9 partly yellow
      ....**confraternus,** p. 92

      Stripes 2 and 3 fused; 9 above wholly black.......**donneri,** p. 94

15   Tibiae yellow externally......................**externus,** p. 90

      Tibiae black...16.

16   Femora of male partly yellow...................**crassus,** p. 92

      Femora of male black....................................17.

17   Expanse 68 mm...........................**fraternus,** p. 90

      Expanse 60 mm...........................**hybridus,** p. 90

27. Gomphus brevis Hagen

Hag. '78, p. 60: Mtk. Cat. p. 90: Currie '17, p. 223 (figs.): Garm. '27, p. 149.
Length 43 mm. Expanse 54 mm.   **Ont., Mass., N. J., to Wis.**

A short stout blackish species striped with greenish. Face cross-lined with black. Labrum all black except for a pair of small pale dots. Thoracic stripes of the first pair parallel-sided, confluent except on the middle of the carina, and separating a pair of pale opposed and inverted 7-marks on the front of the thorax. Legs black except at their bases. The middorsal line of yellowish lanceolate spots of the abdomen disappears on the very base of the 8th segment, 9 and 10 being wholly black above in the male. The lateral margins of 7 to 9 are narrowly orange.

An early season species that inhabits the sandy beds of clear streams at moderate elevations. The senior author found it emerging before the middle of June at Saranac Inn in the Adirondacks and disappearing a few weeks later. Walker ('08) reports it as rather common in Ontario, frequenting well aerated waters, such as rapid streams and the exposed shores of large lakes.

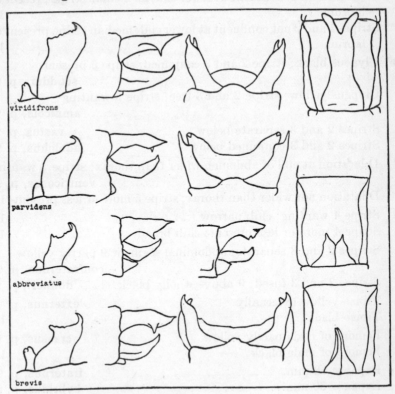

28. Gomphus parvidens Currie

Currie '17, p. 223 (figs.).

Length 37 mm. Expanse 50 mm. **Lakeland, Md.**

Face with a fine black line along the fronto-clypeal suture. Labrum black, except for two small yellow dots. Thoracic stripes of the first pair fused (except on the middle of the carina) into a rather broad triangle, widening forward to the collar, across which they are narrowly connected with the cross band below. Wings hyaline; veins black; stigma brown. Legs black except at base. Abdominal segments 8–10 all black above. A single male has hitherto been found.

Female unknown.

29. Gomphus alleni Howe

Howe '22, p. 19.

Length 44 mm. Expanse 56 mm. **N. H.**

This is another short, thick set, blackish species with a pair of opposed inverted 7-marks on the front of the thorax. Face yellow with a black line across the fronto-clypeal suture. Occiput yellow with a blackish edge. Front of thorax with the stripes of the first pair broad and much widened downward where abbreviated laterally. Stripes 2 narrower, and in a large part, confluent with 3 above and below around a narrow yellow line that extends two-thirds their height; confluent also with 1 above. Stripes 4 and 5 broad, complete, paler, confluent at ends with each other and 3. Abdomen blackish with the usual line of middorsal yellow spots on segment 1 to 8, abbreviated to rearward, very small on 8, very wide on 1 and 2. Sides of 1 and 2 blotched with yellow; of 3 to 7 with small yellow spots; of 7 and 8 with the lower half yellow. 10 black above, yellow beneath. Appendages blackish.

30. Gomphus abbreviatus Hagen

Hagen '78, p. 464: Mtk. Cat. p. 89: Currie '17, p. 223 (figs.): Garm. '27, p. 149.

Length 34 mm. Expanse 52 mm. **Me. to Pa.**

A small greenish species striped with brown. Face pale. Thoracic stripes of the first pair widened a very little to forward, then contracted to a narrow line that crosses the collar, joining the cross stripe just below it. Wings hyaline with brown veins. Legs blackish, paler on the femora beneath. The usual middorsal line of yellowish lanceolate spots on the abdomen ends on the 8th segment, 9 and 10 being wholly black above.

This species occurs sparingly in the rocky gorge of Fall Creek along side the Cornell University Campus, but there appear to be no records of its habits.

31. Gomphus viridifrons Hine

Hine '01, p. 60 (figs.): Mtk. Cat. p. 98: Currie '17, p. 226 (figs.): Wmsn. '20, p. 101.

Length 46 mm. Expanse 60 mm. **Ohio, Ind., Pa.**

A stout but small blackish species, striped with yellowish green. Face greenish. Occiput yellowish; in the male narrowly marked with black around its convex border; in the female, all yellow, and narrowed to the median line. The thoracic stripes of the first pair parallel-sided and narrower than the inverted and opposed bordering pale 7-marks. Wings very faintly tinged with yellow at the base. Legs black, somewhat paler on side of femur and at base. The middorsal line of diminishing yellowish triangles on the abdomen disappears in a dot on the base of 7, 8 to 10 being wholly black above in the male, 9 only so in the female.

32. Gomphus hybridus Williamson

Wmsn. '02, p. 47: Mtk. Cat. p. 93.

Length 49 mm. Expanse 60 mm.   **Ind., Tenn.**

A rather small, stocky species, having much the aspect of the preceding species having the thorax green striped with brown and the abdomen black marked with yellow. Face and occiput green. The thoracic stripes of the first pair fused above and below across the carina. Stripe 2 free above, then shortly fused with stripe 3, and then separated by a pale line below: 2 and 3 of equal width; stripe 4 interrupted above the spiracle; stripe 5 complete, narrow. Legs black, wings hyaline, veins black. Middorsal line of spots on middle abdominal segments long, lanceolate, narrow on 4; 5 and 6, shorter and wider on 7 and 8; 9 and 10 all black above. Segments 8 and 9 are yellow at the sides, including the lateral margins.

33. Gomphus fraternus Say

Say '39, p. 16: Mtk. Cat. p. 93: Whed. '14, p. 94: Garm. '27, p. 163.

Length 54 mm. Expanse 68 mm.   **N. H. to Va. to Wis. to Ark.**

A large, strong-flying, hairy species. The thorax and the swollen basal segments of the abdomen are densely clothed with fine soft short black hair. Face and occiput yellow. Thoracic stripes of the first pair, narrow with parallel sides, narrower than the bordering yellow. Stripe 2 free above, then narrowly fused with 3, then separated by a narrow green line down to the level of the collar. Stripe 4 is interrupted in its upper third and not at all confluent with stripe 5 except at its ends; 5 is narrow and complete. Wings hyaline with black veinss Legs black. Abdominal segments 9 and 10 black above; the preceding segment, marked as usual in related species.

Whedon's ('14, p. 94) notes on the habits of this species are as follows:

Very often taken in pastures and open woodlands back from the rivers. About rapids they dart swiftly here and there above the turbulent waters, dash in and out of the leafy arches along the banks, or rest tightly flattened against the boulders in mid-stream.

34. Gomphus externus Hagen

Hag. '58, p. 411 (figs.): Mtk. Cat. p. 92.

Syn: consobrinus Walsh

Length 54 mm. Expanse 68 mm.   **Me., Wis., Ill., Neb., Tex. and N. Mex.**

A stout fine big species of yellowish or greenish color, striped with brown. Face and occiput yellow. Thoracic stripes of the first pair narrow, parallel-sided.

narrower than the bordering pale bands. Stripe 2 free above, then joined to stripe 3, then separated by a pale line to the level of the collar. Stripe 4 broad, somewhat diffuse and ill-defined on its posterior margin, tending toward confluence through its whole length with stripe 5, which is complete. Wings hyaline, faintly tinged with yellowish at base. Legs black, tibiae yellow externally. The usual middorsal row of pale spots on the abdomen, are broadened on the 9th segment and diffuse and obscure on 10. The yellow lateral spot on segment 9 extends the full length of the side margin of that segment.

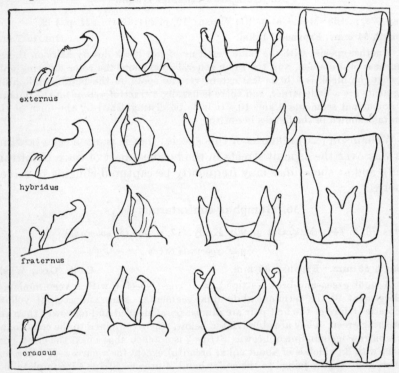

The habits of this species were observed at Havana, Ill. by the senior author in June and July 1896. The males were commonly seen flying about the floating house-boat laboratory, chasing one another, making long irregular sweeps together, and then flying apart and seeming to alight by preference on the boathouse deck, and on a floating cage nearby. They were most in evidence about mid-day. At rest, they sat flat upon the boards or on the bare sand, tail elevated, wings declined, touching the sand, in an attitude of great alertness. Their food was taken in swift sallies from such resting places.

Females were much less frequently seen. When ovipositing they flew over the water, dipping the tip of the abdomen to wash off the eggs. A clutch of 5200 eggs was obtained from a single female by dipping her abdomen in a watchglass of water (see p. 44 for the method).

Transformation occurred in the early morning, and the cast skins were left on the sides of barges, bridge piers and stumps a foot or two above the surface of the water.

35. Gomphus crassus Hagen

Hag. '78, p. 453: Mtk. Cat. p. 91: Wmsn. '19, p. 294: Garm. '27, p. 162.

Length 54 mm. Expanse 70 mm.   Ont. to Tenn.

Another species with the same vestiture of soft black downy hairs on thorax and base of abdomen, and the same general coloration, the color differing only in that the black is a little less extensive; the spots on the middle abdominal segments are a little larger, and there is usually a trace of yellow on the dorsum of abdominal segments 9 and 10. It is to be distinguished by the form of the genitalia shown in the figures herewith.

Williamson ('20) remarks of this species that is is often seen bowling its way over the asphalt streets in the business part of town (Bluffton, Ind), and at such times may frequently be captured clinging to screen doors.

36. Gomphus confraternus Selys

Selys '73, p. 744: Mtk. Cat. p. 90: Kndy. '17, p. 558 (as *sobrinus*)

Syn: sobrinus Selys

Length 55 mm. Expanse 80 mm.   Calif., Ore., Wash.

A stout green-and-brown striped, west coast species, with a very moderate enlargement of the terminal abdominal segments. Face and occiput yellow. Thoracic stripes of the first pair are almost parallel-sided and narrower than the bordering green. They are abbreviated below, where conjoined to the collar band by a narrow median line of brown. Stripe 2 is notched above next the crest, confluent with 3 (which is of about equal breadth) except for a narrow dividing line below, and broadly joined to the collar band of brown. Stripe 4 incomplete, not extending above the spiracle, but almost confluent with 5 at that level. Stripe 5 well developed and broad. Wings hyaline, stigma brown. The middorsal line of yellow triangles on the middle abdominal segments ends in a basal spot on segment 8 or 9. Segment 10 above and appendages black. The yellow spots on the side margins of segments 8 and 9 do not reach the apical border of those segments.

Kennedy ('17) says this is an early spring species, appearing in April and gone by July, and it inhabits the warmer constant streams of moderate size and to a lesser extent the ponds.

In May I found it very abundant on Coyote Creek within the city limits of San Jose, where in a single day's collecting I succeeded in taking over 50 specimens.

On Coyote Creek, a warm sluggish stream with mud banks and much mud bottom, it does not appear about the water in numbers until about 11 in the fore-noon. Earlier than this it can be found on the sunny patches of bare ground back a few yards from the creek bank. It is active about the water during the heat of the day but leaves about four in the afternoon. The males are four or five times as abundant as the females, and usually stay low over the water, seldom rising

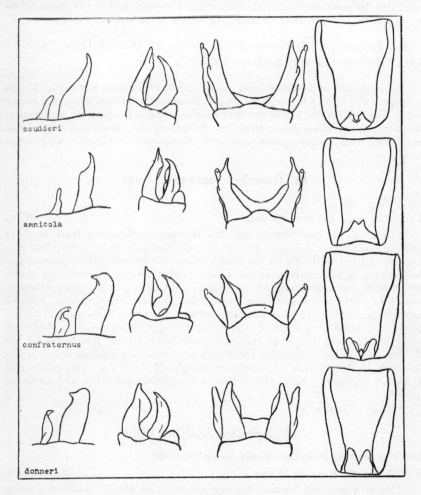

higher than four or five feet above its surface. They usually rest on the bare sandy spots but alight also on logs, brush and willows. The females oviposit by tapping the surface of the water with the abdomen at irregular intervals as they fly close over its surface. It is at such times that the males swoop on them and take them away in copulatory flights, which end in a long resting period in copulation on some tree or bush.

37. Gomphus donneri Kennedy

Kndy. '17, p. 562 (figs.).

Length 55 mm. Expanse 80 mm.   **Calif.**

"An almost black species," similar to the preceding, and doubtfully distinct therefrom; differs from confraternus by having thoracic stripes 2 and 3 wholly confluent, by greater extent of black upon the abdomen, and by the slight differences of form shown in the accompanying figures of the male appendages.

Dr. Kennedy ('17) observed the species at Donner Lake, Nevada Co., California (elevation about 5000 ft.). He says:

It passes most of its time resting on the bare beach or some low stone, though it occasionally lit on a low bush or weed. Along the west shore, where the sandy beach was continuous, it was the only species found, but along the west end of the north shore, where sandy stretches alternated with gravel and rock it was associated with *Ophiogomphus morrisoni, Enallagma cyathigerum,* and *Argia vivida.*

38. Gomphus consanguis Selys

Selys '79, p. 66.

Length 55 mm. Expanse 68 mm.   **N. C.**

This species is unknown to us. We abstract the following from de Selys original description. Face and front yellow, olivaceous, with both front and rear borders and a central spot on the labrum black. Fronto-clypeal suture and two impressions on the postclypeus also black. Occiput yellow, ciliated with black. Front of thorax yellow striped with black. Stripes of the first pair narrowly separated on the carina, and abbreviated below, not touching the collar. Stripe 2 and 3 broader, close together but not confluent, complete. Stripes 4 and 5 complete. Legs black with the front femora pale beneath. Wings hyaline. Abdomen black marked with yellow at the base, there being a three lobed spot on the dorsum of segment 2, and side spots on 1 and 2 that are prolonged into a line inferiorly on 3 to 7. The dilated lateral margins of 8 and 9 are also yellow and there is a vestige of a basal yellow line on 8. Appendages black, as long as 10, subequal.

Female unknown.

39. Gomphus adelphus Selys

Selys '58, p. 413: Mtk. Cat. p. 89: Howe '18, p. 33.

Length 43 mm. Expanse 58 mm.   **N. Y., Mass.**

This is a greenish species, heavily striped with black. Labrum yellow, bordered and traversed by black. Anteclypeus black; postclypeus bordered with black and with two black dots. Occiput yellow, bordered with black. Thoracic stripes of the first pair confluent and truncated at collar but crossing its middle line; stripes 2 and 3 confluent in their lower half, separated above by a pale streak that widens next to the crest. Abdomen with the usual line of mid-dorsal triangles on the bases of the segments. Sides of 8, 9 and 10 black.

40. **Gomphus scudderi** Selys

Selys '73, p. 752: Mtk. Cat. p. 96: Howe '18, p. 35: '23, p. 136: Garm. '27, p. 161.
Length 58 mm. Expanse 75 mm. **Me. to N. Y.**

A stout blackish species, narrowly striped with green. Face green, cross-striped with black on all the sutures. Labrum bordered with black, and more or less divided by a median streak of the same color. Occiput yellow, with a heavy fringe of black hairs. Thoracic stripes of the first pair fused, broadly widened forward, much broader than the two oblique green stripes on the front, which, by confluence with stripe 2 at both ends, they entirely surround. Stripes 2 and 3 broad, confluent in the middle and almost so to the ends. Stripes 4 and 5 broad and more or less confluent, often only an obscure, oblique pale streak showing between them. Wings hyaline, veins black. Legs black. Middorsal line of pale markings of the abdomen almost obliterated on the middle segments; short triangles on 8 and 9; 10 black above. The large side spots of yellow in the greatly dilated lateral margins of 8 and 9 do not touch the lateral margin.

This is a late season species, whose home is in cold spring-fed woodland streams.

41. **Gomphus amnicola** Walsh

Walsh '62, p. 396: Mtk. Cat. p. 89: Howe '23, p. 136: Garm. '27, p. 160.
Length 48 mm. Expanse 72 mm. **Mass. and N. Y. to Iowa**

A very dainty species with much black on the front and yellow on the sides of the thorax. Face greenish, with narrow black cross lines on the upper and lower sutures, and on the ends of the middle suture, and across the lower margin of the labrum. Occiput yellow, with blackened outer angles. Middorsal thoracic stripes of the first pair separated by a yellow carina, narrow (much narrower than the bordering pale stripes), laterally extended below to join stripe 2 above the collar. Stripe 2 very broad, almost entirely confluent with 3, which is narrower. Stripe 4 narrow but continuous. Stripe 5 obsolete. Legs black; front femora more or less greenish beneath. Wings hyaline, veins brown. The middorsal line of triangles on the abdomen is very narrow upon the middle segments, then is broadened on 8 to form a wide triangular spot, with a corresponding dot on 9. The large yellow side spots on 7–9 do not touch the widely expanded lateral margin.

42. **Gomphus vastus** Walsh

Walsh '62, p. 391: Mtk. Cat. p. 97: Howe '18, p. 33: Calv. '21, p. 225 (figs.).
    Garm. '27, p. 165.
Length 54 mm. Expanse 66 mm. **N. H., N. Y., Pa., Tenn., Iowa**

This is a fine species, with yellowish green thorax, brightly striped with brown, and with blackish abdomen, brightly marked with yellow at both ends. Face broadly cross-striped with black on all sutures and on the lower margin of the labrum, the latter more or less divided also by a median black line, leaving only the sides greenish. Occiput yellow, with a fine black long-ciliate margin. Thoracic stripes of the first pair fused and dilated in front to form a broad triangle not meeting stripe 2; the latter is broader than the intervening yellow, is free above but is conjoined with 3 below, and only narrowly separated from it through most of its length. Stripes 4 and 5 narrow but continuous and well defined. Wings hyaline with black veins and stigma. Legs black. There are lanceolate yellow middorsal |basal triangles on abdominal segments 3 to 7; 8 to 10 are black above; 7 to 9 are bright yellow at the sides.

This species frequents the shores of the larger lakes and streams. Wilson ('99, p. 662) says that the banks of the river, with alternating reaches of sand and gravel seem peculiarly attractive to these dragon-flies. Muttkowski says that the males are hard to capture, since they persit in alighting amid the brush near the waters edge.

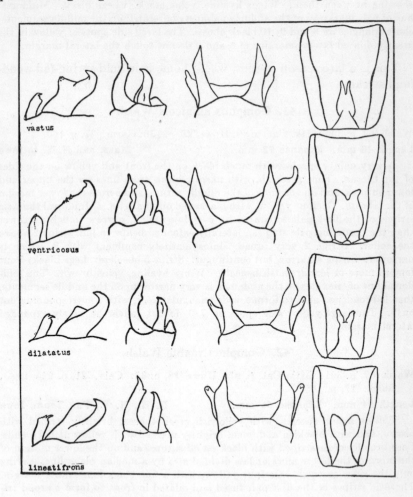

43. Gomphus ventricosus Walsh

Walsh '63, p. 249: Mtk. Cat. p. 98: Howe '18, p. 33: Garm. '27, p. 166.

Length 51 mm. Expanse 63 mm.   **Mass., Pa., Mich., Ill.**

A dainty little club-tail, having a greenish body brightly striped with brown, and a blackish abdomen. Face and occiput yellow, the latter black-margined only next the eyes. Thoracic stripes of the first pair are narrow and parallel-sided, confluent above and below across the carina, and hardly wider than stripe 2. Stripe 2 is rather broad, partly separated above, then confluent with stripe 3 for a space, then separated again lower down by a narrow green line. Stripe 3 is narrower, well defined. Stripe 4 is abbreviated above, extending only a little above the spiracle. Stripe 5 is narrow and obscure, but continuous. Wings hyaline with brown stigma. Legs blackish, the bases paler. The middorsal line of yellow triangles on the black abdomen ends on segment 7. The large yellow spots on the widely expanded sides of 8 and 9 do not touch the lateral margin.

44. Gomphus dilatatus Rambur

Ramb. '42, p. 155: Mtk. Cat. p. 91: Calv. '21, p. 224, and '23, p. 87.

Length 70 mm. Expanse 92 mm.   **Fla., Ga.**

The largest species of the genus. Face with two black cross-stripes and with a black lower border to the labrum. Occiput yellow, narrowly margined with black. Thoracic stripes of the first pair very broad and broadly dilated forward, broader than the adjacent pale stripes which by confluence with stripe 2 below they almost surround. Stripe 2 free above, narrowly separated from stripe 3, but confluent with the cross-band at the collar. Stripes 4 and 5 complete and of moderate width. Legs black; the hind femora and tibiae below armed with very numerous sharp close-set spines. Wings hyaline, lightly tinged with yellowish at base, and with black veins. The dorsal stripe of the abdomen is obsolete on the middle segments, represented by a long triangular basal spot on 7 three-fourths as long as that segment; 8–10, black above; 7–9 broadly yellow on the widely dilated side margins.

This species is common on the lower Chipola River in west Florida. The adult goes steaming along in steady horizontal flight two or three feet above the open river with tail aloft, and wings scarcely showing vibration. It is a striking figure. The slender middle part of the abdomen is inclined upward and the broadly dilated end segments are held parallel with the course of flight, but at a higher level than that of the bulky, striped thorax.

Back and forth it goes, steadily, easily, as ruler of the lesser life over the open stream. Once in a while it picks a blackwing (*Agrion maculatum*) for food, and carries the long, limp captive away to a resting place and feeding place among the willows.

The nymphs live in the muddy banks of the river, and clamber several feet up the swollen bases of the tupelo trees to transform.

45. Gomphus lineatifrons Calvert

Calv. '21, p. 222 (figs.).

Length 69 mm. Expanse 90 mm.   **Mich., O., Ind., Ill., Wis.**

Similar to the preceding species in stature and appearance, but slightly smaller. The uppermost black line across the face is narrow; the thoracic stripes of the first pair are almost parallel sided; the hind lobe of the prothorax is not wholly black in the middle dorsally; stripe 4 is interrupted in the middle, and the spot on the dorsum of the 9th abdominal segment is half as long as the segment.

Subgenus STYLURUS Needham

These are large Gomphines of elongate form having but little dilatation of the club segments of the abdomen. The posterior genital hamules of the male are strongly inclined forward at their tips (the anterior, very small and sequestered), and the subgenital plate of the female is very short, almost rudimentary.

The nymphs of this group are of very elongate form with abdomen narrow, hardly wider than the head, and slowly tapering with lateral spines on 6 to 9; the ninth segment is very long and the tenth is very short. The tibial burrowing hooks are almost wanting. The labium is long and narrow with the sides of the mentum convergent toward the middle hinge. The end hook of the lateral lobe is long and strong, and incurved at almost a right angle; the teeth before it are very few and increase in size proximally. The differences between the known species may be tabulated as follows:

The Nymphs

Name	Length	Relative lengths				Dorsal hooks	Spines of 9	Teeth	Described by
		8	9	10	app.				
spiniceps	40	6	10	2	3	on 9	=10	2–3?	Cabot '72, p. 5†
plagiatus	35–36	8	10	2	2	" 9	⅔ of 10	2–4	Hag. '85, p. 269* †
notatus	36–38	8	10	2	3	" 9	=10	3	Ndm. '03, p. 267†
olivaceous	38	7	10	4	4	" 9	½ of 10	3	Kndy. '17, p. 554†
intricatus	27	8	10	4	4	" 0	=10	3	Kndy. '17, p. 570†

* Also by Ndm. & Hart '01, p. 84.
† Also by Walker '28, p. 79.

KEY TO THE SPECIES

Adults

1 Face brown..................................plagiatus, p. 101
   Face yellow...2.
2 Stripes 4 and 5 broad and fused..............spiniceps, p. 101
   Stripes 4 and 5 very narrow or obsolete...................3.

46. Gomphus intricatus Hagen

Hag. '58, p. 418: Mtk. Cat. p. 94: Kndy. '17, p. 550 (figs.).

Length 41 mm. Expanse 58 mm.   **Tex. to Mo. to Calif.**

A small yellowish species with black feet. Face and occiput yellow. Thoracic stripes of the first pair well separated at the carina, and rather widely diverging forward, and narrower than the adjacent yellow areas, the truncate lower ends parallel with the collar. Stripe 2 free at its lower end, not reaching collar, but touching crest above, and tapering to both ends, wider than 3 and separated therefrom by a yellow stripe its own width. Stripes 4 and 5 obsolete except for a trace of 4 below the level of the spiracle. Wings hyaline, costa yellow. Legs yellow with black feet, black sides to the tibiae and a line on the sides of the femora at the knees. Abdomen more yellow than black, the black being mainly restricted to two pairs of large spots on the sides of each of the middle abdominal segments. Appendages yellow, their tips black.

47. Gomphus olivaceous Selys

Selys '73, p. 749: Mtk. Cat. p. 95: Kndy. '17, p. 557.

Var: nevadensis Kndy.

Length 56 mm. Expanse 72 mm.   **Calif. and Neb.**

This is a pale olivaceous black-footed species. Face and occiput yellow. Thoracic stripe of the first pair narrow, widened below to collar, confluent above

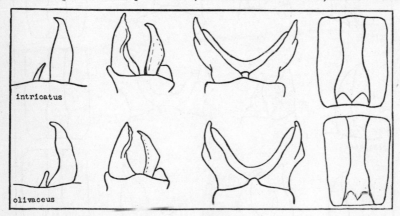

with 2 at the crest; stripe 2 broader, narrowly separated from 3 below, more broadly by a pale yellow triangle above, next to crest; stripes 4 and 5 wanting. Legs blackish beyond the knees and on upper surface of femora. Wings hyaline;

costa yellow, stigma brown, between black veins. Abdomen yellowish at base and sides black above with the usual line of pale spots that are pointed in the middle segments, and abbreviated on 8 and 9; 10 above black. There are round black side spots in the yellow of segments 3–6. Appendages blackish.

48. Gomphus notatus Rambur

Ramb. '42, p. 162: Mtk. Cat. p. 95: Wlsn. '12, p. 191.
Syn: fluvialis Walsh

Length 58 mm. Expanse 75 mm.   **Que. and Mich. to N. C.**

An elegant yellowish species, heavily striped with brown, and with a red-tipped abdomen. Face and occiput yellow. Thoracic stripes of the first pair strongly widened forward, wider than the bordering yellow stripes, separated narrowly by the yellow of the carina, confluent at the crest with the incurving stripes of the second pair. Stripes 2 and 3 fused more or less extensively at the shoulder, usually in such way as to leave a pale spot above and a streak below them. Stripe 2 is much wider than 3. Stripe 4 is narrow and interrupted in the middle, plainest below the spiracle. Stripe 5 is very narrow. Wings hyaline, veins brown, stigma reddish brown when mature. Legs black from a little before the knees, their bases yellow. Dorsum of abdomen obscure blackish, the middle segments obscurely ringed with paler basally. Segments 7 to 10 are reddish brown, yellow at the sides. Appendages yellow.

This species was observed by the senior author at Havana, Ill. in July 1896, where it was emerging daily. On the boathouse of the Illi-

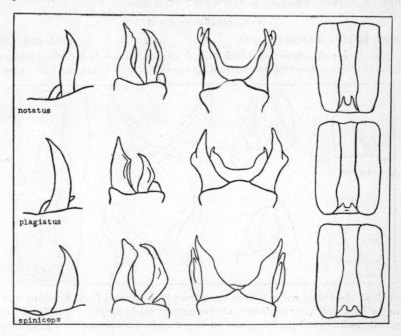

nois State Laboratory of Natural History River Survey, between five and six o'clock in the afternoon it was transforming in great numbers in the sunshine; also in the early morning, from before daylight until seven o'clock—which is a much more usual time for Gomphine emergence. The nymphs live in the sandy bed of the broad river, and cast skins thickly covered the sides of the Havana bridges, piers, etc. at an elevation of one or two feet above the surface of the water.

49. Gomphus plagiatus

Selys '54, p. 57: Mtk. Cat. p. 95: Wlsn. '12, p. 191: Garm. '27, p. 166.

Syn: elongatus Selys

Length 70 mm. Expanse 80 mm.   **N. Y., Ga., N. C.**

A fine large dark brown species. Face obscure brownish, lighter and somewhat greenish on the outer sides of the labrum basally. Occiput green, fringed with long black hairs. Thoracic stripes of the first pair very broad, especially toward the front where they are together widened to form a mid-dorsal triangle of brown, confluent with stripe 2 at collar and crest, leaving an oblique pale mark each side upon the front. Stripes 2 and 3 conjoined above and below, and separated by pale line between. Stripes 4 and 5 complete and distinct. Wings hyaline, veins and stigma brown. Legs blackish, except basal half of the femora which are paler. Abdomen blackish, with a suggestion of rufous on the slightly enlarged terminal segments. Appendages brown.

50. Gomphus spiniceps Walsh

Walsh '62, p. 389: Mtk. Cat. p. 97: Wlsn. '12, p. 191: Howe '18, p. 35: '23, p. 137: Garm. '27, p. 166.

Syn: segregans Ndm.

Length 57 mm. Expanse 75 mm.   **N. Y. and Ill. to Pa., Tenn., Mich.**

A pale obscure-brownish elongate species. Face and occiput yellow. Thoracic stripes of the first pair confluent, very broad, the two covering the front of the thorax, these being fused with stripe 2 around a pair of yellow lines that are strongly divergent forward; stripes 2 and 3 confluent; 4 and 5 very broad, complete, diffuse. Legs brownish, yellowish at base. Wings hyaline, with tawny stigma; slightly flavescent at base; veins black. Abdomen with segments 3–7 with the usual pale middorsal spots, abbreviated behind, nearly obsolete on 7. Laterally segments 1–8 or 9 are yellow; 10 wholly brown. Appendages blackish.

Wilson ('17, p. 191) writes concerning the habits of this species:

Quite a number were present in the immediate vicinity, but it was practically impossible to detect any of them before they flew up out of the grass. One was caught accidentally while sweeping the grass for damselflies. It is a strong flier, and frequents the vicinity of riffles where the water flows rapidly over small stones.

It frequents the riffles flying back and forth over the swift current, and is seldom seen in the long stretches of quiet water between. Frequently it dives into the water for its prey, plunging entirely beneath the surface. It immediately comes forth, spreads its wings, and flies away into the very top of one of the tallest trees along the river bank, there to enjoy its meal in quiet security.

It very seldom alighted on the shore and proved difficult to capture, all the specimens having to be shot either while hovering over the water or while munching their prey in the trees.

It may be recognized when flying near at hand by the reddish-brown posterior end of the abdomen, which stands out in good contrast to the darker color of the rest of the body. In hovering over the water the abdomen is not elevated, but is held nearly horizontal.

Subgenus GOMPHUS

This, the typical group, contains species that are more slender than those of Gomphurus, having the clubbed segments of the abdomen narrower and their lateral margins less dilated. In our species, veins A_1 and A_2 are generally wide apart, at the base, with two rows of cells between. The posterior hamules of the male stand vertically or nearly so, and the subgenital plate of the female is normally short.

The nymphs of this group are depressed, with abdomen wider than head and regularly tapering to a pointed rear end. Burrowing hooks are fairly well developed on fore and middle tibiae. There is a rather well developed end hook on the lateral labial lobe with 4 to 10 teeth before it, and the teeth, if unequal, diminish in size proximally. Low rudi-

The Known Nymphs

Species	Length	Med. lobe	Teeth	Dorsal hooks	Relative lengths				Lat. sp.	Described by
					8	9	10	app		
australis	30	convex 2 teeth	8	r[1] on 9 g[2] on 5-6	7	10	6	6	7-9	Ndm. & Hart '01, p. 78
borealis	30	convex 1 tooth	8-9	0	8	10	5	6	7-9	Ndm. '03, p. 265
cavillaris	30	convex	10	r[1] on 5-9	7	10	6	5	7-9	Brtn. '28, p. 33
descriptus	29-32	hardly convex	7-10	r[1] on 3-9	7	10	4	5	6-9	Ndm. '01, p. 454
exilis	19-26	convex 1 tooth	4-7	low on 6-9	7	10	6	5.5	6-9	Hag. '85, p. 263[3]
graslinellus	32	hardly convex	9	4-6, r on 3 and 9	8	10	5	5	6-9	Hag. '85, p. 264[4]
lividus	30	straight	6-8	humps on 7-9	8	10	4	5	6 or 7-9	Ndm. '01, p. 455
minutus	30	convex convex	8	0	8	10	6	6	7-9	Brtn. '28, p. 32
spicatus	28-31	1 or 0 teeth	7-9	r[1] on 9	7	10	5	5	7-9	Hag. '85, p. 265[3]

[1] Rudimentary
[2] Middorsal groove
[3] Described also in Needham '01.
[4] Described also in Needham and Hart '01.

mentary dorsal hooks are present on a variable number of abdominal segments, and lateral spines are present on segments 6 or 7 to 9.

The following table will assist in determination of the nymphs of those species that have hitherto (1928) been made known.

KEY TO THE SPECIES
Adults

1 Faces faintly cross striped with brown.....................2.
   Face pale..5.

2 Expanse less than 50 mm...............................3.
   Expanse more than 60 mm.............................4.

3 Middorsal yellow stripe on middle abdominal segments
   ....**brimleyi**, p. 106
   Middle abdominal segments obscure brown......**cavillaris**, p. 105

4 Stripes 4 and 5 confluent; top of stripe 2 turns toward 3
   ....**abditus**, p. 110
   Stripes 4 and 5 separate; top of 2 turns toward 1
   ....**australis**, p. 109

5 Tibia yellow externally...................................6.
   Tibiae not yellow externally............................11.

6 Stripe 2 free below; legs yellow..............**intricatus**, p. 99
   Stripe 2 connected with collar..........................7.

7 Abdominal appendages yellow................**militaris**, p. 104
   Abdominal appendages brown or black....................8.

8 Expanse less than 55...................................9.
   Expanse more than 58..................................10.

9 Stripe 2 free above; 1 not fused; 4 and 5 separate; tarsi
    yellow above...............................**minutus**, p. 107
   Stripe 2 not free above; 1 fused; 4 and 5 united; tarsi black above
   ....**exilis**, p. 108

10 Stripe 4 about equal to 5....**graslinellus** and **williamsoni**, p. 107
   Stripe 4 broader than 5......................**lividus**, p. 104

11 Stripes 1 and 2 confluent above and below; 4 broader than 5
   ....**spicatus**, p. 108
   Stripes 1 and 2 separate above collar....................12.

12 Expanse less than 55..................**quadricolor**, p. 111
   Expanse more than 58..................................13.

13 Legs all black.............................**descriptus**, p. 109
   Base of femora yellow.......................**borealis**, p. 110

51. Gomphus lividus Selys

Selys '54, p. 53: Mtk. Cat. p. 94: Howe '18, p. 32: '23, p. 134, Garm. 27, p. 154.

Syn: sordidus Hag., *umbratus* Ndm.

Length 52 mm. Expanse 68 mm.   Mass., Wis., N. C., Ark.

A dull greenish species of medium size, obscurely striped on the thorax and spotted on the abdomen. Face and occiput greenish. Thoracic stripes of the first pair, confluent, slightly widened forward to the collar, each about as wide as the bordering green. Stripe 2 isolated above, then joined with 3, then separated from 3 below by a narrow greenish line, these stripes being of about equal width. Stripes 4 and 5 and the entire area between them pale brown. Wings slightly flavescent at the base. Legs brown, femora pale beneath, tibiae externally yellow. The middorsal line of spots on the abdomen nearly continuous beyond the middle segments but ill-defined, with the spots shortened and widened on 7 and 8. Segments 9 and 10 are obscure yellowish brown, paler dorsally and toward the lateral margins. Appendages blackish.

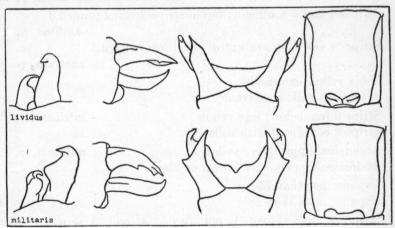

52. Gomphus militaris Hagen

Hag. '58, p. 416: Mtk. Cat. p. 94.

Length 50 mm. Expanse 68 mm.   Tex.

An elegant slender bright yellow species striped with brown. Face and occiput yellow. Thoracic stripes of the first pair confluent at ends of carina, widened a little toward the collar, wider than the bordering yellow. Stripe 2 barely reaching the collar, isolated above and separated from 3 by a yellow line. Stripes 4 and 5 distinct, complete, or the upper half of 4 obscure, and the area between 4 and 5 sometimes a little overspread with brownish. Wings hyaline; stigma tawny; costa yellow. Legs yellow and black, the sides of the femora and the tibiae externally being yellow.   The yellow middorsal line of the abdomen is rather broad and nearly continuous, with segments 8, 9 and 10 mainly yellow, and the appendages.

53. Gomphus cavillaris Needham

Ndm. '02, p. 276: Mtk. Cat. p. 82.

Length 41 mm. Expanse 48 mm.   **N. C. and Fla.**

A small olivaceous species, obscurely striped with pale brown. Face and occiput olivaceous, with pale brownish cross-stripes on the sutures of the former, and with a touch of the same color on the outer corners of the latter. The thoracic stripes of the first pair are confluent across the ends of the carina, widened forward almost to the collar, and are almost confluent with the stripes of the second pair at both ends. Stripes 2 and 3 are of about equal width, and are separated by a pale line, more widely at the ends. Stripe 4 is complete but narrowed above. Stripe 5 complete, narrow, of uniform width. Wings hyaline, crossveins and stigma yellowish. Legs uniformly pale brownish, without color pattern. The middorsal pale stripe of the abdomen is broad on the middle segments, and on segments 7 to 10 it spreads laterally to cover the entire segments. Appendages obscure yellowish brown.

This species was observed by the senior author on Chipola Lake, west Florida, where it is very common. In that waste of drowned cypress trees the adults squat on floating logs most of the time. Often they will settle on the brail of a passing row boat. They make only

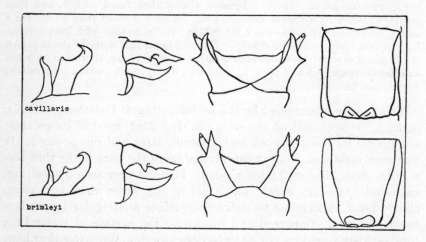

short flights. They sit close with tail and wing tips touching their support. They do not startle easily and are not difficult to capture. A few were flushed from paths on shore in the more open places, and a few pairs were seen together among low shubbery.

The nymphs clamber up the broad sides of mossy cypress stumps and leave their empty skins a foot or more above the surface of the water.

54. Gomphus brimleyi Muttkowski

Mtk. '11, p. 221.

Length 41 mm. Expanse 48 mm.   **N. C.**

Olivaceous green and brown on head and thorax; yellow and black on abdomen. Face greenish narrowly cross-striped with brown on sutures. Vertex
black. Occiput olivaceous. Thoracic stripes of first pair brown, narrowed to a
point at the crest and widened forward but not reaching the collar; stripe 2
narrowed and pointed above; twice as wide as surrounding pale stripe; stripe 3
distinct, complete, widened upward; 4 and 5 complete, 5 half as wide as 4. Legs
brown, femora beneath and tibiae externally and first two joints of tarsi superiorly paler. Abdomen blackish with the usual middorsal yellowish line on segments 1–8, interrupted at sutures, abbreviated on 8; apex of 7–9 edged with
yellow; 9 above black; 10 brown. Appendages brown, black at tips.

55. Gomphus graslinellus Walsh

Walsh '62, p. 394: Mtk. Cat. p. 93: Garm. '27, p. 164.

Length 48 mm. Expanse 60 mm.   **Md. to Wis.**

A slender greenish species, striped with brown. Face and occiput greenish.
Thoracic stripes of the first pair confluent, parallel sided, about as wide as the
bordering pale areas. Stripe 2 isolated above, then fused with 3, and then
separated below by a narrow greenish line. Stripe 2 is wider than 3. Stripes 4
and 5, broad and complete, and a bit diffuse. Wings hyaline with brown veins.
Legs brown, tibiae yellow externally. The middorsal pale stripe of the abdomen
is composed of nearly continuous and rather wide triangles, shortened on 8 but
lengthened again on 9 and 10. The sides of 8, 9 and 10 are marked with yellow.
Appendages blackish.

This species was studied by the senior author at Galesburg, Illinois,
in 1895. It appeared on the wing on May 23rd, reached its greatest
abundance in about a week and a month later had disappeared. It
was seen most commonly when flushed from the bare paths that ter-
raced a steep hillslope beside a pond. Females were seen ovipositing,
unattended, moving slowly along above the water close to a steep
clayey bank, descending to strike the surface at irregular intervals a
few feet apart. Captured and dipped to the surface of water in a
tumbler they would let fall 30 to 50 eggs at a dip. When free they kept
at the egg-laying process for a surprisingly long time. They certainly
lay many thousands of eggs.

The nymphs burrow in the steep clayey banks. Tail tip upturned
for respiration, they leave a shallow groove in the bottom marking
their trail. Transformation occurs between daybreak and sunup,
flat on the bank or on low grass, a foot or two from the water's
edge.

56. Gomphus williamsoni Muttkowski

Wmsn. '03, p. 253 (figs. no name): Mtk. Cat. p. 98.

Length 48 mm. Expanse 62 mm.   **Ind.**

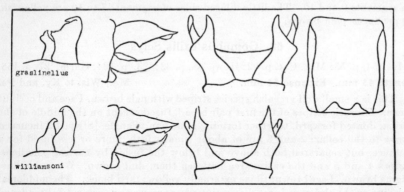

Similar in appearance to the preceding species. The figures presented herewith are copied from Williamson, who considered it a hybrid between that species
and *G. lividus*. Muttkowski merely applied the name given above, without
further characterization. Is it a distinct species?

57. Gomphus minutus Rambur

Ramb. '42, p. 161: Mtk. Cat. p. 94.

Length 44 mm. Expanse 55 mm.   **Fla., Ga.**

This is a dainty little greenish species, heavily striped with brown. Face and
occiput green. Thoracic stripes of the first pair broad, widened forward toward
the collar, broader than the bordering green stripes. Stripe 2 isolated above and
separated from 3 (which is of equal width) by a narrow green line. Stripes 3 and

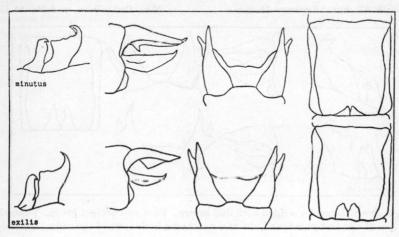

4 complete and rather broad, the area between them sometimes obscure. Wings hyaline, costa yellow, stigma brown. Legs brown, marked with yellow underneath the femora, on the outer face of the tibiae, and the tarsi. Abdomen brown with the pale middorsal line obscure, yellowish, continuous, becoming diffuse on segments 9 and 10. The little dilated sides of segments 7 to 10 are yellowish. Appendages pale brown.

58. Gomphus exilis Selys

Selys. '54, p. 55: Mtk. Cat. p. 92: Howe '18, p. 32: '23, p. 134: Garm. '27, p. 153.

Length 43 mm. Expanse 54 mm.   **Me., Wis. to Ky. and Pa.**

This is a small dull greenish species striped with pale brown. Face and occiput green. Thoracic stripes of the first pair broad, fused except on the middle of the carina, dilated forward, together forming a median triangle. Striped 2 incurved above to the collar: 2 and 3 are of about equal width, more or less fused for a distance, but separated both above and below the fusion by narrow pale lines. Stripes 4 and 5 and the entire area between them dull brown. Wings hyaline, stigma brown. Legs brown; tibiae externally yellow; tarsi black. The middorsal pale line on the abdomen is nearly continuous, narrowed on segment 8, broadened and diffused on 9 and 10. The slightly dilated side margins of segments 7 to 9 are dull yellow. Appendages brown.

A common species of the northeastern United States, about the shores of canals lakes and ponds, frequenting the more sheltered places. Williamson ('20) noted it "resting on blue grass heads and on the leaves of maples not over two feet high." "On dead weed stems, and on the windrow of debris along the lake."

59. Gomphus spicatus Hagen

Hag. '54, p. 54: Mtk. Cat. p. 97: Stout '18, p. 68: Howe '18, p. 34: '23, p. 133. Garm. '27, p. 156.

Length 47 mm. Expanse 56 mm.   **Me., Ont., Wis., and Pa. to Ill.**

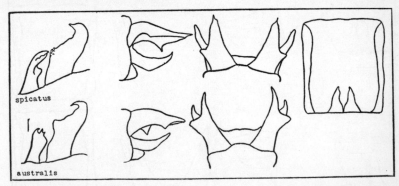

A greenish species striped with dull brown. Face and occiput green. Thoracic stripes of the first pair broad, diffuse, widened a little toward the collar; laterally spreading at both crest and collar to unite with stripe 2 around the ends of an isolated green line. Stripes 2 and 3 confluent or very nearly so. Stripes 4 and 5 and the entire area between them brown, with an additional brown oblique bar extending rearward from 5 below. Wings hyaline with brown veins. Legs blackish with tibiae yellow externally. The pale middorsal markings of the abdomen are very obscure, nearly continuous, shortened on segments 7 and 8; the side margins of segments 7, 8 and 9 are narrowly yellow. Appendages black. May to July; about the shores of the larger lakes and streams.

60. Gomphus australis Needham

Ndm. '97, p. 184: Mtk. Cat. p. 90.

Length 52 mm. Expanse 58 mm. **Fla.**

An olivaceous species striped with black. Face yellow with short blackish pubescence and two blackish cross stripes, one on base of labrum, the other across frons. Vertex black. Occiput yellow. Thoracic stripes of the first pair fused except on middle of carina, widened forward, not reaching collar, confluent above with incurved stripe 2; stripes 3, 4, and 5 distinct, entire, narrow. Legs black. Wings hyaline, costa yellow, stigma brown. Abdomen with middle segments black; sides of 1 and 2 pale; middorsal lanceolate pale spots on 7 and 8; sides of 7 apically, and of 8 and 10 entirely, yellow. Appendages brown.

61. Gomphus descriptus Banks

Banks '96, p. 194: Mtk. Cat. p. 91: Garm. '27, p. 151.

Length 50 mm. Expanse 60 mm. **N . Y. to Ill.**

This is a greenish species striped with brown and with blackish abdomen. Face and occiput green. Thoracic stripes of the first pair confluent except on the

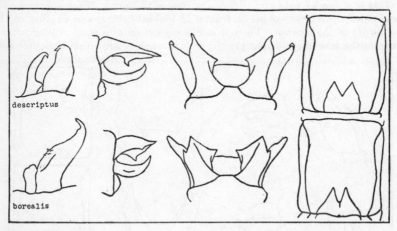

middle of the carina, nearly parallel sided, rounded to the collar where narrowly connected forward with the collar band. Stripe 2 free above, then fused for a distance with 3, then separated below by a narrow green line. Stripes 2 and 3 are of about equal width; the latter is sometimes narrowly divided by pale greenish on the upper part of the suture. Stripes 4 and 5 complete, angulated, variable, more or less overspreading the intervening area. Wings hyaline; stigma tawny. Legs blackish, with only the sides of the front femora pale. The middorsal spots of the abdomen are shortened on segments 6 and 7; 8, 9, and 10 are black above, yellow at the side margins. Appendages black.

This rather local species is not uncommon at Ithaca, N. Y. in the latter part of May. The males sometimes occur in large numbers, foraging over meadows half a mile back from the streams in the lee of the forests. The senior author once found a number of them going to roost at 3 in the afternoon in a pine tree, and clubbed them out and caught them with a net.

Transformation occurs very early in the morning within from one to three feet of the edge of the stream.

62. Gomphus borealis Needham

Ndm. '00, p. 454: Mtk. Cat. p. 90: Howe '18, p. 33: Garm. '27, p. 157.
Length 49 mm. Expanse 62 mm.   **N. H., N. Y., N. C.**

Similar to the preceding species (*G. descriptus*); distinguishable only by the form of the appendages.

63. Gomphus abditus Butler

Butler '14, p. 347.
Length 50 mm. Expanse 66 mm.   **Mass.**

This is a slender pale green species striped with brown. Face obscure, with broad pale brown cross-stripes on frontal and labral sutures and another on the free border of the labrum. There is also a suggestion of a median longitudinal stripe on the labrum. Occiput yellow, with a touch of brown on the outermost

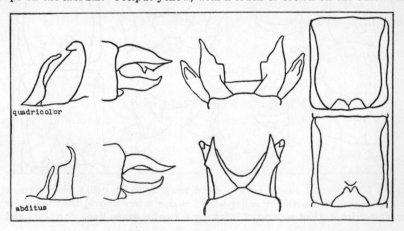

corners. Thoracic stripes of the first pair narrow above and widened below to a confluence with stripe 2 above the collar, leaving only an isolated oblong stripe of yellow between. Stripes 2 and 3 confluent above and below, and separated in the middle by a narrow line of yellow. Stripe 2 is broader than 3. Stripes 4 and 5 are complete, and the area between is washed with pale brown. Wings hyaline, with brown veins and tawny stigma. Legs brown, paler basally to the middle of the femora. Tibiae brown externally. The middorsal line of pale triangles on the abdomen is slender, abbreviated on segments 6 and 7, widened and further abbreviated on 8; 9 and 10 brown above. The side margins of the very moderately dilated segments 7, 8 and 9 are broadly washed with obscure yellow. Appendages brown.

64. Gomphus quadricolor Walsh

Walsh '62, p. 394: Mtk. Cat. p. 96.

Length 44 mm. Expanse 54 mm.   **Mass., Wis. to Tenn.**

A small green species striped with blackish brown, and with blackish abdomen. Face and occiput greenish. Rear of eyes black, with a mid-lateral pale spot. Thoracic stripes of the first pair fused except in the middle of the carina, and parallel sided, each not as wide as the bordering greenish stripe, truncate below at the collar, but narrowly conjoined with the brown collar band on the median line. Stripe 2 reaches the brown of the crest by a narrow prolongation, fuses with stripe 3, isolating a triangular greenish spot above, then separates from 3, leaving a green stripe below. Stripe 3 is broadest at the point of fusion with 2, and tapers downward therefrom. Stripes 4 and 5 are complete, narrow, and conjoined at the upper end. Wings hyaline; veins black. Legs black. The usual middorsal pale stripe of the abdomen is reduced to basal triangles on the middle segments. Segments 8, 9 and 10 are wholly black above and yellow at side margins. Appendages black.

Subgenus ARIGOMPHUS

These are graceful and strong flying Gomphines of less distinct coloration than the preceeding, the dark stripes of the thorax and the pale spots of the abdomen becoming diffuse or obsolete. The hind femora of the male are hairy, and of the female are spiny beneath. The apical margin of the eighth abdominal segment is cut obliquely, being longest on the dorsal side. The posterior genital hamules of the male slope backward.

The nymphs of this group are lanceolate in outline, the wide abdomen being narrowed before the end and then drawn out in a long tapering point so that the side margins of the long ninth segment are concave. The tibiae have strong burrowing hooks. The mentum of the labium has parallel sides and a convex median lobe that usually bears one or more teeth in the middle of the front border. The lateral lobes are blunt at the tip and bear, within, a series of jagged and widely spaced teeth that diminish in size proximally. Dorsal hooks are wanting except for a low rudiment on the ninth abdominal segment. Sometimes there is a median ridge before it but there is no median groove or impressed line. Segment 10 is long and cylindric and the long vertically flattened spines of 9 are closely applied to its sides. There are lateral spines on 7, or 8 to 9, only.

The following table sets forth the more salient characters of the nymphs of the species hitherto described.

The Known Nymphs

Name	Length	Teeth	Dorsal hooks	Relative lengths				Lateral spines*	Described by
				8	10	10	app.		
furcifer	33	6–7	0	8	10	6	4	8–9 = 1/5 of 10	Walk. '04, p. 358
pallidus	38	8	9	8	10	6	5	7–9 = 10	Hag. '85, p. 266
submedianus	38	6–7	9	7	10	5	4	7–9 = 10	Ndm. & Hart '01, p. 79
villosipes	35	6	0	7	10	6	4	8–9 = 1/5 of 10	Ndm. '01, p. 460

* And length of 9 in terms of length of 10.

KEY TO THE SPECIES

Adults

1　Occiput bordered with black.................villosipes, p. 116
　　Occiput not bordered with black............................2

2　Abdominal appendages black...............................3
　　Abdominal appendages not black..........................4

3　Superior appendages of male forked and with a long external tooth
　　......................................cornutus, p. 115
　　Superior appendages of male merely angulate externally........
　　......................................whedoni, p. 115

4　Stripe 5 complete...........................lentulus, p. 113
　　Stripe 5 obsolete or wanting................................5

5　Stripes 2 and 3 conjoined above...............furcifer, p. 115
　　Stripes 2 and 3 not conjoined above.........................6

6　Femora and tibiae uniformly pale..............pallidus, p. 114
　　Femora and tibiae partly black..............................7

7　Stripes 2 and 3 subequal...................subapicalis, p. 114
　　Stripes 2 and 3 reduced to a line..........submedianus, p. 113

65. Gomphus lentulus Needham

Ndm. '12, p. 275: Mtk. Cat. p. 94.

Length 49 mm. Expanse 64 mm.   **Ill.**

An olive species striped with brown. Face yellowish. Vertex brownish. Occiput yellow. Thoracic stripes of the first pair obscure, narrow, well separated, parallel; stripe 2 abbreviated above and diffuse at borders, well separated from 3 which is of equal breadth; 4 wanting; 5 complete, diffuse. Legs blackish with tibiae and 2 basal segments of tarsi yellow externally. Wings hyaline; costa yellow; stigma fulvous. Abdomen brownish with mid-dorsal and lateral streaks of yellow, basally and suffused with rufous toward the apex. 10 and appendages yellow.

66. Gomphus submedianus Williamson

Wmsn. '14, p. 54: Howe '18, p. 35: Kndy. '21, p. 596 (figs.): Howe '23, p. 133 (as *pallidus*).

Length 52 mm. Expanse 63 mm.   **Ill.**

This is another, slightly smaller and less hairy, northern species, with face and occiput pale, thoracic stripes of the first pair narrow and obscure, stripe 2

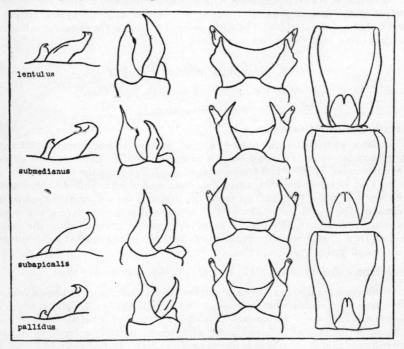

broader, stripe 3 a narrow line and 4 and 5 wanting (or, sometimes, a trace of 5 on the upper part of the suture). Wings hyaline with costa yellow and stigma tinged with rouge. Legs rather heavily lined with black on the femora before the knees and on the under side of the tibiae. Tarsi wholly black. Middle abdominal segments obscure greenish olivaceous; 3 to 6 each with an incomplete basal blackish ring, 7, 8 and 9 rusty brown; 10 and appendages yellow.

This species was observed near Galesburg Ill. by the senior author in 1896. It was common about the sloping shores of a small artificial lake. It rested much on the flat dirt roads and paths and on the mud close to the water's edge. Its flights were short, much like the flights of robber-flies, direct from one objective to another, at low elevation. It has a long season, being collected first on May 28th, and being most abundant about July 4th. Transformations occurred between daylight and sun rise, and the cast skins were left lying flat on the mud from one to three feet from the edge of the water.

67. Gomphus subapicalis Williamson

Wmsn. '14, p. 54: Kndy. '21, p. 596 (figs.).
Length 56 mm. Expanse 68 mm.   **Tex.**

A similar southwestern species, with unmarked face and occiput, the thoracic stripes of the first pair usually present but narrow and incomplete, stripes 2 and 3 of about equal width. The rusty color of the tip of the abdomen is less extended, being little developed on segment 7.

68. Gomphus pallidus Rambur

Ramb. '42, p. 163: Mtk. Cat. p. 95: Wmsn. '14, p. 54 (figs.).
Syn: pilipes Hag

Length 56 mm. Expanse 68 mm.   **Ga.**

A large pale olivaceous species, almost without thoracic stripes and with long hairy hind legs. Face and occiput pale greenish. The usual thoracic stripes are represented by indistinct traces, that of the 3rd pair (on the humeral suture) being best developed. Wings hyaline, costa and stigma yellow. Legs pale, blackened at tip of tibia and on tarsi; the first and second tarsal segments are yellow on the dorsal side. The middle abdominal segments have a somewhat annulate appearance, the pale color of the dorsum overspreading the sides, leaving them darker apically. Segments 7–9 are rusty brown; 10 and appendages yellow dull yellow.

Wilson's observations ('17, p. 192) on this species are that:

It flies comparatively slowly and hovers a great deal; its wings have a yellowish tinge, very visible when hovering. When it alights on a pebbly beach it hovers a moment and apparently feels the rock, testing it before settling, and meanwhile holdings its abdomen pointing upward. It then settles down slowly, lowering the abdomen until it is flat against the rock. In this position its colors harmonize so well with the surroundings that it can be seen only in a favorable light. It also frequently alighted on the boat, holding its abdomen elevated at an angle of 45.

This species was also fairly common at the riffles but unlike *plagiatus* it frequently alighted on the river bank and was then comparatively easy to capture.

69. Gomphus cornutus Tough

Tough '00, p. 17: Mtk. Cat. p. 91: Mtk. '10, p. 110: Mtk. & Whed. '15, p. 88, 90, 97.

Length 50 mm. Expanse 63 mm. **Ont. to Iowa, Wis.**

A yellowish green species with black and brown markings. Face and occiput greenish. Thoracic stripes of the first pair obscure, separated, abbreviated below, divergent towards both ends; stripe 2 wanting; 3 better developed, entire, confluent at crest with 1; 3 and 4 entire but diffuse and obscure. Legs black, front femora green beneath. Wings hyaline, veins black, costa pale, stigma yellowish. Abdomen blackish with middorsal row of spots on 1–8; small and basal on 9; also a small quadrangular spot on 10. Appendages blackish.

Found by Whedon ('15 p. 95) "transforming at a little kettle-hole near Mankato (Minn.). A fresh female and a dozen exuvia were picked up from floating sticks, algae, etc., at this time."

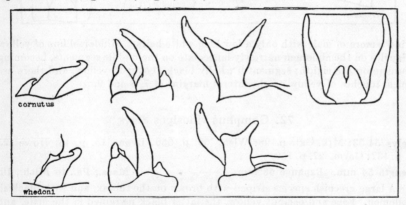

70. Gomphus whedoni Muttkowski

Mtk. '13, p. 167.

Length 50 mm. Expanse 63 mm. **Wis.**

This species though appearing to differ from *G. cornutus* strikingly in form of superior appendages of the male (as stated in the key), according to the describer, shows no other differences and is perhaps only a specimen in which these appendages have suffered an arrested development. Doubtfully distinct.

71. Gomphus furcifer Hagen

Hag. '78, p. 458: Mtk. Cat. p. 93: Howe '18, p. 34: '23, p. 133: Garm. '27, p. 158.

Length 46 mm. Expanse 64 mm. **Mass., N. Y., Ohio, Mich.**

A dark colored greenish species, striped with black. Face and occiput green. Thoracic stripes of the first pair well separated at the carina, ill defined, rather narrow and divergent, and abbreviated below, not reaching the collar. Stripe 2 wider than 1 but not as wide as the intervening spaces, and well separated from stripe 3 by a green line. Stripe 3 is narrower than 2 except at a depression toward its upper end. Stripes 4 and 5 are very incomplete. Wings hyaline with black veins and tawny stigma. Legs black, yellow to middle of femora, black beyond.

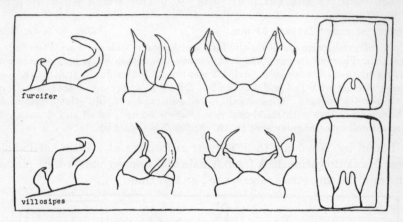

Hind femora of male with only a few long white hairs.   Middorsal line of yellow triangles on the abdomen narrowly lanceolate on the middle segments, becoming obsolete on the eighth; segment 9 wholly black above; 10 yellow, and there are apical touches of yellow on the lateral margins of 7, 8 and 9.

72. Gomphus villosipes Selys

Selys '54 53: Mtk. Cat. p. 98: Wlsn. '09, p. 656: Lyon, '15, p. 46: Howe '23 p. 132: Garm. '27, p. 159.

Length 54 mm. Expanse 68 mm.   **Mass., Pa., to Mich., Ill.**

A large greenish species striped with brown on the thorax, and with blackish abdomen. Face and occiput yellow, the latter black margined in the male, and with a median marginal tooth in both sexes. Thoracic stripes of the first pair narrower than the adjacent green areas, a little widened forward, abbreviated in front and separated by the carina. Stripe 2 free above, separated from 3 by a pale line. Stripe 3 complete, 4 and 5 obsolete, except at extreme ends. Wings hyaline; costal margin yellow; stigma yellowish. Legs black except at base. Hind femora of male densely clad with long soft hairs commingled with numerous slender spines. Tibiae pale externally. Middorsal pale line of abdomen obscure, abbreviated on segments 3–7; 8 and 9 black above on male, paler in female; 10 and superior appendages yellow, blackish at sides.

This is a common species at Ithaca N. Y., where its nymphs burrow in the mud of the settling basins of all the larger hill streams. The middle of May is the time of emergence. The handsome strong-flying greenish gray adults are hard to follow with the eye as they dart about over the riffles. Half submerged boulders in mid-stream seem to be their preferred resting places.

Wilson ('09, p. 656) found it.

Common, squatting on bare ground, logs and rocks; strong and pugnacious; catches and eats smaller dragonflies such as Leucorrhinia and Sympetrum.

11. DROMOGOMPHUS Selys

These are large yellowish green Gomphines with spiny hind legs. The venation is as in Gomphus, and only the legs show distinctive characters. The hind femora are armed beneath with a row of 5 to 7 long, strong spines.

The nymph of this genus (page 60, no. 7) bears a sharp median abdominal ridge that ends posteriorly on each segment in a straight spine. The lateral abdominal appendages are considerably shorter than the inferiors.

The genus includes only the three following nominal North American species.

KEY TO THE SPECIES

Adults

1 Face with a cross stipe of brown on the fronto-clypeal suture
....**armatus**, p. 117
   Face yellow.. ..2
2 Thoracic stripes 4 and 5 present.............. **spoliatus**, p. 117
   Thoracic stripes 4 and 5 wanting............. **spinosus**, p. 118

73. Dromogomphus armatus Selys

Selys '54, p. 59: Mtk. Cat. p. 100.

Length 54 mm. Expanse 76 mm. **Ga.**

A yellowish species with faint thoracic stripings. Face yellow with a narrow brownish line across the middle suture. Thoracic stripes of the first pair very narrowly linear and separated by the yellow carina, isolated from 2 above and below. Stripes 2 and 3 narrow and separated by a still narrower yellow line. Stripes 4 and 5 broader, continuous, diffuse. Wings hyaline with yellowish costa and stigma. Abdomen very much dilated on the terminal segments, yellow with a broad brownish black stripe each side.

74. Dromogomphus spoliatus Hagen

Hag. '57, p. 409: Mtk. Cat. p. 100: Wmsn. '20, p. 101: Garm. '27, p. 169.

Length 62 mm. Expanse 75 mm. **Wis., Ind., O., Tex.**

A fine big yellowish species striped lightly with brown. Face and occiput yellow. Thoracic stripes of the first pair widely separated at the carina, and strongly widened downward; prolonged at both ends to a narrow confluence with 2, leaving a rather wide yellow included stripe each side. Stripes 2 and 3 of about equal width, widened at a point of convergence near the upper end, and rather widely separated by yellow both above and below this point. Stripes 4 and 5 complete, narrowly linear, deep in the sutures. Legs brown yellowish toward the base. Wings hyaline with tawny stigma and yellowish costal margin. Ab-

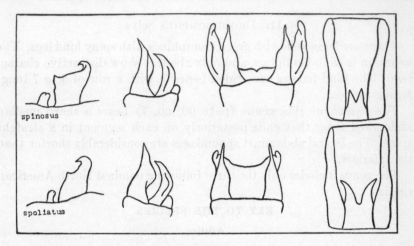

domen brownish basally and reddish on the slightly expanded apical segments. Paired pale dots invade the brown on the dorsum of segments 1 to 6 and a blackish narrow line borders the apical and inferior lateral margin of segments 8 and 9. 10 and appendages yellow.

Williamson ('01, p. 119) characterizes it as "An active, inquisitive species, relentless in love and war, more wary than *D. spinosus* and most numerous about the water from 9 A. M. to 4 P.M.: conspicuous by reason of the yellow, or reddish yellow, 7th to 9th abdominal segments" He found them abundant along the old canal-feeder of the St. Josephs River in Indiana and observed them capturing cabbage butterflies (*Pieris rapae*) and damselflies (*Hetaerina americana* and *Argia putrida*).

75. Dromogomphus spinosus Selys

Selys '54, p. 40: Mtk. Cat. p. 100: Wlsn. '12, p. 192: Brim. '03, p. 151: Howe '18, p. 75: '23, p. 138: Garm. '27, p. 168.

Length 58 mm. Expanse 78 mm.   **Me., Wis., Fla., Tex.**

A fine slender yellowish species with rather conspicuous brown shoulder stripes. Face and occiput yellow, the latter with blackish touches on the outermost angles. Thoracic stripes of the first pair very narrowly linear and widely separated by yellow at the carina and narrowly connected at the ends with stripe 2 to surround a wide yellow trapezoidal stripe. Stripes 2 and 3 of about equal width, broad and confluent except for a slight divergence at the lower end. Stripes 4 and 5 wanting. Legs blackish, yellowish at base. Wings hyaline with yellow costal margin and brownish stigma. Middorsal stripe of abdomen wide and trilobed on 2, narrow and continuous on 3 to 7, abbreviated triangular on 8 and 9, and rounded on 10. Side margins of the moderately expanded segments 7, 8 and 9 largely yellow with a blackish external border. Appendages blackish.

Inhabits still water: a common species about the shores of the finger lakes in central New York; found by Professor G. W. Herrick transforming abundantly on the shore of Canandaigua Lake in June 1897. Taken in transformation by Mrs. P. Babiy on the shore of Keuka Lake at Penn Yan, N. Y. July 12th 1925.

12. LANTHUS Needham

These are dainty little Gomphines conspicuously striped with black and yellow. In the venation of the wings there are several distinguishing characters. The stigma is short, hardly more than twice as long as wide. The upper section of the arculus (undivided portion of vein M) is short; vein M_{1-3} departing from it in a descending rather than in an ascending curve. There are usually but weak antenodal cross veins in the costal space between the thickened antenodals. The triangle of the hind wing is larger than that of the fore wing and tends to be angulated externally at the point where a weak trigonal supplement originates. The cell between the bases of A_2 and A_3 is often very long. The genital hamules of the male are inclined to rearward. The genus includes only two species of the eastern United States.

The nymphs of this genus are stocky little fellows with short abruptly pointed depressed abdomen and with the flat broadly oval, third antennal segment overspreading the face. The labium is short, the sides of the mentum are parallel; the front border of its median lobe is straight and scale-fringed with some low chitinous teeth in the middle. The lateral lobe is obliquely rounded to the first of a series of coarse teeth on its inner margin, and there is thus, no distinct end hook. The second of this series of 6 or 7 teeth is largest and the others diminish in size proximally. There are very short lateral spines on abdominal segments 8 and 9, and there are no dorsal hooks at all.

These nymphs inhabit the sandy places in the beds of rocky spring-fed brooks where they burrow shallowly, and whence they are easily obtained by sifting. They do not at once make themselves evident by action, however; instead they feign death for some minutes after being taken from the water and are apt to be thrown away with the trash, undiscovered by the careless collector.

KEY TO THE SPECIES
Adults
1 Abdominal appendages pale; thoracic stripe 4 complete........
....**albistylus,** p. 120
Abdominal appendages black; thoracic stripe 4 interrupted......
....**parvulus,** p. 120

76. Lanthus albistylus Hagen

Hag. '78, p. 460: Mtk. Cat. p. 88: Howe '18, p. 31: '23, p. 130: Garm. '27, p. 139
Syn: naevius Hag.

Length 36 mm. Expanse 46 mm.   **Me. to N. C. and Tenn.**

The smallest and daintiest of our clubtails, a greenish species heavily marked with black. Face pale, cross lined with black on all the sutures, the upper and middle sutures conjoined by an inverted black 7, the lower stripe runs down on the middle of the labrum and the latter is bordered with blackish. Thoracic stripes of the first pair are broad and broadly confluent and strongly widened downward. Stripes 2 and 3 are of about equal width and well separated by a pale stripe. Stripes 4 and 5 are complete. Legs black. Wings hyaline with stigma and costal margin brown. Middorsal pale line of abdomen narrows at the third segment and disappears at the fourth. Sides of 8 and 9 yellow. Appendages yellow.

77. Lanthus parvulus Selys

Selys '54, p. 56: Mtk. Cat. p. 88: Howe '18, p. 31: '23, p. 132: Garm. '27, p. 140.
Length 38 mm. Expanse 48 mm.   **N. S., N. Y., N. C.**

A very pretty little blackish species. Face greenish cross lined with black on the sutures and overspread with the same between the two lower ones (ante-

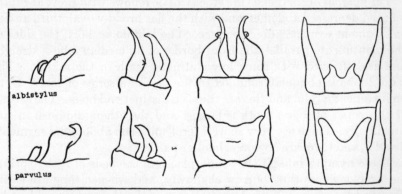

clypeus). Labrum bordered with black. Thoracic stripes of the first pair very broad, confluent, widened below and conjoined there with the 2nd, whereby the isolated intervening pale stripe is narrowed downward and abbreviated. Stripe 2 rather broad and broadly confluent with 3, leaving usually only a little green triangle between them below the crest. Stripe 4 broadly interrupted above the spiracle. Stripe 5 continuous. Legs black. Wings hyaline with brownish stigma. The yellow middorsal line of the abdomen narrows on 3, disappears on 4, and the posterior part of the abdomen including the appendages is black.

The nymphs of this species (Ndm. '01, p. 442) frequent the sandy beds in the deeper parts of small spring brooks. They dig rapidly. They feign death for a few minutes when taken from the water.

13. OCTOGOMPHUS Selys

These are elegant little black and yellow Gomphines that are easily recognized by the broad yellow patch that almost covers the front of the thorax (stripe 1 being wanting) and that has the shape of an inverted urn. In venation they resemble Lanthus, except in the minor characters stated in our key to the genera.

The abdominal appendages of the male terminate in 8 points (whence the generic name), the inferior being four-lobed, and the superiors each two-lobed, as shown in our figures.

The sole known species occurs along the mountain streams of our Pacific slope.

The nymphs burrow in the sandy places in the edges of snow-fed mountain stream beds or lie amid the loose trashy sediment, whence they are easily obtainable by sifting the surface layer. The senior author found them associated with larvae of soldier flies (Euparyphus) and midges (Chironomous and Tanytarsus) at the edges of the current in Cucamonga and other Cañons in the San Gabriel mountains in Southern California. A few were found in the sand bars of the Santa Ana River, where it meanders over the hot plain. These nymphs, when placed in a dish of gravel or sand, quickly buried themselves by digging deeply into it. Kept for weeks in a small dish with the big predacious nymphs of Cordulegaster, they managed to escape being eaten. They are quite agile. They are the cleanest of Gomphine nymphs, as befits their dwelling in the clear, cold streams.

78. Octogomphus specularis Hagen

Hag. '59, p. 544: Mtk. Cat. p. 101: Kndy '17, p. 574: Smn. '26, p. 20.

Length 50 mm. Expanse 66 mm. **Calif.**

A very pretty little Western club-tail with a yellow inverted-urn shaped mark covering the front of the thorax, and very broad shoulder stripes of black. Face pale cross-lined with black on the sutures, the lower stripe running down on the middle of the labrum; the latter is margined with black. Occiput black, with yellow hind border. Thoracic stripes of the first pair wanting, so that there is a very wide median yellow area. Stripes 2 and 3 unusually broad, often wholly confluent. Stripe 4 wanting below the spiracle, stripe 5 continuous but narrow, conjoined with 3 and 4 below. Legs black. Wings hyaline with black veins and brown stigma. The middorsal pale stripe of the abdomen becomes very narrow on segments 3 and 4, disappears on 5 to 9, and reappears as a diffuse pale round spot on 10. The extreme apical margin of 8 and 9 is pale above, and 8 has an isolated yellow spot on the slightly expanded lateral margin.

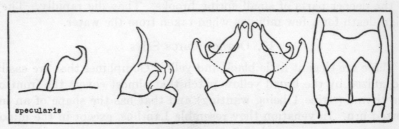

specularis

Kennedy ('17, p. 574) found this species on the wing from April to August—a rather long season of flight for a Gomphine. He studied its habits carefully in the coast streams of California. He says of it:

As with most gomphines, the males of this species stay near the water while the females are seldom seen there. The males are usually found in the sunlit openings of the streams where they perch on stones, driftwood, or on the foliage of the surrounding alders. But while preferring the sunny spots they do not hesitate to hunt up and down stream through the shade. The four females I have taken were found along a road on the side of the gorge several hundred feet above the stream. They appear to resort to the stream only to oviposit.

After having spent various days wading down mountain streams observing *Octogomphus* more often than catching them, I was rewarded on July 7 by seeing a female oviposit. She came volplaning down through an opening in the canopy of alders and, while going through evolutions involving several figures, 8's and S's, she touched the surface of the pool lightly with the tip of her abdomen at intervals of 2 to 6 feet. After 20 seconds of this she airily spiraled up and out into the sunshine, where she alighted on a bush on the hillside above the creek.

Kennedy found the cast nymphal skins sticking to exposed roots of alder trees a foot or two above the surface of the pools in the streams. Judging by sizes of nymphs found together, he thinks that three years are required for development. He has published a careful description and figures of the nymph (l.c., p. 579).

Subfamily AESCHNINAE

The Darners

Very large and strong flying dragonflies, with nearly smooth bodies and rather brilliant coloration. The eyes meet broadly on the top of the semiglobular head, crowding between the visible part of vertex and occiput. The labium is cleft at the apex on the median line. The moderate stigma generally has a strong brace vein at its proximal end. The triangles are elongated in the axis of the wing and a trigonal planate springs from a prominence in the outer side of each. The female has a well developed ovipositor.

This family contains a large proportion of our biggest dragonflies. They dominate the upper air over pond and meadow. They venture far from water. They invade city streets and fly into open laboratory windows.

These are the true "mosquito hawks"; but their diet is by no means restricted to mosquitos. Midges and mayflies, and moths and crane-flies are eaten freely. When the evening swarms of mayflies rise by the waterside, these big darners may be seen coursing through the swarms, in and out again repeatedly, gathering a meal. At noon, when the midges are settled on the tree trunks by the water side, a big darner may often be seen searching a tree, his face a few inches from the bark as he slowly moves along it up and down on the leeward side, rustling his wings as if to flush the midges, and now and then seizing one of them. They all eat other smaller dragonflies.

The nymphs of this group are smooth and slender of body with long thin legs. The labium is flat and lacks raptorial setae (except in Gynacantha); its median lobe is cleft at the front. The prothorax bears prominent tubercles at the sides. The abdomen is widened beyond the base. There is a considerable development of color pattern, suited to different types of environment.

The nymphs are active climbers. They live amid green vegetation in still waters or in trash fallen in the edges of streams. They are predatory and cannibalistic, and often approach their prey by stealth.

KEY TO THE GENERA

Adults

1 Radial sector simple...2.
   Radial sector bearing an apical fork (except in Oplonaeschna)..4.

123

2   Two cubito-anal cross veins; vein M_2 undulate; supratriangle
    without cross veins; one cross vein under stigma............
    ....**Gomphaeschna**, p. 125
    Three or more cubito-anal cross veins; vein M_2 not undulate;
    supratriangle divided by cross veins; several cross veins under
    stigma...3.

3   Basal space traversed by cross veins...........**Boyeria**, p. 126
    Basal space open.......................**Basiaeschna**, p. 126

4   Sectors of the arculus separating from the arculus at or below
    its middle...5.
    Sectors of the arculus springing from above the middle of the
    arculus.......................................**Anax**, p. 128

5   Radial sector apparently unbranched; 2 cross veins under the
    stigma............................**Oplonaeschna**, p. 129
    Radial sector distinctly branched; three or more cross veins under
    stigma...6.

6   Fork of radial sector under the middle of the stigma; outer end of
    radial planate gently curved...........**Coryphaeschna**, p. 131
    Fork of radial sector before the stigma; outer end of planate bent
    forward abruptly.......................................7.

7   Radial sector symmetrically forked; one or two rows of cells be-
    tween it and its planate...............................8.
    Radial sector strongly deflected towards the stigma at the base
    of its fork, unsymmetric; 3 to 7 rows of cells between it and its
    planate...9.

8   Face strongly produced above, the upper margin of the frons very
    acute; veins M_1 and M_2 parallel to the level of the stigma; the
    radial planate subtends one row of cells...**Nasiaeschna**, p. 132
    Face vertical, not sharply angulate at upper edge of frons; veins
    M_1 and M_2 approximated at the stigma; the radial planate
    subtends..............................**Epiaeschna**, p. 133

9   Two rows of cells between Cu_1 and Cu_2 beyond the anal loop of
    the hind wing............................**Aeschna**, p. 134
    One row of cells between Cu_1 and Cu_2 beyond the anal loop of
    the hind wing.........................**Gynacantha**, p. 149

Nymphs

1   Lateral lobes of labium armed with strong raptorial setae
                                          Gynacantha, p. 150
    Lateral lobes of labium lacking raptorial setae.............2.

2 Hind angle of head strongly angulate.....................3.
   Hind angle of head broadly rounded....................5.

3 Superior abdominal appendages as long as inferiors...........
   ....**Coryphaeschna**, p. 131
   Superior abdominal appendages much shorter than inferiors...4.

4 Lateral lobe of labium squarely truncate on tip..**Boyeria**, p. 127
   Lateral lobe of labium with taper pointed tip **Basiaeschna**, p. 126

5 Lateral spines on abdominal segments 7–9.........**Anax**, p. 128
   Lateral spines on abdominal segments 6–9......**Aeschna**, p. 135
   Lateral spines on abdominal segments 4 or 5–9...............6.

6 Low dorsal hooks on segments 7–9........**Nasiaeschna**, p. 132
   No dorsal hooks on abdomen..............**Epiaeschna**, p. 133

14. GOMPHAESCHNA Selys

These are small brown darners of rather secretive habits and of very local distribution. The stigma of the wings is short, with only two cells bordering it behind. Between the two thickened antenodal cross veins there are usually but two weak ones. The triangles are divided by a single cross vein. There are but two cubito-anal cross veins. A single row of cells is subtended by the radial planate. The anal loop is small, enclosing usually but four cells. This is a large array of venational characters setting off this genus from all our other Aeschnines, allying it somewhat with the preceding subfamily (as the generic name suggests), as does also the forking inferior appendage of the male abdomen.

The single species is restricted in its distribution to the eastern states. Its nymph is still (1928) unknown.

79. Gomphaeschna furcillata Say

Say '39 p. 14: Mtk. Cat. p. 104: Howe '19, p. 43: Hag. '74, p. 354: Garm. '27, p. 177.

Syn: quadrifida Ramb. *Var: antilope* Hag.

Length 50 mm. Expanse 70 mm.   **Me. and Mich. to Pa. and Ga.**

A dull brownish species with obscurely spotted abdomen. Face and frons obscure bluish or dirty whitish including sides of frons above and tip of vertex. Base and middle of frons above and occiput black. Thorax obscure brownish thinly clothed with greyish hairs. Front of thorax greenish brown with carinae narrowly blackish, occasionally showing a pair of obscure pale, parallel stripes. Sides greenish brown striped with black narrowly on the humeral suture (stripe 2) broadly on the lower half of the middle suture (stripe 4) and on all the third lateral suture (stripe 5). These side stripes are widened and confluent below around the leg bases. Legs shining brown, darker on knees. Wings hyaline wth tawny stigma and brown veins. Abdomen brown with yellow auricles in the male and equivalent side spots in the female; with 3 tawny yellowish spots on the dorsum of the middle segments, one broad basal spot and a pair of large triangular apical spots on each segment. Lower lateral margin of 1–8 pale beneath. 9 and 10 are obscure. Appendages thinly fringed on inner side with long brown hairs.

A somewhat large form (Length 58 mm.) with brownish face, black stigma, more elongate abdomen and appendages, and generally more obscure coloration, has been described under the name *G. antilope* (Hagen).

15. BASIAESCHNA Selys

These are slender brownish darners with brown spots on the bases of both wings. The radial sector is unbranched and the anal loop encloses two vertical rows of cells. They are common about woodland streams in early summer. They fly rather slowly and unwarily and are not especially difficult to capture. The one known species is restricted in range to the eastern states.

Its nymph was described by the senior author ('01, p. 466) and by Ndm. & 'Hart ('01, p. 38).

80. Basiaeschna janata Say

Say '39, p. 13: Mtk. Cat. p. 103: Howe '19, p. 42: '23, p. 127: Garm. '27, p. 174.
Syn: minor Ramb.

Length 56 mm. Expanse 76 mm.   **Me. and Wis. to N. C. and Mo.**

This is a pretty brownish darner with conspicuous yellow side stripes. Face obscure. Frons with a black T spot above, whose base envelops the vertex except at its pale transverse summit. Occiput brown. Front of thorax brown with 2 obscure parallel yellowish streaks that disappear superiorly. Sides of thorax with 2 brown yellow oblique stripes that are rendered more conspicuous by borders of darker brown. Legs brown. Wings hyaline with yellowish stigma and brown veins, and with a brown spot at their extreme bases. Membranule white. Abdomen pale on the swollen basal segments, ringed with brown on the carinae; segments 2–9 ringed with black and with a very obscure pattern of broad paler parietal areas covering most of the segments; 10 paler above, except (male) around its low median tubercle. Appendages brown.

16. BOYERIA McLachlan

These are large brown species with two big pale spots on each side of the thorax, by which they may be recognized even in flight. A distinctive structural character is the presence of cross veins in the space before the arculus, (the first median space).

They are inhabitants of woodland streams where the adults fly near the water, especially on sunny afternoons. They glide along but little above the shining surface, on well poised, transparent wings, which, against the background of the water, are well nigh invisible. They do not fly very rapidly. They haunt the shadows in the edges of the woods, and when discoverable they are not hard to capture.

The nymphs are blackish and smooth of body with obscure rings of paler color on the legs. The hind angles of the head are sharply angulate. There is a minute brown tooth on the front border of the median lobe of the labium, a little remote from the median cleft. The superior appendage of the male is narrowly cleft lengthwise at the tip.

They cling to timbers, fallen trash and drift wood and to roots that trail in the stream.

Nymphs

Name	Length	Lateral spines	Width by length of labium	Described by
vinosa	35	5–9	1×2	Cabot '81, p. 29*
grafiana	38	4–9	less than 1×2	Walk. '13, p. 164

* Also by Ndm. '01, p. 465 & Ndm. & Hart '01, p. 36, fig.

KEY TO THE SPECIES
Adults

1 Side spots of the thorax yellowish; abdominal segments 9 and 10 unlike in color, 10 more yellowish..............**vinosa,** p. 127

   Side spots of thorax bluish; abdominal segments 9 and 10 alike in color, greenish blue .... **grafiana,** p. 128

81. Boyeria vinosa Say

Say '39, p. 13: Mtk. Cat. p. 102: Wlsn. '12, p. 192: Howe '19, p. 41: '23, p. 126. Garm. '27, p. 172.

Syn: quadriguttata Burm.

Length 64 mm. Expanse 80 mm.   **Me. and Wis. to Ark. and Tenn.**

A slender brownish species with conspicuous yellow side spots on thorax. Face and thorax pale except for a very obscure brownish T spot above on the latter. Occiput yellow, brown at the sides. Thorax brown in front with very obscure pale stripes diverging forward and dilated above. Sides of thorax brown with the 2 round spots of bright yellow. Wings hyaline except for a short brownish basal spot; veins brown and stigma tawny. Abdomen with moderately expanded basal segments and very obscure coloration; wholly brown with black apical carinae and the sides of the tenth segment paler. Appendages brown, the lower one paler.

Mr. J. L. Graf (Wmsn. '07, p. 5) observed this species ovipositing in damp algae while at rest on rocks just above the water.

82. Boyeria grafiana Williamson

Wmsn. '07, p. 1: Mtk. Cat. p. 102: Walk. '13, p. 161: Howe '19, p. 42: '23, p. 127.

Length 64 mm. Expanse 88 mm.   **Mass. and Ont. to Pa. and Ky.**

A handsome brown species with bluish face and side spots. Face and frons bluish or yellowish with an obscure diffuse T spot on the top of the latter. Vertex brown with a pale hind border. Front of thorax with 2 narrow bluish yellow spots that strongly diverge forward and that are dilated at their upper end before the collar. Sides with 2 large bluish yellow spots on the lower more convex portion. Legs obscure brownish. Wings hyaline with brown costa and tawny stigma. A diffuse brownish spot at extreme base along the veins. Abdomen brown, auricles of male yellow; 3 narrow pale spots on dorsum of second segment, one basal, two lateral and transverse; segments 3–7 with broad, smooth, basal brown cross bands followed by encircling yellow line narrowed at sides, and a pair of submedian, narrow, transverse, pale dashes. 9 and 10 paler on sides. Appendages brown.

17. Anax Leach

The Green Darners

These are large, strong flying dragonflies. The males lack auricles on the second abdominal segment, and the adjacent wing margin is not notched, nor stiffened with an anal triangle. The upper section of the arculus (undivided portion of vein M) is very short, so that both its sectors spring from the upper half.

The nymphs are active climbers in submerged vegetation. Their long, smooth bodies are decorated in a neat protective pattern of greens and browns. There are lateral spines only on segments 7–9 of the abdomen.

The genus is world wide in its distribution. It contains some 27

The Nymphs

Species	Length	Teeth on Med. lobe*	Cleft of Med. lobe	End hook** Character	Movable hook Setae	Described by
junius	40–62	0	closed	rounded	moderate	Cabot '81, p. 15
longipes	62	at cleft	open†	truncate		
amazili	53	at cleft	open‡	truncate	coarse	Byers '27, p. 67
walsinghami	58	wide apart	open	truncate	fine	Byers '27, p. 66

* Median lobe of labium.
** Of lateral lobe of labium.
† Reaching the level of the cord: caudal app. more than 8 mm. long.
‡ Not reaching the level of the cord: caudal app. about 6 mm. long.

species, of which only one is generally distributed in this country, while three others of tropical coastwise distribution are found in our borders.

KEY TO THE SPECIES

Adults

1   Top of frons yellow............................**longipes, p. 129**
    Top of frons with a black spot.............................2.
2   Black spot on frons surrounded with blue ....3.
    Black spot on frons not surrounded with blue....**amazilli, p. 129**
3   Expanse 105 mm...............................**junius, p. 129**
    Expanse 120 mm.......................**walsinghami, p. 130**

83. Anax longipes Hagen

Hag. '61, p. 118: Mtk. Cat. p. 106: Howe '19, p. 44: '23, p. 120: Garm. '27, p. 179.
Length 79 mm. Expanse 107 mm.   **Mass. and Ohio to Fla.**

    This is a fine green-bodied species with long red legs. Face yellow, including top of frons. Thorax green. Hind femora 15 mm. long. Wings with costa and stigma yellow. Abdomen green on 1 and on side of 2; brick red beyond with some spots of yellow on sides. Appendages red.

84. Anax amazili Burmeister

Burm. '39, p. 841: Mtk. Cat. p. 105: Calv. '19, p. 37: Byers '27, p. 67.
Syn: maculatus Ramb.
Length 79 mm. Expanse 108 mm.   **La., P. R.**

    This is a fine greenish species with black legs. Face yellow. Frons with a triangular brown spot above on each side of which is a spot of blue. Thorax green. Legs black, paler basally. Costa greenish; stigma brown. Abdomen thick, much swollen at base where green; brown on segments 3–10, with a dorsal blackish stripe that is narrowed on the middle of segments, and two touches of blue or green each side on segments 3–7. Large spots of same color on 9. 10 brown, unspotted. Appendages brown.

85. Anax junius Drury

Drury 1773: Mtk. Cat. p. 105: Osburn '16, p. 90: Howe '19, p. 43: '23, p. 120. Ndm. '23, p. 129: Smn. '26, p. 24: Byers '27, p. 67: Garm. '27, p. 168: Calv. '28, p. 12.
Syn: spiniferus Ramb.
Length 76 mm. Expanse 104 mm   **N. Am.**

    This is a fine big darner with a green thorax and bluish abdomen. Face yellow. Frons above blue, margined with black and with a round black central spot within a ring of blue surrounded by yellow. Thorax wholly green. Legs blackish beyond femora, which are reddish. Wings hyaline, often tinged with

amber yellow, except at the ends; costa yellow; stigma tawny. Abdomen pale
at base on sides of much swollen segments, and blue beyond with a very obscure
pattern of paired pale, dorsal markings. Appendages brown. Distinguishable,
even in flight, from all other northern dragonflies, by the big, green body.

The nymphs are cannibals. They climb rapidly, and swim well by
means of ejections of water from the gill chamber. They are often
seen half hiding behind submerged stems with the head poised low,
and the abdomen lifted in a position of great alertness. Transformation occurs before daybreak, usually not far from the water's surface.
The nymphs are sometimes found in brackish water having a high degree of salinity.

This species is discussed at length in Part I, page 7, and is illustrated
in our frontispiece.

86. Anax walsinghami McLachlan

The giant green darner

McL. '82, p. 127: Mtk. Cat. p. 106: Ndm. '23, p. 129: Smn. '26, p. 24: Byers
'27, p. 66.

Length 105 mm. Expanse 122 mm.   **Calif.**

This is our largest dragonfly. Face yellow. Top of frons with an elongate
brown spot surrounded by yellow outside of which is a circle of blue. Thorax
green. Legs black with the front femora yellowish beneath. Wings broad with
yellow costa and a short, narrow, brown stigma. Abdomen very long, narrow,
blue except the first segment which is red. A mid-dorsal brown line on the following segments widens posteriorly almost covering 7–9 dorsally, leaving on 10
only two blue spots. Appendages brown, short, somewhat spatulate.

18. OPLONAESCHNA Selys

These are brownish darners with rather short thick abdomens. Vein
R_s is unbranched, veins M_1 and M_2 are strongly convergent just before the stigma. Vein M_4 bends away from M_3 at the beginning of the
terminal curve. The tenth abdominal segment of the male bears a
high median tubercle.

There is a single Sonoran species. Nymph unknown.

87. Oplonaeschna armata Hagen

Hag. '91, p. 124: Mtk. Cat. p. 104.

Length 68 mm. Expanse 100 mm.   **Ariz. and N. Mex.**

This is a short brownish species with blackish side stripes and black ringed
abdomen. Face pale greenish with yellow labrum and a broad black transverse
spot on rounded summit of frons, often forming a T spot. Very small black
vertex is tipped with yellow. Occiput and summit of carinae yellow. Front of
thorax brown with 2 obscure greenish blue narrow stripes more or less interrupted

above. Sides of thorax with 2 bluish stripes that become yellowish below where they are bordered by black, with a general background of brown; pubescence of thorax whitish, short in front, long below and to rearward, grading down the sides. Legs brown. Wings hyaline with yellow costa and brown veins and yellow or brown stigma. There are rather conspicuous roundish black spots upon and above the base of the wing roots. The swollen basal segments of the abdomen are tufted above with tawny hairs; apical margins of segments 2–8 are narrowly ringed with shining black at apex and on dorsum there are 2 pairs of yellow spots, the hinder pair well separated, adjacent to an apical black ring; the other pair subbasal, approximate, laterally tapering and confluent with obscure yellow, submarginal, lateral, streaks; 10 brown with conspicuous mid-dorsal spines. Appendages blackish.

19. CORYPHAESCHNA Williamson

These are huge, neotropical darners that enter only the southeastern U. S. The head is very wide and the abdomen is very long; likewise, the slender abdominal appendages, which may reach 10 or 12 mm. Veins M_1 and M_2 converge behind the stigma. The fork of the radial sector is very unsymmetrical and its base is under the middle of the stigma. The apical planate takes origin far beyond the stigma.

These are swift-flying, powerful insects, very difficult to capture with a net. One of them, at least, is of economic importance as an enemy of the honeybee. Two species are said to occur within our limits, and a third lives farther southward. Ours may be distinguished as follows:

KEY TO THE SPECIES

1 Dorsum of thorax brown with green stripes.......**ingens,** p. 131
   Dorsum of thorax green with brown stripes.......**virens,** p. 132

The nymph is at once distinguished from all our other darners by the possession of a pair of long, sharp parallel spines besides the median cleft of the labium. Kennedy ('19, p. 107) has described the nymph of *C. ingens*.

88. Coryphaeschna ingens Rambur

The Bee Butcher

Ramb. '42, p. 192: Mtk. Cat. p. 115: Kndy. '19, p. 106.

Syn: abbotti Hag.

Length 88 mm. Expanse 120 mm.   **N. C., Ga. and Fla.**

This is a gigantic species with stout thorax and very long abdomen. Face greenish with brown-bordered yellowish labrum. Frons above with a pale brown T-spot and a basal half ring. Occiput yellowish. Front of thorax brown with 2 broad green stripes, divergent and tapering below, and dilated at the top in a recurrent lobe surrounding a stripe of brown (stripe 2). Sides of thorax green with a broad median stripe widened below to cover the spiracle, and confluent with the brown of the under surface. Legs blackish. Wings hyaline, sometimes tinged with yellow beyond the triangles and at the base; stigma brown. Abdomen slender; sides of basal segments clothed with white hairs; auricles small; segments 3–8 cross-banded with greenish yellow, interrupted middorsally and confluent at sides with submarginal streaks of the same color; 9 with paler apical half-ring, which on 10 becomes a pair of dorsal spots. Appendages long, straight smooth, hairy within.

89. Coryphaeschna virens Rambur

Ramb. '42, p. 192: Mtk. Cat. p. 115.

Length 87 mm. Expanse 115 mm.   **Ga.?**

Face, occiput and tip of vertex green. Thorax similar to that of the preceding but with the dorsum greenish, marked with brown, in a line on each side of the carina (stripe 1) and another short, very oblique one on each side (stripe 2); sides greenish with brown lines on first and last sutures (stripes 3 and 5). Feet black with only base of femora reddish. Wings hyaline, sometimes a little tinted with brown; costa black; stigma brown; anal triangle of 2 cells. Abdomen slender a little enlarged on the second segment or narrowed on the third; blackish spotted with green; 3–8 with middorsal streaks and a terminal ring of green; 10 flat above. Appendages brownish.

20. Nasiaeschna Selys

These are big, angular, greyish blue and brown darners of rather archaic aspect, built on lines that are rather less graceful than those of related genera. The frons projects forward above the sloping clypeus in a sharp-edged snout-like shelf (whence the generic name). The radial sector is symmetrically forked. The radial planate subtends but a single row of cells. Veins M_1 and M_2 are not convergent behind the stigma.

There is a single species distributed well over the eastern United States, but it seems to be rare and local.

The nymph is at once distinguished from all the other darner nymphs of our fauna by the possession of a series of dorsal hooks on the abdomen. It was described by the senior author ('01, p. 468) and by Ndm. and Hart ('01, p. 34).

90. Nasiaeschna penthacantha Rambur

The Blue-nosed Darner

Ramb. '42, p. 208: Mtk. Cat. p. 116: Howe '19, p. 50: '23, p. 125: Garm. '27, p. 194.

Length 68 mm. Expanse 98 mm.   **Ill. and New England to Fla. and Tex.**

This is a blue-nosed, black-legged creature of rather elongate form and slender abdomen. Face yellowish with brownish margin to the labrum below and to the frons above. Top of frons porcelain blue, more obscure basally. The bifid summit of the vertex is blue. The lateral ocelli, inserted upon its upper surface, are narrowly ringed with yellow. The occiput is very narrow, limited to the rear of the very long eye seam. Thorax compact, smooth, shining with very short obscure vestitute. Front brown with 2 broad bluish green stripes abbreviated below, where there points are directed laterally, dilated above into T-shaped or 7-shaped summits near the crest. Sides greenish blue between 3 broad bands of brown, the first on the humeral suture (stripes 2 and 3) emarginate below; the second on the second lateral suture (stripe 5) widened below and with a spur running forward; the third covering the rear of the thorax. Legs black, becoming rufous basally. Wings hyaline, becoming a little rufous; stigma narrow tawny. Abdomen slender, little widened at base, little constricted on 3, slowly tapering; auricles of male large, triangular; sides of 1, 2, 3, bluish green below. Remainder of abdomen very obscurely spotted with paler on a background of brown with shining subbasal and apical rings of black encircling all the segments Appendages short and slender, shining brown.

21. EPIAESCHNA Hagen

These are among the largest of our dragonflies, attaining a wing expanse of 116 mm. The face is vertical and not acutely angulated at top of frons; the head is very wide, due to the huge, bulging eyes. The radial sector is forked rather symmetrically. The radial planate subtends 2 rows of cells. Veins M_1 and M_2 converge behind the stigma.

These are voracious swift flying dragonflies, widely and generally distributed throughout the eastern United States. Due to their strikingly large size, their fearless approach and their habit of flying into open windows betimes, they are rather well known. They are exceedingly hard to capture in flight. There is but a single species.

The nymph is a very large smooth, greenish creature with a somewhat spindle shaped abdomen. It has no dorsal hooks but it has lateral spines on segments 5–9 of the abdomen. The mentum of the labium is parallel sided in its basal half and then suddenly and roundly widened to the base of the rather slender lateral lobes. The front border of the mentum is divided into 2 smoothly rounded lobes whose convergent curves meet in a median acute notch. The inner border of each lateral lobe is armed with a dozen sharp denticles, and there is a longer, stronger, internal tooth at its tip.

The senior author collected a cast skin of this species at Dead Pond near Rock Bluff P. O., Florida, on April 2nd. It was clinging to the bark of a cypress tree more than 6 feet above the surface of the water. The tree stood in a sphagnum filled pond.

91. Epiaeschna heros Fabricus

Fabr. 1798, p. 285: Mtk. Cat. p. 117: Howe '19, p. 50: '23, p. 125: Garm. '27, p. 196.

Syn: multicincta Say

Length 82 mm. Expanse 116 mm.   Me., Ont. and S. D. to Fla. and Tex.

This is a very large and handsome, strong flying species with brown body and more or less smoky wings. Face brownish, paler on sutures. Frons with diffuse blackish border next the transverse apical carina. Vertex bilobed, black. Occiput brown. Thorax brown in front with 2 broad greenish stripes divergent below, with long, slender points, and dilated above beneath the collar. Sides brown with 2 very broad greenish stripes; the rear one widened superiorly. Legs black. Wings subhyaline, the membrane more or less deeply tinged with amber brown; costa and subnodus yellow; stigma brown. Abdomen brown with black carinae; a half ring of greenish on the base of segment 2 includes the small scale like auricles in the male; a middorsal ridge on 10 ends in a triangular spine. Appendages black, hairy internally in the male, smooth and leaf like in the female.

22. AESCHNA Illiger
The Blue Darners
By Elsie Broughton

Expanse 78–100 mm.

This cosmopolitan genus is represented in our fauna by eighteen species. The wings are moderately broad with a well developed anal loop. The radial sector is more or less sinuate and is forked unsymmetrically. Vein M_1 rises either just before the stigma or opposite its inner end. The males have an anal triangle of two or three cells and a pair of auricles on the second abdominal segment. The eyes are broadly contiguous. The thorax has on each side a pair of lateral pale stripes the form of which is more or less characteristic of the species. These stripes are of four main types (Fig. 33): (1) moderately broad, the anterior margins nearly straight and parallel; (2) the anterior margin, especially of the first, excavated by the body color of the thorax; (3) the anterior margin, of the first at least, excavated, sometimes rectangularly, and with a dorsal posterior spur; (4) slender, the first one bent twice, nearly at right angles. One species, *interrupta*, shows great lack of conformity, possessing lateral pale stripes ranging from long, slender, parallel stripes, through broader ones with excavated anterior margins,

FIG. 31. Nymph of *Aeschna umbrosa*.

to a complete constriction of the stripes into two pairs of small spots.

The abdomens of fresh specimens are conspicuously patterned with yellow, blue or green, but this color was so faded in our specimens that it is not here described, (see Walker '12).

, These strong-flying dragonflies may be found foraging miles away from their breeding places. In the humid East they fly unceasingly on the hottest days, and take prolonged rests in the shade when the weather is cool; but in the arid West, according to Kennedy ('17):

Both *A. californica* and *multicolor* hang in the shade from the underside of leaves of trees on very hot days. . . . . I have not noticed them resting when the temperature was less than 100. These rests last for a few minutes only but occur at short intervals. It is only at such times that they are easily taken away from the water.

While ovipositing the female is not accompanied by the male. She lays her eggs a little beneath the surface in the tissues of soft stems, making oblique rows of punctures with her ovipositor. Walker ('12) says that:

In most species the males seize the females while ranging over the reeds and rushes which grow in their breeding places. Very frequently the females are picked up while ovipositing. If copulation ensues, the pair usually fly off to the nearest trees, often circling about in the air a few times.

The Known Nymphs

Species	Length	Lat. sp.	of 9[1]	ap. b ×1[2]	Lat. lobe	Described by
californica	36	6–9	3/5	subequal	rounded	Walk. '12, p. 188
canadensis	37	6–9	1/2	5/7+	hooked truncate	Walk. '12, p. 141
constricta	37	6–9	2/5	6/7	pointed	Ndm. '01, p. 470
clepsydra	38	6–9	2/3	5/7	hooked	Walk. '12, p. 134
eremita	45	5–9	3/5	7/9	truncate	Cabot '81, p. 23[3]
interrupta	40	5 or 6–9	3/5 of 10	5/7	truncate	Walk. '12, p. 109
juncea	41	6–9 r. on 6	1/2 of 10	3/5	truncate	Lucas '00, p. 193
multicolor	38	6–9 r. on 9	1/2	8/9	squarely truncate	Walk. '12, p. 195
palmata	41	6–9	3/5 or 2/3	4/5	squarely truncate	Walk. '12, p. 162
subarctica	40	6–9 r. on 9	1/2 of 10	3/5	truncate	Walk. '12, p. 98
tuberculifera	41–45	6–9 r. on 9		1/2+	truncate	Walk. '14, p. 370
umbrosa	40	6–9	1/2	3/4	squarely truncate	Cabot '81, p. 24[3]
verticalis (?)		6–9			hooked	Ndm. & Hart '01, p. 41

[1] In relation to length of segment 9.
[2] Proportion of apical breadth to length of mentum.
[3] Also Ndm. & Hart '01, p. 42.

The *nymphs* are climbers among the submerged, standing aquatic plants in still shallow waters, where they await almost motionless the coming of their prey. Some are exceedingly voracious (see Walk. '12, p. 53) and will attack animals considerably larger than themselves.

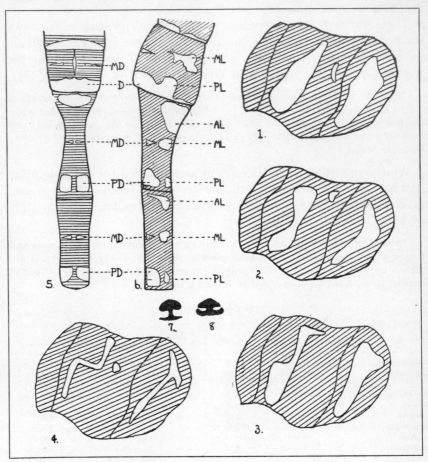

FIG. 32. Color patterns. Thoracic stripes of *1, juncea; 2, eremita; 3, canadensis; 4, caerulea. 5,* Dorsum of abdominal segments 1 to 4 to show naming of spots after Walker. *6,* Lateral aspect of same. *7,* T-spot on top of frons of *caerulea; 8,* same of *sitchensis.*

KEY TO THE SPECIES†

Adults

1 Lateral thoracic pale stripes bent twice, almost at right angles..2.
  Lateral thoracic pale stripes not so bent.....................3.

2 Labrum with a black upper border and a brownish lower margin; T spot with long stem (Fig. 32)...............**caerula,** p. 139

Labrum margined narrowly with black above and below; *T* spot with a short stem........................**sitchensis,** p. 139

3 Ventral tubercle present on segment 1.....................4.

Ventral tubercle not present on segment 1..................6.

4 Fronto-clypeal stripe present...............**californica,** p. 140

Fronto-clypeal stripe not present...........................5.

5 Ventral tubercle prominent; vein *M1a* rising beyond the stigma; outer side of anal loop longer than the inner side of triangle ....**multicolor,** p. 141

Ventral tubercle low; *M1a* rising under the distal end of stigma; outer side of anal loop equal to the inner side of triangle.....

....**mutata,** p. 142

6 Dorsum of 10 smooth, without tubercles or spines; anal triangle of male three celled..7.

Dorsum of 10 with a median tooth between one or two pairs of spines; anal triangle of male two celled.................11.

7 Rear of head black..8.

Rear of head with some brown or yellow......**umbrosa,** p. 142

8 Abdominal spots *ML* (Fig. 32) on 3–6, minute...**walkeri,** p. 143

Abdominal spots *ML* on 3–8.............................9.

9 Abdominal spots *PL* (Fig. 32) on 5–8; lateral thoracic pale stripes of female entirely surrounded by black.........**arida,** p. 144

Abdominal spots *PL* on 3–5, 6 or 7; lateral stripes of female not surrounded by black...................................10.

10 Abdominal spots *MD* on 3–7; cross bar of *T* spot straight, its stem parallel sided.........................**palmata,** p. 144

Abdominal spots *MD* on 3–8; cross bar of *T* spot curved, its stem wider at base............................**constricta,** p. 145

11 Dorsal thoracic stripes reduced to 1 or two spots............
....**interrupta,** p. 145

Dorsal thoracic stripes present............................12.

12 Black stripe on fronto-clypeal suture.....................13.

No black stripe, sometimes a fine brown line, on fronto-clypeal suture..16.

13 Pale spots between two lateral thoracic stripes large and conspicuous, sometimes confluent with first lateral stripe; fronto-clypeal stripe not reaching lateral margins....**clepsydra,** p. 146

Not as above..14.

14   Vein *M1a* rising under the proximal third of the stigma or before
     its inner end..............................**eremita,** p. 146
     Vein *M1a* rising under the middle or distal third of stigma....15.

15   Sides of lateral thoracic pale stripes more or less straight; first
     one without dorsal posterior spur..............**juncea,** p. 147
     Sides of lateral thoracic pale stripes excavated; with a dorsal
     posterior spur on first stripe..............**subarctica,** p. 148

16   Abdominal segment 10 black..............**tuberculifera,** p. 148
     Abdominal segment 10 with pale spots.....................17.

17   Anterior margin of first lateral thoracic pale stripe rectangularly
     sinuate*.................................**canadensis,** p. 148
     Anterior margin of first lateral thoracic pale stripe obtuse-
     angularly sinuate..........................**verticalis,** p. 149

† In the determination of species the final criteria must be the genitalia
Characters such as the color of the face and the dark markings on it, and even
the thoracic color pattern, are dependent too much upon state of preservation of
the specimen to be reliable; the dorsal thoracic pale stripes are often too faded
to be discernible. For a careful and detailed description see Dr. Walker's mono-
graph: *The North American Dragonflies of the genus Aeshna*, University of
Toronto Studies, Biological Series No. 11, 1912. This very excellent work is
indispensable to any worker in the genus. It has been drawn upon to a very large
extent in assembling the material herein.

* Not constant; see figures of genitalia.

Nymphs

1   End hook of labium curving to an internal terminal tooth.....2.
    End of labium truncate....................................4.

2   End hook broadly curved to a point........................3.
    End hook abruptly curved, almost truncate.........**canadensis.**

3   End of lateral lobe slender, 9×1.5; lateral spine on 6 less than one
    fourth as long as segment........................**constricta.**
    End of lateral lobe broader, 7×3; lateral spine on 6 one half as
    long as the segment............................**clepsydra.**

4   Lateral spines on 5–9....................................5.
    Lateral spines on 6–9....................................6.

5   Lateral spine on 9 reaching beyond the posterior margin of 10..
    ....**interrupta.**
    Lateral spine on 9 reaching three fifths of the margin of 10 (all
    spines shorter than in the above)..................**eremita.**

6   Femora concolorous......................................7.
    Femora striped..8.

7   Lateral spine on 9 reaching to the middle of 10 . . . . **juncea.**
    Lateral spine on 9 not reaching to the middle of 10
    . . . . **subarctica.**

8   Mentum of labium 1 and one fourths times as long as broad. . .9.
    Mentum of labium not much longer than broad. . . . . .11.

9   Lateral lobes of labium with an internal apical tooth; lateral lobe
    nearly twice as long as broad. (See Walk. '14, p. 372). . . .10.
    Lateral lobes of labium with no internal apical tooth; two-
    thirds as long as broad. . . . .**palmata.**

10 Mentum of labium twice as long as width of its base. . . . .
    . . . .**interrupta.**
    Mentum of labium three times as long as width of its base. . . . . . .
    . . . . **tuberculifera** and **umbrosa.**

11 Lateral spine of 6 rudimentary. . . . .**multicolor.**
    Lateral spine of 6 well developed. . . . .**californica.**

92. Aeschna caerulea Burmeister

Burm. '39, p. 839: Mtk. Cat. p. 113: Walk. '12, p. 72: Howe '19, p. 47.

Syn: septentrionalis Burm.

Length 47 mm. Expanse 78 mm.   **N. H. and Labr. to Gr. Slave L.**

Face brownish with a heavy black line on the fronto-clypeal suture, labrum
bordered above and below with brown. Occiput yellow. Lateral thoracic pale
stripes exceedingly narrow, stripe one bent twice at alternate right angles, second
stripe nearly straight sometimes divided at middle, two small spots sometimes
present between.

93. Aeschna sitchensis Hagen

Hag. '61, p. 119: Mtk. Cat. p. 114: Walk. '12, p. 77: Whts. '17, p. 99: Walk.
'21, p. 221.

Length 51 mm. Expanse 80 mm.   **N. F. and Mich. to Alaska**

Face dull greenish or olivaceous with a black line on the fronto-clypeal suture
increasing in width laterally. Anteclypeus dark, labrum bordered narrowly above

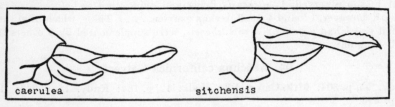

caerulea   sitchensis

and broadly below, with black. Lateral thoracic pale stripes narrow and sinuate;
the first pair bent twice at alternate right angles. Legs dark brown, femora
darker beneath. Wings hyaline, costa and stigma brown.

Whitehouse ('17) says:

I incline strongly to the opinion that the true breeding ground of this northern insect is muskeg, which may account for the nymphs being still unknown.

And then in '21 Walker writes:

. . . . I found at the foot of a mountain, a small mossy bog, fed by springs and by the seepage from a small cold mountain brook. The bog was partly enclosed by spruce forest and supported a scattered growth of stunted white spruce and willows, shrubby cinquefoil, and a few other swamp plants, but, excepting the moss, which was partly submerged, there was practically no aquatic vegetation, neither standing nor floating. Here were 2 species of dragonflies flying and ovipositing. One was *Somatochlora franklini* Selys, the other *Aeshna sitchensis*. The latter was the commoner of the two, but was far from numerous, the bog often appearing for many minutes at a time to be devoid of dragonfly life.

The males of *A. sitchensis* flew low, as a rule, only a foot or two from the ground; sometimes apparently at random over the bog sometimes following the stream for some distance, but not covering a definite beat. They flew less swiftly than most Aeshnas and frequently dropped to the surface of the water for an instant, in a manner somewhat suggestive of an ovipositing female.

The females were frequently observed ovipositing in the wet moss about the edges of the small puddles in the bog, many of which were less than a square foot in area. The manner of oviposition was quite like that of other Aeshnas. The insect would light on the moss and thrust the abdomen into it in various directions, following no regular plan. Usually she remained at one spot less than half a minute, then flew on a few yards and repeated the operation. Once or twice copulating pairs were seen to rise from the bog and fly to the neighboring trees.

A prolonged search was made for nymphs and exuviae, but although *Somato chlora* exuviae were found, no traces of the early stages of *sitchensis* appeared.

I was now, however, on the right track. I had at last penetrated the mystery of this strange dragonfly's haunts, which proved to be the same as those of the equally little-known Somatochlora. It may be recalled, however, that the correct solution of this puzzle was already hinted at by Mr. F. C. Whitehouse.

He then reports his experiences at another bog a few days later:

The upper and middle parts of the bog were mossy and practically without standing aquatic plants and the open areas of water were mere puddles. . . . . The water here was also warmer. . . . . There were very few dragonflies here, but I soon observed *A. sitchensis* flying and ovipositing as before, ... At length, however, I found 4 small Aeshna exuviae. . . . . These, which from their small size I had no doubt were *sitchensis*, were supplemented by 3 others the following day.

94. Aeschna californica Calvert

Calv. '95, p. 504: Mtk. Cat. p. 109: Walk. '12, p. 184: Kndy. '15, p. 343: '17, p. 596.

Length 50 mm. Expanse 80 mm.   **B. C. and Calif. to Utah and Ariz.**

Walker '12 describes this as a species of somewhat less than medium size, with a rather short broad abdomen. Face greenish with a black line on the fronto-clypeal suture and another at the base of the labrum. Lateral thoracic pale stripes narrow, diffusely edged with blackish behind. First stripe with more or less parallel sides, slightly wider below. Legs black, femora yellowish basally. Wings hyaline, costa yellow, stigma brown.

Dr. Walker says that this is the earliest North American Aeschna to appear in the adult state. He found it in Calif. and Wash. as early as the second week in April. Mr. Kennedy ('17) found it very abundant in Washington the first of May. He observed it, ('15) swarming about alkaline ponds as well as on the cold torrents of the Yakima Reservation.

95. Aeschna multicolor Hagen

Hag. '61, p. 121: Mtk. Cat. p. 113: Walk. '12, p. 190: Wmsn. '14, p. 226: Kndy. '15, p. 344: '17, pp. 596, 607: Ndm. '23, p. 129: Smn. '26, p. 25.

Syn: furcifer Karsch

Length 55 mm. Expanse 90 mm. **B. C. to Tex., Colo. and So. Calif.**

Mr. Walker describes this species as: "Of average to rather large size, the thorax robust and the abdomen somewhat short. Frons and postclypeus pale blue or grey-blue with a narrow yellowish white submarginal area; fronto-nasal suture ochraceous. . . . . Rhinarium (anteclypeus) and labrum greenish, the latter narrowly margined above and below with dark brown." Lateral thoracic pale stripes straight, the second one slightly wider above. Legs black, first femora with a basal pale streak externally. Wings hyaline, costa yellow, stigma brown.

Kennedy ('15) says that both this species and *californica* are wide fliers, being found at times several miles from the nearest water. And later ('17) he writes:

This species was observed catching insects on the market street of the city (Sacramento, Calif.) at twilight. . . . . They flew among the wagons and buggies entirely indifferent to the numerous passers-by. This habit of familiarity with man's haunts is very noticeable in *multicolor*. It is the most domestic of all the western Odonata.

Williamson ('14) says that it is associated with *Anax junius* and is of similar habits. A like reference in Needham ('23) says that it was: "Nearly as abundant (at ponds near Laguna Beach, Calif.) on the wing as was *Anax junius*, but the nymphs and nymph skins were far less common.   Two adults were found ensnared in the strong webs of the spider *Argiope trifasciata*."

Abundant about alkaline ponds from June to August.

96. Aeschna mutata Hagen

Hag. '61, p. 124: Mtk. Cat. p. 113: Walk, '12, p. 198: Garm. '27, p. 192.

Length 58 mm.   Expanse 93 mm.   **Ind., Ohio, Mass.**

Walker ('12) describes this as a "species of average size and build, with a rather short abdomen, and somewhat long and narrow wings."

Face pale bluish, yellowish near ocular margin.   Occiput yellowish, edged laterally with black.   Lateral thoracic pale stripes distinct and straight, the first parallel sided, the second slightly wider above.   Legs black, femora with a basal external pale streak.   Wings hyaline; costa brownish yellow; stigma dark brown.

Williamson ('08) reports it as flying slowly in and out, with much stationary fluttering among the leaf stems.

On bright mornings when the eastern sky was unobscured they were hunting low over the western side of the marsh at 4:45 o'clock.   One cloudy morning they did not appear at all.   After 9 or 10 o'clock their visits to the marsh were rare and they were more wary, leaving the marsh when any effort was made to approach them and flying directly to or above the tree tops.   *A. mutata* spends most of the day after 9 or 10 A.M. either resting in the trees or flying about over the tree tops, very probably the latter.   As is usual in the genus the night is spent clinging to the tree trunks or larger limbs at some elevation.

97. Aeschna umbrosa Walker

Walk. '08, p. 380, 390: Mtk. Cat. p. 114: Walk. '12, p. 165: '12a, p. 31: Davis 13, p. 22: Kndy. '15, p. 344: Howe '19, p. 44: '23, p. 124: Ndm. '27, p. 19: Garm. '27 p. 191.

Var: occidentalis Walk.

Length 64 mm.   Expanse 96 mm.   **Atlantic to Pacific Coast**

Face and occiput pale brownish. Labrum pale, margined above and below by a narrow black line.   Lateral thoracic pale stripes darkly margined and with more or less parallel sides, although the first stripe is often widened and bulbous below.   Abdominal segment 2 has a similarly conspicuous stripe with a sinuate anterior margin. Legs brown, paler externally. Wings hyaline with a slight violet tinge and touches of brown anteriorly and basally; costa brown, stigma tawny.

Walker ('12a) says it is an exception to all other eastern species in that it frequents small woodland streams and ditches or small pools on the edges of woods, never being found associated with the other species in open marshes and shows a marked preference for more or less shady haunts while its near ally *constricta* is most often seen ranging over open fields or bushy pastures. It habitually flies till well after dusk.

Kennedy ('15) reports that it is closely associated with *palmata* both in season and habits.

98. Aeschna walkeri Kennedy

Kndy. '17, p. 587.

Length 65 mm. Expanse 94 mm.   **Calif.**

The following description is taken from that of Dr. Kennedy. Face bluish gray, labrum grayish white, occiput creamy. Lateral thoracic pale stripes usually with nearly straight parallel edges. Legs dark brown except tibiae and tarsi which are black. Wings hyaline, stigma brown.

Dr. Kennedy says of it:

It is a stream species with habits similar to those of *palmata*. It inhabits the warmer frost-free streams of the coast mountains, while *palmata* lives mostly in the colder streams of the Sierras. . . . .

Aeshna walkeri was most abundant on the stream flowing down at Fry's Harbor (Santa Cruz Island, Calif.). In several quarter mile stretches the course of the stream was so deep that its bed was a fairly smooth trough of rock, being too steep to retain the rocks and sand washed down from above. Such stretches frequently contained pools, mere rock bowls, 6 to 10 feet in diameter, filled with water, in which green clouds of filamentous algae floated over the black leaves and vegetable trash in the bottom. Such pools were alive with *A. walkeri* nymphs, tadpoles, and *Archilestes* nymphs. . . . . At no place in the stream did aquatic vegetation occur and in only a few places did roots hang in the water. Because of this lack of vegetation in which *Aeshna* usually oviposits, the habits of this species were unusual.

During the sunny part of the day the males are found coursing up and down the creek. As there is usually a morning fog on the island, which does not clear up until 9 o'clock, it is frequently 11 o'clock before the *Aeshna* males are on the creek. They then persist in flying up and down until the middle of the afternoon, when they leave the water one by one to hunt insects in the sunshine above on the hill tops. In the patrolling of the creek they combine feeding and hunting for females. A male will slowly fly along the rocky wall overhanging the water, inspecting every nook and cranny, and only give a hurried inspection to the open side of each pool. After being satisfied that he has not overlooked a female he will rise over the waterfall at the head of the pool and proceed to inspect, in the same manner, the stream above. . . . .

The females do not spend as much time on the creek as the males. Few were found on the creek before 3 o'clock, but when it had become almost twilight in the depths of the gorge they were nervously hurrying up and down the creek ovipositing. The method of this was so unusual that I did not recognize at first what they were doing. A female would alight on one of the rock walls overhanging the pool and would try to insert her ovipositor in the rock. After an attempt or two she would fly a few inches or feet and make another attempt. As the rocks over the pools in the shadier spots were seamed with lines of green moss, she would soon locate each seam and drive her ovipositor into the vein of moss. The eggs thus were laid in the thin seam of moist earth which supported the moss. Usually less than half a dozen stabs would be made in one seam when she would fly to another and repeat the laying. In two places where tree roots hung into the water, females were flushed that were probably ovipositing in these. Oviposition was going on as late as 5 o'clock when it was almost twilight in the shadier portions of the gorge.

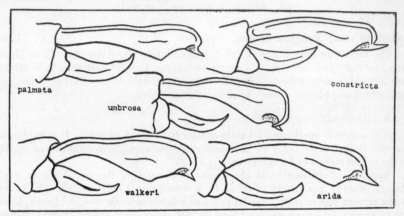

In copulation a male usually found a female while she was seated on a vertical wall of rock, and picking her off the two would fly away in copulation. This usually lasted some time while the pair hung to some live oak bush on the hillside. Pairs did not fly in couple as does *Anax*.

99. Aeschna arida Kennedy

Kndy. '18, p. 298.

Length 78 mm. Expanse 112 mm.   **Ariz.**

Face greenish with a narrow line on the fronto-clypeal suture and across the base of the labrum. Lateral thoracic pale stripes broad and straight, the first one slightly excavated on its anterior margin and narrower in its upper half. Each stripe bordered on both edges of its entire length with a wide dark brown band. Legs black with the bases of the femora dark brown. Wings hyaline. (From Kennedy.)

100. Aeschna palmata Hagen

Hag. '56, p. 369: Mtk. Cat. p. 113: Walk. '12, p. 157: Kndy. '15, p. 329: '17, p. 610.

Length 57 mm. Expanse 89 mm.   **Pacific Coast**

A smaller species with black feet. Face yellow with a black stripe on the fronto-clypeal suture and a black border on the labrum which also has a median transverse strip on its upper half. Occiput brownish broadly bordered with black. Dorsal thoracic pale stripe rather narrow and separated above into a distinct spot. First lateral thoracic pale stripe parallel sided with but a slight excavation of the anterior margin. One or two spots between the 2 lateral pale stripes. Wings hyaline with black veins; costa brownish, stigma black.

Kennedy ('15) reports it as occurring commonly on streams from August until September. He says of it:

It was in company with *A. umbrosa occidentalis* and had apparently identical habits, as both patrolled the smaller, more stream-like sloughs, especially where they were surrounded by trees. Both seemed to prefer such sunny glades to the more open spaces. In both species the males were much more abundant than the females.

He adds ('17)

Several were easily netted, as they flew in short beats among the willow thickets to escape the wind. This species in such a situation is very easily victimized by the collector. They fly low and slowly and are very bull-headed about keeping to their short protected beat, two or three passes with the net sometimes failing to drive one away.

101. Aeschna constricta Say

Say '39, p. 11: Mtk. Cat. p. 109: Walk. '12, p. 176: Whed. '14, p. 95: Howe '19, p. 49: '23, p. 123: Garm. '27, p. 189.

Length 58 mm. Expanse 93 mm.   **Atl. Coast to Dakotas**

Face yellowish; occiput yellow with black lateral angles; a fine pale line on the fronto-clypeal suture; labrum narrowly margined with black. Thorax brownish; lateral pale stripes wide, the first one with a sinuate anterior margin, narrowing a little above the middle and the giving off a posterior spur; the second broadly widened above by expansion on both margins. Legs black, femora paler basally. Abdominal segment 1 with a pale dorsal spot and sometimes with an apical annulus; 2 with a lateral pale spot and a large dorsal basal spot extending down lateral margins; 3–10 with all spots present.

Whedon ('14)

A pair in copulation was captured in an open, pastured woodland. . . . . The insects hung quite motionless from the lower branches of oak trees, allowing the net to approach them without seeming to heed it. Three females were taken on a wooded roadside which skirts Lake Madison, most of them as they clung to the underside of trees or leaves, devouring their prey. All of the above females were heterochromatic.

102. Aeschna interrupta Walker

Walk. '08, p. 381, 387: '12, p. 100: Kndy. '15, p. 336: '17, p. 581: Howe '19, p. 45: '23, p. 122.

Syn: *propinqua* Scud., *Var*: *nevadensis*
Walk., *lineata* Walk., *interna* Walk.

Length 58 mm. Expanse 95 mm.   **N. F. to Ont. and Mich.**

Occiput dull yellow. Face yellowish green, paler on sides and top of frons and vertex; vertex with a dark margin. A black or dark brown line on front-clypeal suture. T spot heavy, sides of stem straight or a little convex. Labrum green, margined narrowly above and broadly below with black. Thorax dark olive brown. Dorsal thoracic pale stripes reduced to small isolated spots, or wanting. Lateral pale stripes either straight and very slender or divided into an upper and lower spot. Abdominal spots well developed.

103. Aeschna clepsydra Say

The Time-keeper

Say '39, p. 19: Mtk. Cat. p. 109: Walk. '12, p. 129: Howe '19, p. 45: '23 p. 124: Garm. '27 p. 184.

Length 65 mm. Expanse 94 mm.   **Ont. and N. E. to Ind.**

Face brownish green with a heavy dark line on the fronto-clypeal suture usually not reaching the margin; occiput yellow. Anteclypeus darker. Labrum bordered below with black. Readily distinguished by the large pale spots between the wide lateral thoracic pale stripes; these are sometimes confluent with sinuate stripe 1. Abdominal segments 1 and 2 (often 3 and 4) with large pale spots. Dorsum of 10 yellow with median posteriorly pointing black triangles. Legs brown, paler externally. Wings hyaline, stigma and costa tawny.

Muttkowski ('08) reports this species as being common in the woods and about the lakes of Wisconsin from June to Sept. Walker ('12) observed it at Go Home Bay flying over shallow reed-grown bays and adjacent marshes, and on one occasion took two specimens from tree trunks on the edge of a wood, about half a mile from the nearest possible breeding place.

104. Aeschna eremita Scudder

The Hermit

Scud. '66, p. 213: Mtk. Cat. p. 110: Walk. '12, p. 119, 42: Howe '19, p. 46: '23, p. 122.

Syn: hudsonica Selys.

Length 65 mm. Expanse 100 mm.   **Labr., N. H. to Alaska and Wyo.**

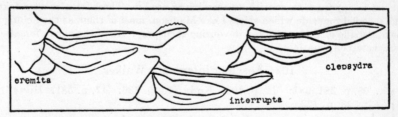

A large dark species. Face greenish with a dark stripe on the fronto-clypeal suture and on the upper and lower margin of the labrum, that of the upper margin running down into a median dark spot; clypeus brownish. Occiput yellow with black lateral angles. Dorsal thoracic pale stripe narrow, sometimes separated from a pale spot above. Lateral stripe 1 strongly constricted in the middle. Stripe 2 also very much constricted in the middle and much widened dorsally. One or more pale stripes between the two lateral stripes. Wings hyaline costa yellow, stigma brown.

Mr. Walker ('12) describes oviposition of this species from several careful observations:

The insect when first seen was clinging to the blade of a bur-reed (Sparganium) close to the surface of the water with about half the abdomen immersed (see initial figure page 00). She was watched for about 5 minutes at the end of which she suddenly flew away. During this time the end of the abdomen was thrust against the stem every 2 or 3 seconds and was gradually lowered until wholly under water. Soon after this depth was reached she flew away.

I then examined the reed and found the punctures . . . . were confined to the 2 narrow surfaces of the 3 cornered reed and the great majority were on one surface. They tended to be grouped in oblique rows, although the arrangement is by no means regular. They were found to lie a little beneath the surface and very obliquely placed, occupying more nearly a vertical position than a horizontal one. The pointed anterior ends were in all cases outermost.

On the following day another ovipositing female of the same species was observed at closer range, in fact I was almost directly above the insect while watching her. She was supported on a collection of dead floating reeds among a thick growth of living ones and was thrusting the ovipositor, seemingly at random, into any piece of reed within reach. She did not remain more than a minute or so, but the lever-like thrusts of the ovipositor could be seen distinctly when the abdomen was turned sideways. In making these thrusts the terminal abdominal segment served as a fulcrum.

105. Aeschna juncea Linnaeus

Linne. 1758, p. 544: Mtk. Cat. p. 111: Wlsn. '09, pp. 656, 665: Walk. '12, p. 83: Howe '19, p. 46: '23, p. 123.

> *Syn: ocellata* Mueller., *rustica* Zetterstedt, *picta* Charpentier,
> *caucasica* Kolenati, *propinqua* Scud.

Length 55 mm. Expanse 92 mm.   **N. F. and N. H. to Alaska and Col.**

A stout medium sized species. Face yellowish with a heavy dark line on the fronto-clypeal suture; anteclypeus brownish with a yellowish upper margin.

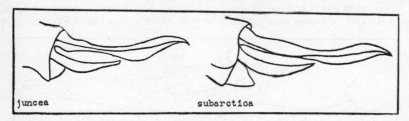

juncea   subarctica

Labrum yellow bordered with black anteclypeus dark brown. Lateral thoracic pale stripes wide the first pair narrowed slightly above and the second pair narrowed below. Legs black, femora paler basally. Wings hyaline, costa and stigma brown.

Walker ('12) says " . . . . it flies over the open marshes and shallow reed-grown waters which border the river . . . . . The weather was dull and one was taken in flight during a light rain." Ris ('85) has given an interesting account of the habits of this holoarctic insect in Switzerland.

106. Aeschna subarctica Walker

Walk. '08, p. 385, 390: '12, p. 93.
Length 57 mm. Expanse 90 mm.   **Manitoba to Atl. Coast**
    Face yellow with a heavy black line on the fronto-clypeal suture, broadest in the middle; anteclypeus dark brown and labrum bordered narrowly above and broadly below with black; occiput yellow. Lateral thoracic pale stripes excavated by an obtuse angle; the first stripe bearing a posterior spur. Legs reddish brown, femora paler beneath. Wings hyaline, costa yellow, stigma brown.

    Mr. Walker says that *Aeshna subarctica* is closely related to *Aeshna juncea* . . . . and that he was unable to distinguish them in flight; nor could he detect any differences in habits.

107. Aeschna tuberculifera Walker

Walk. '08, p. 385, 387: '12, p. 152: Howe '19, p. 48: '23, p. 124: Garm. '27, p. 187.
Length 58 mm. Expanse 98 mm.   **N. H. and Ont. to Wis.**
    Face olivaceous with a fine brown line on the fronto-clypeal suture; labrum with very narrow upper and lower marginal black lines. Occiput pale bluish green, the anterolateral margins black. Legs dark brown. Wings hyaline, sometimes slightly flavescent at the base; costa and stigma brown.

108. Aeschna canadensis Walker

Walk. '08, p. 382, 389: Mtk. Cat. p. 109: Walk. '12, p. 135: Howe '19, p. 48: '23, p. 123: Garm. '27, p. 182.
        Syn: clepsydia Selys, *juncea* Wmsn., *verticalis* Walk.
Length 58 mm. Expanse 92 mm.   **N. E. U. S. to Wash.**
    Occiput yellow margined on sides with black. Face bluish or yellowish green; frons olivaceous, darker above, paler near ocular band. Fine brown line on fronto-

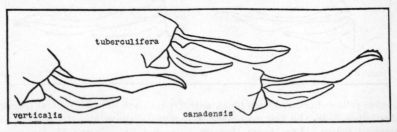

clypeal suture. Anteclypeus dark brown in center. T spot heavy, strongly convex in front; stem broad, sides straight. Dorsal thoracic pale stripes straight and broad. Lateral pale stripes broad, the first one deeply constricted on its anterior margin by a rectangulate excavation, and with a posteriorly projecting spur on the upper end; the second, broad, wider above. Legs brown, tarsi and under sides darker; first femora with an external, basal pale streak. Wings hyaline; stigma and costa brown.

Walker ('12) says: "This species breeds among reeds and sedge in shallow sluggish creeks, lakes and bays. With the exception of *Ae. californica* and the *multicolor* group it is the earliest species to appear in the adult state. Individuals may sometimes be seen as early as the middle of June but the usual time of appearance in the Transition Zone in Ontario is during the last week of June and the first week of July. By the middle of July they are numerous and may sometimes occur in very large numbers about the sunny borders of woods, especially conifers. Here they may be seen sunning themselves on the trunks of trees or hanging from the twigs. On hot sultry days they fly restlessly to and fro in small openings among the trees, on the lookout for their prey. In August they are less frequently seen in the woods. They appear to return to their breeding-grounds, where they may be observed in large numbers, gliding over the reeds or skirting the water's edge. Such individuals are all males and may often be observed to drop down among the reeds and then emerge with a female *in copula*. Apparently copulation does not take place far from the water as commonly occurs *in constricta* and other species."

109. Aeschna verticalis Hagen

Hag. '61, p. 122: Mtk. Cat. p. 114: Walk. '12, p. 145: Howe '19, p. 47: Garm. '27, p. 188.

Syn: propinqua Scud.

Length 59 mm. Expanse 96 mm. **Wis., Ill. to Atl. Coast**

Occiput and face greenish yellow, with a fine brown line on the fronto-clypeal suture; anteclypeus reddish brown. T-spot heavy; stem short with divergent sides. Labrum brownish green, margined narrowly above and broadly below with black. Dorsal thoracic pale stripes conspicuous; lateral ones fairly broad; the first with an obtuse angulate excavation on the anterior margin and the dorsal posterior projecting spur; the second narrower below and with a slight suggestion of a dorsal anterior spur. Legs brownish, tibiae and tarsi black. Wings hyaline; costa and stigma brownish.

23. GYNACANTHA Rambur

These are slender graceful darners with broad heads and very long eye seams. The venation is much as in Aeschna. The legs and abdomen are slenderer, and the apex of the abdomen in the female is variously spined.

This is a large tropical genus, of which but three species have been found within our southern limits.

The nymph is similar to that of Aeschna, but is readily distinguished from all other Aeschnine nymphs by the possession of a row of long strong raptorial setae upon the upper and inner edge of the lateral lobe of the labium.

KEY TO THE SPECIES
Adults

1 Expanse less than 90.........................trifida, p. 150

  Expanse usually more than 100..........................2.

2 Superior appendage of the male with a dorsal ridge...........
  ....nervosa, p. 150

  Superior appendage of the male without a dorsal ridge..........
  ....bifida, p. 151

110. Gynacantha trifida Rambur
The Vixen

Ramb. '42, p. 210: Mtk. Cat. p. 108.
Syn: needhami Mrtn.

Length 65 mm. Expanse 84 mm.   **Fla. and Calif.**

A slender graceful species with greenish thorax and brown abdomen. Face obscure yellowish. Apex of frons above suffused with black. Vertex blackish and very narrow. Occiput brown. Thorax brown and green, thinly clad with short, pale pubescence. Front brown, with two broad, green, obscure stripes. Sides more green than brown with an ill-defined oblique brown stripe upon the middle (stripe 4) and touches of brown upon the other sutures. Legs brown with black tarsi. Wings hyaline with brown veins and tawny stigma. Abdomen brown with blackish carinae and obscure median and subapical pale rings; the median ones are dilated toward the middle line on segments 3–7. The swollen basal segments are greenish at the sides and obscurely lineate above along the sutures. Appendages brown. Female with 3 black downwardly directed spines on segment 10 beneath.

111. Gynacantha nervosa Rambur

Ramb. '42, p. 213: Mtk. Cat. p. 107.
Length 75 mm. Expanse 106 mm.   **Fla. and Calif.**

A fine, big, brownish species with little differentiation of color pattern. The face is tawny; the frons above is diffusely blackish around the margin; the minute occiput is yellow. The thorax is wholly brown except for a blackish spot at the spiracle. The abdomen is brown with narrow black lines on the sutures encircling the segments. Segment 10 of the female has two black, decurved spines below.

Williamson who has observed this species in the tropics says ('23, p. 40) that it

seems essentially crepuscular in its flight. Where the species occurs abundantly the numbers on the wing and in sight at once, the mobile active flight, and the rapidly coming darkness of the tropical night combine to form a scene to fire the imagination. They come from everywhere, the air is filled with them, some fly erratically, others patrol regular beats, apparent spots of greater density lure the collector from one point to another. As suddenly as they appeared, only a few are seen, and then they are gone, and the disappointed collector with possibly only two or three specimens in his bottle, realizes that the twenty or thirty minute flight is at its end, and that he will not see **nervosa** again for twenty-four hours.

Dr. W. T. M. Forbes reports that the night-jars take their toll of Gynacanthas during this same half hour of evening flight.

The brownish coloration of this species is of a type that seems to go with crepuscular habits of flight. Dusk-flying and shade-dwelling dragonflies run to somber browns.

112. **Gynacantha bifida** Rambur

Ramb. '42, p. 213: Mtk. Cat. p. 107.
Length 74 mm. Expanse 104 mm. **Fla.**

Face yellow. Top of frons with an ill-defined T-spot. Occiput yellow. Thorax brownish on a yellowish background. Feet yellowish. Wings hyaline, broad, with open venation; costa and stigma yellowish red; membranule whitish, very small; a brownish streak along the subcostal space extends beyond the nodus the length of the wing, and overlaps a little into the costal area before the nodus; anal triangle of three cells. Abdomen brown with streaks of black on the second segment and median streaks of yellow on the following segments. Appendages brown.

Subfamily CORDULEGASTERINAE

Large black and yellow dragonflies, with eyes approximated or meeting at a single point on the top of the head. Labium with a median terminal cleft. Stigma with no brace vein at proximal end. Females with a rather crude ovipositor.

The group is a small one, pertaining to the northern hemisphere and there is in our fauna but a single genus.

24. CORDULEGASTER

The Biddies

These are clear-winged stout, hairy, dragonflies, of rather primitive aspect. The thorax is blackish, with a pair of oblique pale stripes on the front and two additional pairs on the sides. Legs black. Wings hyaline. Face mostly greenish or yellowish, but with the clypeus always fuscous. The occiput and the abdominal markings are very different in the different species. All the species frequent clear-flowing woodland streams, where their nymphs dwell in the bottom ooze of the settling basins.

In terms of the stripings of the Gomphus thorax (fig. 30) the stripes of the 1st pair have fused to form a middorsal triangular spot, those of the 2nd and 3rd pairs have fused completely (except for a little rift in *C. diastatops*). Those of the 4th and 5th have likewise fused and a 6th has developed behind, and all have become conjoined longitudinally by their ends.

Nymphs of this genus agree in the following points: the body is stout, rough hairy, cylindric, tapering beyond the middle of the abdomen to a pointed apex, the longitudinal axis upcurved at both ends, the tips of the eyes and the abdominal appendages being the highest points. The antennae are seven-jointed, slender. The eyes cap the angular antero lateral prominence of the head and extend a pair of sharp points internally on the vertex from their hind angles. Hind angles of the head rounded, the hind margin not obviously concave posteriorly. The labium is very large, extending posteriorly between the bases of the middle legs, its dilated, spoon-shaped anterior end covering the face up to the antennae, and meeting above a convex frontal prominence, whose margin is fringed with sensory hairs. The mentum is triangularly widened beyond the middle; its median lobe is produced in a median tooth which is bifid on the median line; its lateral lobes are broad,

152

triangular, concave, and bear a row of short raptorial setae just within the external margin, a stouter, but not longer movable hook at the end of this row, and a series of coarse, irregular interlocking teeth on the distal margin.

Prothorax with a transverse dorsal flattened area, which is fringed with stiff hairs; legs slender and not very long, adapted for raking the sand aside; femora and tibiae with dorsal and ventral rows of long hairs, the ventral row on the tibiae graduating into spines at the tip, these becoming arranged in a double row on the ventral side of the tarsal segments; tarsi three-jointed; wings a little divergent on the two sides, when grown, reaching the fourth abdominal segment.

Abdomen, subcylindric, arcuately upcurved toward the tip; no dorsal hooks; lateral appendages less than one fourth as long as superior and inferiors; the transverse apical rings on the abdominal segments are somewhat remote from the apices of the segments and bear rows of very stiff hairs, which are incurved at the tip and serve to hold a layer of sand, dirt, etc. about the body.

The nymphs live on the bottom in shallow water, buried in clean sand or in silt. Though buried they do not burrow, but descend by raking the sand from beneath them by sweeping, lateral movements of the legs. When deep enough, they kick the sand up over the back till only the elevated tips of the eyes and the respiratory aperture at the tip of the abdomen are exposed. By placing a live nymph in a dish of sand and water and watching, its method may be observed in a very few minutes. The whole comical performance reminds one strongly of the descent of an old hen in a dustbath (whence the common name suggested for this group).

Once adjusted in the sand, a nymph (unless food tempts) remains motionless a very long time, even for weeks. Let any little insect walk or swim near the nymph's head, and a hidden labium springs from the sand with a mightly sweep and clutches it. The nymphs will capture and eat young brook trout as long as themselves, when placed in their cage. So eager are they, they will rise partly from the sand on approach of a trout. Like the nymphs of the Aeschninae, they seem to have a decided preference for big game, if one may judge by the strenuous efforts they put forth when something at the limit of their capacity for capturing approaches.

KEY TO THE SPECIES*
Adults

1 Abdomen with transverse yellow bands on the segments......2.
   Abdomen with yellow spots................................4.

2   Frons dark with a superior transverse oval yellow spot. Size large,
    (Length 73 mm.)..........................**diadema,** p. 155
    Frons uniformly colored. Size smaller, (length 62 mm.)........3.

3   Face yellow......................................**sayi,** p. 155
    Face blackish.............................**erroneous,** p. 155

4   Abdomen with a mid dorsal line of spots....................5.
    Abdomen with lateral spots...............................6.

5   Spots bifid on middle segments................**dorsalis,** p. 156
    Spots spear shaped on middle segments.........**obliquus,** p. 158

6   Length of abdomen less than 60 mm..........................7.
    Length of abdomen 65 mm..................**fasciatus,** p. 158

7   A single pair of lateral spots on each segment. Eyes not contiguous
    ....**diastatops,** p. 158
    A median and an apical pair of spots on the middle segments.
    Eyes contiguous..........................**maculatus,** p. 159

  * By C. F. Byers.

Nymphs*

1   Segments 8 and 9 without lateral spines....................2.
    Segments 8 and 9 with lateral spines.......................3.

2   Each division of the bifid middle tooth of the mentum truncate on
    the end, and with a very shallow secondary intendation, followed
    by a straight row of small denticales. Lateral setae 6–7......
    ....**dorsalis.**
    Mentum with each half of the middle tooth again strongly bifid,
    the lower half being smaller and almost hidden among the hairs
    at its base. No denticles. Lateral setae 5...........**diadema.**

3   Lateral spines on 8 and 9 stout, straight, and conspicuous. Teeth
    on the lateral lobes comparatively broad and blunt..........4.
    Lateral spines on 8 and 9 small, cylindric and hidden among scurfy
    hairs. Teeth of the lateral lobes long and sharp.............
    ....**maculatus.**

4   Median tooth of the mentum secondarily bifid into two equal
    parts...**sayi.**
    Median tooth of the mentum secondarily bifid into two unequal
    parts, the lower being the smaller........................5.

5   Lateral setae 5. Mental setae 10–11...............**diastatops.**
    Lateral setae 6. Mental 13........................**obliquus.**
    The nymphs of **erroneous** and **fasciatus** are still (1928) unknown.

  * By C. F. Byers.

The Known Nymphs

Species	Length	Lat. spines on 8 & 9	Lat. Set.	Ment. Set.	Described by
diadema	35	none	5	8–9	Ndm. '04, p. 697
diastatops	40	stout	5		Cabot '72, p. 13
dorsalis	35	none	6–7	8–9	Ndm. '04, p. 696
maculatus	41	minute	5	10–11	Ndm. '01, p. 477
obliquus	39	stout	6	13	Ndm. 06', p. 3
sayi	34	stout	5	11	Ndm. '03, p. 267

113. Cordulegaster diadema Selys

Selys '68, p. 68: Mtk. Cat. p. 76: Kndy. '17, p. 515 (figs.).

Length 78 mm. Expanse 100 mm. **Ariz.**

A fine big species of the southwest, its black body striped on the thorax and ringed on the abdomen with yellow. Face pale, with a blackish cross-stripe just below the ridge of the frons and a black clypeus and labral border. Occiput brown, low, hair-fringed. Pale stripes of the thorax pointed downward and strongly divergent. Those of the sides of the thorax broad and regular. Legs black. Wings hyaline; costa yellow; stigma brown. Abdomen black, ringed with yellow. Segments 3 to 8 each with a single median ring that is angulated at the side and bent forward at its lower end; on 9, similar, but broader and nearly divided in the middle; on 10, broken into three small spots. Segment 2 mostly yellow. Appendages black.

114. Cordulegaster sayi Selys

Selys '54, p. 104: Mtk. Cat. p. 78.

Length 62 mm. Expanse 78 mm. **Me., Va., Wis., Ga.**

A fine eastern species. The face is pale, with clypeus and border of labrum brown. The occiput is pale with very narrow black edging next the eyes. The black of the thorax is a little more extensive, so that the pale stripes of the front are shortened and rounded below; those of the sides are broad, and the black that intervenes between these stripes is undivided. Legs black. Wings hyaline with yellow costa, and tawny stigma. Abdomen half-ringed above with yellow on segments 2 to 9, the rings on 2 to 6 being double, and on 7 to 9 single but broader. Segment 10 and appendages black.

Muttkowski ('08, p. 79) reports that this species is found about Wisconsin lakes from June to August.

115. Cordulegaster erroneus Hagen

Hag. '54, p. 688: Mtk. Cat. p. 76: Garm. '27, p. 121.

Length 78 mm. Expanse 102 mm. **Pa., N. C. to Ky.**

A fine large species with cross-banded abdomen. Face yellowish, except for the clypeus and labral border, and the extreme side margins of the frons which are blackish. Occiput small, pale, clothed and fringed with tawny hairs. Stripes of the front of the thorax abbreviated and narrowed to a point below, and strongly divergent. Legs black. Wings hyaline; costa yellow; stigma black. The pale dorsal crossbands of the abdominal segments are dilated forward at the sides and incised by the black of the mid dorsal line on segments 2 to 6, and on 2 to 4 there is an additional side spot below. The crossband on 7 is broader; on 8, narrower and narrowly divided in the middle line; and on 9, reduced to a pair of widely separated pale dashes in the midst of the black; 10 and appendages black.

116. Cordulegaster dorsalis Hagen

Hag. '57, p. 347: Mtk. Cat. p. 76: Kndy. '17, p. 515 (figs.): Smn. '26, p. 26: Ckll. '19, p. 22.

Length 76 mm. Expanse 94 mm.   **Pacific Coast, Alaska to Calif.**

A fine big black west-coast species with thorax conspicuously striped and abdomen dorsally spotted. Face yellow with a faint wash of brown above across the upper margin; clypeus and labral border brown. Occiput brown, with marginal fringe of tawny hairs. Pale stripes of the front of the thorax rather broad, regular, strongly divergent downward. Those of the sides broad and regular. Legs black, brownish at base. Wings hyaline with brown stigma. Pale spots of the abdomen more or less saddle-shaped on segments 2 to 9, diminishing in size to rearward, bilobed behind on most of the segments; 10 mostly black. Appendages black.

Kennedy, who studied this species in the coast Mountains of California, ('17, p. 516) observes,

Cordulegaster dorsalis is found usually on those swift mountain torrents which do not freeze in the winter time. It is found in the swift upper reaches of all the perennial streams. It does not occur on the lower reaches of these same streams after they have emerged onto the level floors of the valley, and have lost their swiftness to become warm and muddy. In the steep and narrow mountain gorges where the rushing torrents pour down through the shade of the redwoods and alders, this dragonfly adds a note of mystery to the scene; for the individuals with their strange ophidian coloration glide noiselessly up stream and down, never showing that curiosity towards strangers or unusual surroundings which is exhibited by the Libellulines of the sunny valleys, but always moving straight ahead as though drawn irresistibly onward. Only males are common on the streams, the females seldom resorting to the water except to oviposit.

The males, as indicated above, fly on the longest beats I have observed for any dragonfly, for they fly continuously up stream and down, until they come to the head of the stream or to the slow water below, or until some unusual obstruction turns them aside, when they face about and fly as steadily in the opposite direction. The course is usually a foot or two above the surface of the stream and goes through dense shade and any loose brush or foliage which may hang over the water. Because of this habit of flying in long beats this dragonfly is not easily taken, as the collector has but a single chance at each individual.

In the streams of the Coast Mountains of California, where I have had opportunities to observe the habits of *Cordulegaster* most, it shows a marked upstream migration of the imagoes. The eggs are laid in the shallow water along the edges of the stream and the nymphs wander aimlessly over the bed. Because the nymphs are free on the stream bottom each freshet during the three or four years of nymphal life serves to wash them farther downstream so that when they come to emerge they may be far downstream from the place where the eggs were deposited.

I have never observed copulation in this species, but in the matter of oviposition I was more fortunate. August 16, on Stevens Creek, I saw a female oviposit. She flew hurriedly up the creek and every few yards stopped and with a sudden backing or downward stroke, while hovering with the body in a perpendicular position, stabbed her large ovipositor into the coarse sand along the stream edge, where the water was about an inch deep. She thus thrust her abdomen down through the inch of water driving her ovipositor into the sand beneath. Four to ten such perpendicular thrusts were made at each stop. Some stops were along the open beaches, but more were in quiet nooks between large rocks where she would have barely room enough for her wing expanse. She usually faced the center of the stream while ovipositing, though once she faced upstream and once she faced the bank. The peculiar perpendicular position with the up and down motion reminded me strongly of the manner of oviposition of some crane flies, except that the latter oviposit in damp soil and support themselves on their slender legs while making the vertical thrusts. Fig. 11 shows the position of the female while ovipositing.

The nymphs are shortlegged, slow moving creatures and are usually abundant in the streams of the Coast Mountains. They occur with Octogomphus nymphs in the leafy trash of the eddies, but are also found crawling slowly about over the bed of the stream. Their very slow and apparently cautious movements do not betray them, and they carry with them further protection in the coat of long hairs which collects dirt and on which flourishes a thick growth of filamentous algae. Because of this covering of dirt and algae the nymph, though on an otherwise barren bottom, will usually escape the closest scrutiny of the collector, for it does not appear any different from a stick or a stone covered with dirt and aquatic growths. On Mission Creek, Santa Barbara, California, I found nymphs of *dorsalis* buried in flocculent silt, as described for the various eastern species of the genus.

At emergence, which takes place in June, the nymphs crawl from 1 to 5 feet up the trunk of the nearest alder tree. This species spends 4 years in the egg and nymphal stage.

The senior author kept nymphs of this species alive in a dish of water and sand for some weeks on his desk in California in order to observe their feeding habits. A half grown nymph, thrown out of the sand, chanced to wander in front of a grown nymph and was seized by the cannibal and wholly devoured in half an hour. Damselflies (mostly Enallagmas) were used for regular feeding. Several were eaten daily by each nymph.

A large Enallagma nymph seized by its abdomen clung with its feet to the back of the head of the biddy nymph and would not let go until the latter compelled it by repeated forward thrusts of its tail spines turned forward over its head. A big nymph taken in the fingers will often use its tail spine defensively.

The normal food of these nymphs in the streams of southern California, as determined by stomach examinations, is mayfly nymphs and midge larvae.

117. Cordulegaster obliquus Say

Say '39, p. 15: Mtk. Cat. p. 77: Garm. '27, p. 123.

Length 74 mm. Expanse 96 mm.   **Me., Pa., Wis., Ill.**

A fine large species having a peaked occiput with a bald spot in the middle, and a Gomphus-like middorsal line of spots on the abdomen. Face pale, with the clypeus and labral border obscure brownish. Hind border of the yellow occiput hair fringed only at the sides. Pale stripes of the front of the thorax narrowed to a point below and strongly divergent, the pale side stripes strong and regular. Legs black, brownish at base. Wings hyaline, with costa and stigma brown. The middorsal line of pale spots on the abdomen is widened in the middle on each of segments 2 to 6; it is still more widened on 7 and 8; and reduced to a little basal transverse dash on 9; 10 and appendages wholly black.

The senior author has published an extended account of the habits of this species in *Entom. News*, 16: 3–6, 1905.

118. Cordulegaster fasciatus Rambur

Ramb. '42, p. 178: Mtk. Cat. p. 77.

Length 73 mm. Expanse 92 mm.   **S.E. States**

This is a fine, large, reddish brown species. Face yellowish, with brown bordered labrum and brown anteclypeus. There is a narrow brown line before the ocelli. The occiput is brownish black clothed with thin brown hairs. The two yellowish stripes on the front of the red brown thorax are cuneiform, pointed and divergent downward. The pale side stripes are broad and regular, and in the dark area between them there is a suggestion of an included narrow pale line. Legs black, reddish at base. Wings hyaline, a little tinged with yellow or brown in old specimens; stigma reddish. Abdomen blackish with two midlateral rows of yellow spots on segments 2 to 8; the spots are triangular on 7, and almost bifid on 8. Auricles of the male yellow. Appendages black.

119. Cordulegaster diastatops Selys

Selys '54, p. 101: Mtk. Cat. p. 76: Garm. '27, p. 119.

Syn: lateralis Scud.

Length 60 mm. Expanse 80 mm.   Atlantic States **Me.** to **N. C.**

A trim blackish species with greenish stripes on the thorax and a line of obscure pale spots along the sides of the abdomen. Face greenish except for the clypeus and a narrow front border to the labrum. Occiput yellowish, except for a narrow line of black on the lateral margins next the eye, and a black hair fringe. Pale stripes of the front of the thorax rather broad, strongly divergent forward and pointed downward. The broad black shoulder stripe is divided above by a little greenish triangle (due to incomplete fusion of black stripes 2 and 3). Likewise, the two oblique pale stripes of the sides are broad and parallel, with the intervening black, paler in the middle (due to the incomplete fusion of black stripes 4 and 5). Legs black. Wings hyaline with a tawny stigma. The pale markings of the abdomen consist of a line of lateral triangles each side, continuous on segments 2 and 3, abbreviated progressively on 4 to 8, reduced to a squarish spot on 9; 10 and appendages black.

This is the common species in the northeastern states. In the glades of the woods the adult males course the streams in persistent flight during hours of sunshine in hot weather. Females are less in evidence, but are seen sometimes ovipositing by vertical thrusts in the sand in shoal riffles up-stream from the settling basins in the brooks. The cast skins left behind by the nymphs at transformation are found commonly sticking to roots and logs at the edges of these basins.

120. Cordulegaster maculatus Selys

Selys '54, p. 105: Mtk. Cat. p. 77: Garm. '27, p. 122.

Length 68 mm. Expanse 84 mm. Atlantic Coast, N. S. to N. C.

A stout hairy species with attingent eyes, and a small brownish occiput that is clothed all over its upper and front surface with brown hairs. Face pale, with obscure brownish clypeus and labral border. Pale stripes of the front of the thorax abbreviated and pointed below and strongly divergent downward; those of the sides broad and regular. Legs blackish, brown at base. Wings hyaline with tawny stigma. Abdomen with pale spots in two rows on the abdomen well up toward the middorsal line, double on segment 2, single and diminishing in size to rearward on segments 3 to 8; 9, 10 and appendages black.

Davis ('13, p. 18) reports this species as often found flying up and down brooks. Williamson ('07, p. 144) thus writes of its egg-laying habits:

Two females were observed to fly down from trees alighting on algae covered rocks in the stream bed. On the portions of these rocks not covered by water they crawled about in an awkward manner thrusting the abdomen with much commotion into the algae beneath the water. Males alternated between the trees and short flights over the water.

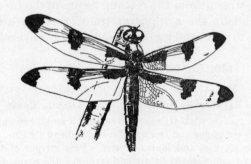

Family LIBELLULIDAE

The Skimmers

These are the commonest and best known of dragonflies. On shining, tremulous wings they hover over every pond and pool. They range in size from the little blue bell (*Nannothemis bella*), less than an inch long, up to the big belted skimmers of the genus Macromia.

These are mostly showy dragonflies. The body is stout and the abdomen is generally less elongated than in the preceeding groups. The head is bulged laterally by the huge compound eyes which overspread its upper surface meeting in the median line above, in a short seam. The triangles are elongated in different directions; that of the fore wing cross-wise and that of the hind wing length-wise of the wing. They are situated much nearer the arculus in the hind than in the fore wing. The antenodal cross veins mostly matched in position across the subcostal vein. Some of the more proximal postnodals do not extend to the median vein. There is no brace vein to the stigma. The anal loop is generally well developed. The female generally lacks an ovipositor.

The coloration of members of this family is often strikingly beautiful. Often there are wing patterns in brown, red and gold, and sometimes these are different in the two sexes. Often there is a development of pruinosity (like a hoary bluish white powder) with age, completely changing the appearance of the body by obscuring the original color pattern.

KEY TO THE SUBFAMILIES

Adults

1 Anal loop compact, little longer than wide, the bordering basal portion of vein Cu_2 straight, included cells not in two rows and not separated by a distinct bisector or mid rib; triangle of hind wing remote from the arculus; arculus with long stalked sectors; more than 2 cubito-anal cross veins present..............
.....................................**Macromiinae, p. 163**
Anal loop elongate, becoming foot-shaped, divided length-wise into 2 rows of cells by a bisector or mid rib; the bordering basal portion of vein Cu_2 sinuous; triangle of hind wing close to the arculus; one or two cubito-anal cross veins present.........2.

161

2 Anal loop somewhat foot-shaped but with little development of the toe; males with auricles on the sides of the second abdominal segment, and with the adjacent inner margin of the hind wing notched .... **Corduliinae, p. 171**

Anal loop (in ours) generally distinctly foot-shaped with a well developed toe; males without auricles on 2, and inner margin of hind wing rounded.................... **Libellulinae, p. 201**

Nymphs

1 Head with a prominent frontal horn; abdomen flat and subcircular; legs very long; teeth on lateral lobe of labium with very deep incisions between them................. **Macromiinae, p. 163**

Head with no prominent frontal horn; abdomen more elongate and less depressed; teeth on lateral lobes of labium with only shallow incisions between them.................................**2.**

2 Hind femora longer than the head is wide; when the lateral spines are long there is a full series of big dorsal hooks on the abdomen ....**Corduliinae, p. 171**

Hind femora not longer than the head is wide; when lateral spines are long there is generally no full series of big dorsal hooks on the abdominal segments.................... **Libellulinae*, p. 203**

* These last alternatives are of uncertain application. When in doubt try both routes.

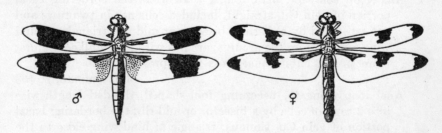

Fig. 32a. Sexual differences in color pattern in *Plathemis lydia*.

Subfamily MACROMIINAE
The Belted Skimmers

These are very large, strong flying, clear winged dragonflies, with robust bodies and long legs. In the hind wing the triangle is remote from the arculus (though nearer it than in the fore wing); the anal loop is never foot-shaped, but is short and compact, lacking a bisector. The distinctive feature of their coloration is a conspicuous band of yellow encircling the synthorax at the middle sutures, showing as a single oblique, middle yellow stripe upon the sides.

These dragonflies are the monarchs of the upper air. They fly high and forage widely and are exceedingly difficult to capture. They go volplaning about the shores of lakes and large ponds and the more quiet places in the large streams.

The nymphs are short and flat with widely sprawling legs. The eyes are very prominently elevated on the superolateral angles of the head, and between them is a conspicuous frontal horn. There is a row of strong, cultriform mid dorsal hooks running length-wise of the abdomen.

These nymphs are not found in the weed beds, but on the bare areas of the bottom, amid the silt which spreads over them.

The group is a small one, including in our limits but 2 genera, which may be distinguished as follows:

KEY TO THE GENERA
Adults

1 Dorsal surface of the head with the occiput larger than the vertex; subtriangle of the fore wings usually divided by a cross vein; 4 to 6 cross veins in the space above the bridge............
....**Didymops**, p. 169
Dorsal surface of the head with the occiput much smaller than the vertex; subtriangle of the fore wings generally open; 2 or 3 cross veins in the space above the bridge........**Macromia**, p. 164

Nymphs

1 Head hardly as wide across the eyes as across the bulging hind angles; lateral spines not incurved, those of the ninth abdominal segment hardly surpassed by the tips of the appendages; dorsum of the tenth abdominal segment with no trace of a dorsal hook
....**Didymops**, p. 169
Head widest across the eyes; spines of the ninth abdominal segment shorter, not nearly reaching the level of the apices of the appendages; dorsum of the tenth segment with a very rudimentary dorsal hook.....................**Macromia**, p. 165

25. Macromia Rambur

These are fine clear-winged dragonflies of brownish color and very robust form. The top of the vertex is a double cone, with the two apices rather sharply pointed. The legs are black. The wings are hyaline. A girdle of yellow encircles the thorax and there is a saddle of yellow upon the dorsum of the seventh abdominal segment more or less well defined.

Most species seem to prefer the larger streams over which they sweep boldly and erratically here and there, betaking themselves often in

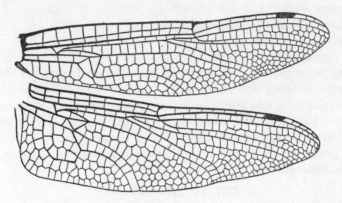

FIG. 33. Wings of *Macromia pacifica*.

high flights above the neighboring tree tops. Their season of greatest activity is midsummer and they are most in evidence on clear hot days. The females oviposit unattended by the males.

Williamson has studied the species of this genus occurring in Indiana, and has this to say about their habitat and habits ('15, p. 386): "The Wabash River at Bluffton during recent years has been overrun at the ripples by willow herb, so the river in summer is reduced to a succession of pools of greater or less length. On the banks *Hibiscus militaris* has become throughly established at the water's edge. These pools seem to be an ideal home for the Macromias.

"Individuals follow the same track over and over, crossing the river at a certain point, returning over a certain patch of willow herb, turning out from the shore line at a certain clump of Hibiscus, and going and coming over the same or nearly the same course, and not following the pools in a circular manner. Moreover, individuals of successive generations have followed the same course as their predecessors, as I have observed at the pools where I have found individuals most numerous, and where I have collected for several years. The configuration of vegetation and water is a positive factor in determining the course of flight."

Their flat, long legged, freckled *nymphs* sprawl on the botton silt, which their colors match perfectly. They clamber far out away from the water to transform, leaving their empty skins often many meters distant from it, attached to tree trunks or walls.

The nymphs of this genus differ from those of Didymops chiefly in that the head is widest across the eyes and slowly narrowed to rearward. They seem to prefer clayey bottom among the roots of trees where a net may hardly be used to get them.

Nymphs of but three of our species have hitherto been described. Their chief characters may be tabulated as follows

The Known Nymphs

Species	Length	Tip of Horn	Ment. Setae	Lat. Setae	Lat. sp.* on 9	Described by
illinoiensis	30	acute	5+1	6	straight	Cabot '90, p. 16
magnifica	31	acute	4+1	6	straight	Cabot '90, p. 18**
taeniolata	36	obtuse			incurved	Cabot '90, p. 19

* Lateral spines.
** Kennedy ('15, p. 313–322) has adequately described and illustrated this species, and has given a key to these nymphs.

They are of wide distribution, especially in the northern hemisphere. About a third of the species occur within our limits. They may be distinguished as follows:

KEY TO THE SPECIES

Adults

1 Pale stripe on front of thorax obsolete or nearly so............2.
   Pale stripe on front of thorax well developed reaching at least half
     way to the crest.......................................4.

2 Yellow ring on second abdominal segment divided dorsally.....
     ....**australensis**, p. 169
   Yellow ring on second abdominal segment entire..............3.

3 Yellow cross band of abdominal segment 7 in male, reaching lateral
     border...............................**alleghaniensis**, p. 167
   Yellow cross band of seventh abdominal segment of male not
     reaching lateral border..................**illinoiensis**, p. 166

4   Costa brown...5.
    Costa yellow...6.
5   Expanse over 115...........................**taeniolata**, p. 167
    Expanse less than 100 mm.................**georgiana**, p. 169
6   Pale stripe on front of thorax abbreviated and pointed above....
    ....**wabaşhensis**, p. 167
    Pale stripe on front of thorax broader and reaching almost to
    carina..7.
7   Pale spots of middle abdominal segments divided on median line
    ....**pacifica**, p. 168
    Pale spots of middle abdominal segments not divided on median
    line; vertex pale..8.
8   Transverse pale spot on abdominal segment 2 entire; antenodals of
    fore wing 14 to 15.......................**annulata**, p. 168
    Transverse pale spot on abdominal segment 2 divided; antenodals
    of fore wing 11 to 12.....................**magnifica**, p. 168

121. **Macromia illinoiensis** Walsh

Walsh '62, p. 397: Mtk. Cat. p. 120: Wlsn. '12, p. 193: Howe '19, p. 52: Garm.
'27, p. 204.

Length 70 mm. Expanse 100 mm.   **N. Eng., N. Y., Pa., Del., N. C.**

Another darkly colored species, lacking pale stripes on the front of the thorax.
Face brownish, paler on middle of labrum and on most of the postclypeus.
Top of frons with four yellowish spots on a brown ground, two within and two
without the median furrow. The single median side stripe of the thorax is well
defined and there is another obscurer one on the hind margin below. Legs black.
Wings hyaline, except for a tinge of brown in the membrane at the extreme base.
Costa and stigma brown. Pale spots of abdomen of slight extent, divided by
black on the middorsal line except on segment 7, where fused into the usual
saddle mark, which does not extend down to the lateral margin of the segment.
Segments 8, 9, and 10 and appendages black.

Walker ('08, p. 17) says:

This insects frequents woodland paths and glades in the neighborhood of large lakes and rapid streams, coursing swiftly back and
forth over its chosen part with almost tireless energy. It appears about
the end of June or first week in July, and remains until the latter part
of August.

This species frequents lakes as well as rivers. Williamson ('09, p. 369)
observes that

At Sandusky, Ohio, where **M. Illinoiensis** has been taken in large numbers, many
collect toward evening in the cedars on Cedar Point, several individuals fre-

quently choosing the same twig for a resting place. It is probably that during the day these same individuals seek insect food at a considerable elevation, and hence escape observation.

Williamson further says (*l, c,* p. 386) that when this dragonfly is in flight one gets the "impression of a black insect largely yellow at apex of the abdomen."

122. **Macromia allegheniensis** Williamson

Wmsn. '09, p. 376: Mtk. Cat. p. 120.

Length 70 mm. Expanse 98 mm.   **Va., Pa., Ky.**

Differs but little from the preceding species, the pale markings of the abdomen being a little more extensive, especially the cross stripes on abdominal segments 2 and 8; on 2 it is continuous across the middorsal line, and on 8 it extends lower down on the sides, in the male, reaching the lateral margin.

123. **Macromia taeniolata** Rambur

Ramb. '42, p. 139: Mtk. Cat. p. 121: Wlsn. '12, p. 193: Garm. '27, p. 204.

Length 90 mm. Expanse 122 mm.   **N. Y. and Wis. to Kan. and Fla.**

This is the largest species of the genus. The face is brownish with the middle of the labrum and all of the clypeus pale. The vertex is metallic blue and hairy, double pointed and peaked. The two pale stripes of the front of the thorax are rather narrow and abbreviated and taper upward, reaching a little more than half way to the crest. The pair of yellow dashes on the crest a little overspread its front margin. Legs black. Wings hyaline with brown costa and stigma. The pale markings of the dorsum of the abdomen are separated by black on the median line except on the 7th segment, where the narrow yellowish line is continuous, its ends curving forward on the sides of the segment. Segments 9 and 10 and the appendages are black.

Wilson ('09) found it in late May and in July along streams in damp woods. It is a species of very swift and long sustained flight, and is very difficult to capture.

124. **Macromia wabashensis** Williamson

Wmsn. '09, p. 374: Mtk. Cat. p. 121.

Length 74 mm. Expanse 102 mm.   **Ind.**

"Very similar to *taeniolata*, but may be recognized by the following characters: Costa (and antenodals and postnodals) yellow or yellowish as far as the tips of the wings; labrum less obscured, face paler and brighter colored; lateral spots on frons distinct; dorsal abdominal spot on 8 similar in shape and extent, relative to the transverse carina, to the spot on 7. Wings tinged with pale yellowish, or hyaline, the extreme apex frequently slightly fumose."—From Wmsn. '09, p. 374.

125. Macromia pacifica Hagen

Hag. '61, p. 134: Mtk. Cat. p. 121.

Syn: flavipennis Walsh

Length 70 mm.   Expanse 94 mm.   Wis., Ind., Tex., Calif.

A fine western species, with yellow costal wing margin, and double row of spots on the abdomen. Face greenish yellow across the postclypeus and dull yellow on the labrum. Top of frons pale, scarcely showing the outline of the four usual spots. The pale stripes of the front of the thorax are well developed, parallel sided, and reach upward nearly to the crest. Side stripes broad and well defined, with an inferior pale stripe on the hind margin of the thorax. Legs black. Wings hyaline, with yellow costa, and blackish stigma. Pale markings of the top of the abdomen divided on the median line on segments 2 to 8; on 2, an elongate and rather wide transverse band; on the other segments spots, largest as usual on 7. Segments 9, 10 and appendages black.

Williamson, who has observed this species at Bluffton, Indiana, says ('09, p. 386) that it is readily recognized at some distance on the wing, and that "In flight one gets the impression of an insect largely yellow in color."

126. Macromia annulata Hagen

Hag. '61, p. 133: Mtk. Cat. p. 120.

Length 68 mm.   Expanse 95 mm.   Carolina, Tex., Ill.

A rather pale species with whitish face and yellow costa. The vertex is pale. The pale stripes of the front of the thorax are well developed, parallel sided, and reach upward nearly to the crest. The hind margin of the thorax also is yellow lined beneath. Legs black with bases of the femora paler. Wings hyaline with yellow costa and brown stigma. Pale markings of the abdomen continuous across the middorsal line, there is a narrow band across segment 2, a broad spot on 7 and shorter spots on 3 to 6 and on 8. Segments 9, 10 and appendages, blackish.

127. Macromia magnifica McLachlan

McL. '74, p. 22: Mtk. Cat. p. 121: Kndy. '15, p. 313.

Length 70 mm.   Expanse 96 mm.   Calif., Ariz.

A fine brownish western species rather brightly marked with yellow and with venation rather more open than in the other species. Face with the usual two pale cross bands and with the top of the frons and the vertex yellowish. Stripes on the front of the thorax broad, and reaching well up toward the crest. Legs blackish. Wings hyaline; costa yellow; stigma brown. Pale marks of the dorsum of the abdomen undivided except on the 2nd segment and rather broad on the succeeding segments; there are represented by narrow transverse basal lines on 9 and 10. Appendages brown.

Kennedy ('15, p. 313) reports interesting observations on this species, made by him on Satus Creek, Umatilla flats, Oregon, from which we gather that he found the males patrolling the larger pools of the stream, most abundantly on calm clear forenoons. The females he saw ovipositing in the larger pools. They flew back and forth 40 to 50 feet, touching the water at 3 to 5 foot intervals to liberate eggs, and generally persisted at their task until seized and carried away by a male. He found the cast skins of the nymphs sticking to the trees whose bare roots dipped into the water on under-cut banks of the pools.

128. Macromia georgina Selys

Selys '78, p. 197: Mtk. Cat. p. 120.

Length 71 mm. Expanse 96 mm. **N. C., Ga., Tex.**

A pale-faced brownish species that has in addition to the usual paler areas on the middle of the labrum and on the postclypeus, a rather broad transverse band of the same color just beneath the ridge on the frons. There are the usual four obscure pale spots on the frons above. The vertex is peaked, bifid, bare and brown. The pale stripes of the front of the thorax are rather narrow, and taper upward and end far below the crest. Legs black. Wings hyaline; costa and stigma brown. The pale markings of the abdomen are continuous across the middorsal line on segments 2, 7 and 8, on 2 linear, on 7 saddle shaped, on 8 smaller but similar, on 3 to 6 broken on the middle line to form pairs of spots. Segments 9, 10 and appendages black.

129. Macromia australensis Williamson

Wmsn. '09, p. 381: Mtk. Cat. p. 120.

Length 75 mm. Expanse 104 mm. **Okla., Tex.**

A large dark colored species with a minimum of pale markings for the genus. Face brownish, with the middle of the labrum and most of the postclypeus pale. Top of frons scarcely spotted. Peak of vertex, bifid, brown, bare. No stripe on front of thorax, the single median side stripe conspicuous. Legs black. Wings hyaline, costa and stigma brown. Pale markings of the abdomen are continuous across the median dorsal line on segments 2 (where transversely linear), and on 7 (where a broad saddle mark), and on 8, and divided by black of the mid dorsum on 3 to 6. Appendage and segments 9, 10 and appendages black.

26. Didymops Selys

These large dragonflies differ from Macromia chiefly in the conformation of the top of the head, as indicated in the key, and in small details of venation. The subtriangle of the forewing is generally divided by a cross vein, and the membranule is very broad.

The flat, long-legged *nymphs* (Ndm. '01, p. 481) dwell in the silt in the beds of lakes and ponds and in settling basins of streams. They sprawl on the bottom, usually in the midst of trash, and are oftenest found where falling silt has partly covered them, leaving only the tips of their eyes and the curious un-lifelike hooks and spines exposed. Thus situated, their concealment is perfect. They crawl a considerable distance from the water to transform, and leave their skins sticking to trees and posts often a good many meters distant from the margin of the water, and often as many meters above the ground.

The adults are strong flying and rather widely ranging. They are fairly common in wooded districts flying along the margins of lakes and slow streams in the Eastern United States.

This indigenous eastern genus includes but 2 species that may be separated as follows:

KEY TO THE SPECIES
Adults

1 Wing expanse 77 mm. Basal antenodal cells of both wings tinged with brown.............................**transversa, p. 170**

Wing expanse 82 mm. Basal antenodal cells of both wings hyaline ....**floridensis, p. 170**

130. Didymops transversa Say

Say 1839, p. 19: Mtk. Cat. p. 118: Howe '19, p. 51: Garm. '27, p. 202.

Syn: cinnamonea Burm., *servillei* Ramb.

Length 58 mm. Expanse 77 mm.   **Alta, Me., Mich., to S. C. and Ga.**

A large, hoary, brown species with rusty red tail. Face pale with the front edge of the labrum darker. On the top of the frons there is an 8-spot, dilated at the ends longitudinally. The conical vertex and the low occiput are pale olivaceous. The thorax is brown with a broad, oblique pale stripe on the middle of the sides. Legs brown, tarsi black, tibiae yellow externally. Wings hyaline, except for a short basal brown streak in front of the basal space and covering hardly more than the first antenodal cross vein. Stigma brown and costa tawny. Abdomen very obscurely half ringed with black above on the middle segments; the paler apical half of each segment being palest on segment 7, becoming more or less rusty red on the apical segments, whose extreme apical margins are encircled with black. Appendages tawny.

131. Didymops floridensis Davis

Davis '22, p. 110.

Length 65 mm. Expanse 82 mm.   **Fla.**

This is similar to the preceding species but larger and it has the base of the wings less extensively tinged with brown. The venation is black except for a somewhat paler costa. The frons above is shining black, the occiput is lemon yellow and narrower than in *D. transversa*. Behind the eye there is a long, narrow, black, shining area, chiefly above the eye tubercle, extending to the occiput, where *transversa* is dull yellow. Otherwise the two are quite similar. The *nymph* is unknown.

Subfamily CORDULINAE

Strong-flying dragonflies of large size and often of brilliant metallic coloration. Eyes very large and broadly attingent, with an angulation or low tubercle on their hind margin at the side of the head. Sectors of the arculus separate at their origin. Triangle of hind wings retracted to the arculus. Anal loop somewhat foot-shaped (in ours), with well developed bisector, but with little development of the "toe." Males with auricles on the sides of the second abdominal segment, and corresponding notches in the inner margin of the hind wings.

The nymphs are sprawlers upon the bottom. They are generally hairy, dark colored, and stout bodied, and the dorsal hooks when developed are rather heavy and not spinelike.

Our genera have a predominantly northward distribution. They may be separated as follows:

KEY TO THE GENERA

Adults

1 Fore wing, veins M_4 and Cu_1 divergent to wing margin . . . . 2.
  Fore wing, veins M_4 and Cu_1 convergent to wing margin . . . . 4.

2 Fore wing triangle equilateral. Size large (expanse 75) . . . . 3.
  Fore wing triangle long and narrow. Small size (expanse 46) . . . .
  . . . . **Williamsonia,** p. 199

3 Ante- and post-nodal cross veins all blotched with brown . . . . . .
  . . . . **Platycordulia,** p. 172
  Only basal ante-nodal cross veins blotched with brown . . . .
  . . . . **Neurocordulia,** p. 173

4 Wings with nodal and apical spots . . . . **Epicordulia,** p. 175
  Wings with only basal spots or with none . . . . 5.

5 Basal brown spots large; basal ante-nodal cross veins spotted with
    brown except in (*Tetragoneuria stella*) . . . . 6.
  Basal brown spots small or wanting; basal ante-nodal cross veins
    not spotted with brown . . . . 7.

6 Hind wing with 6 ante-nodal cross veins . . . . **Helocordulia,** p. 181
  Hind wing with 4 to 5 ante-nodal cross veins . . . .
  . . . . **Tetragoneuria,** p. 178

7 Hind wing with two cubito-anal cross veins . . **Somatochlora,** p. 183
  Hind wing with one cubito-anal cross veins . . . . 8.

171

8   Fore wing triangle crossed cross veins..........**Cordulia**, p. 197
    Fore wing triangle free from.............**Dorocordulia**, p. 198

Nymphs

1   Lateral setae four or five; mentum about as long as wide........
    ....**Epicordulia**, p. 175
    Lateral setae five or six: mentum longer...**Neurocordulia**, p. 173
    Lateral setae seven; mentum of labium longer than wide......2.

2   Abdomen with large, laterally flattened, generally cultriform dorsal
    hooks...3.
    Abdomen with no dorsal hooks, or with these rudimentary, not
    flattened laterally or cultriform, but small obtuse or pointed
    prominences.......................................5.

3   Lateral spines of the ninth segment longer than half the length of
    that segment; dorsal hooks on segments 3–9, highest on 6, cul-
    triform, and sharp....................**Tetragoneuria**, p. 179
    Lateral spines of the ninth segment shorter than half of that seg-
    ment; dorsal hooks less developed........................4.

4   Dorsal hooks on segments 4–9 laterally flattened, but obtuse at
    apices, and not cultriform..............**Somatochlora**, p. 184
    Dorsal hooks on segments 6–9, longest on 8 and cultriform......
    ....**Helocordulia**, p. 182

5   Hind angles of the head rounded; lateral spines of the ninth abdo-
    minal segment one-fifth as long as that segment...........6.
    Hind angles of the head angulate superiorly; spines of the ninth
    abdominal segment one-third as long as that segment........
    ....**Dorocordulia**, p. 198

6   Teeth on lateral labial lobes deeply cut and separated by rather
    wide notches.........................**Somatochlora**, p. 184
    Teeth low, separated only by shallow crenulations.............
    ....**Cordulia**, p. 197

27. PLATYCORDULIA Williamson

These are large yellowish cordulines with densely veined wings that
are prettily spotted with yellow along the whole front margin. The anal
loop is widened at the end, where there is some doubling of the included cell rows, and two rows of cells intervene between the loop and
margin of the hind wing. The superior appendages of the male are
armed with a tooth on the inner side beneath their arched basal portion.
The nymph is unknown.

132. Platycordulia xanthosoma Williamson

Wmsn. '08, p. 432: Mtk. Cat. p. 124.

Length 46 mm. Expanse 75 mm. **Okla.**

This is a yellowish dragonfly, with the abdomen darker than the thorax except at the ends. The eyes are contiguous for a distance about equal to the width of the vertex. The wing membrane is yellowish hyaline with diffuse, yellow spottings on most of the cross veins that lie in front of a line through triangles and subnodus, and around behind the stigma to the wing apex. The yellow overspreads the membrane of the interspaces at base, nodus and apex, spreading especially to rearward at base of hind wing. Membranule white, posterior third dark brown, this brown color in the hind wing broadly margining adjacent cross veins.

Williamson obtained two male specimens (all that are as yet recorded for this species) at Wistar, Oklahoma, flushing one of them himself from some bushes which overhung the edge of the Pateau River. "Its flight and manner of alighting and its position at rest suggested a teneral Libellula."

28. NEUROCORDULIA Selys

These are crepuscular dragonflies of non-metallic coloration. The wings have basal markings of brown. Both triangle and subtriangle of the fore wing are normally divided into three cells. There are two cubito-anal cross veins. Veins M_4 and Cu_1 diverge toward the wing margin.

The nymphs are stocky, short legged and rather smooth. The head has a low rounded shelflike frontal ridge between the antennae and a pair of obsolescent tubercles on top. Its hind angles are obtusely

The Known Nymphs

Species	Length	Lateral spines of 9	Dorsal hooks of 3	Dorsal hooks of 8	Described by
obsoleta	20	surpass abd. app.	erect	low	Ndm. '01, p. 486
yamaskanensis	23	not so	curved	absent	Walk. '13, p. 165

angulate with the hind margin concave between them. The labium is short and wide, with 7 to 9 mental setae each side and 5 or 6 laterals. The teeth on the inner margin of the lateral lobes are semi-elliptic, and separated by deep incisions, almost as in the Macromiinae. The abdomen is oval with sharp lateral margins. There is a row of prominent dorsal hooks, sharp and spinelike on basal segments, becoming thick and blunt and highest on the middle segments. There are lateral spines on segments 8 and 9. Segment 10 is short, annular and included.

KEY TO THE SPECIES

Adults

1 Wings with a brown spot covering the nodus......**obsoleta**, p. 174
   Wings with no brown spot covering the nodus...............2.
2 Wings with brown basal spots...........**yamaskanensis**, p. 175
   Wings with only faint yellow clouds on basal cross veins........
   ....**virginiensis**, p. 175

133. Neurocordulia obsoleta Say

Say '39, p. 29: Mtk. Cat. p. 123: Mtk. '10, p. 174: Howe '19, p. 53: Garm. '27, p. 234.

Syn: polysticta Burm. *molesta* Walsh, *Var. clara* Mtk.

Length 43 mm. Expanse 6 mm.   **Mass. and Ill. to N. C. and La.**

This is a large brown species of rather dull coloration. Face olive with a yellow labrum. Thorax very hairy, brownish olive, with a darker middorsal stripe that is divided by a yellow carina, and a little yellow spot at each side on the collar. There are cuneiform dark spots on the sides of the thorax near the base of the legs. Legs pale brown. Wings spotted with brown on the antenodal cross veins in the subcostal space with a larger spot on the nodus. Wing roots brown with this color confluent with the large brown spot at the hind angle which may reach to the triangle. Stigma yellow. Abdomen long, swollen at the base, narrowed on the third segment, then gradually enlarged to the apex. Olive brown, yellowish on sides of segments, especially each side of segment 2. Appendages light brown, hairy.

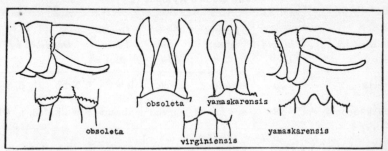

The senior author found numerous cast skins sticking to the swollen bases of cypress trees in Chipola Lake, Florida, in early April. Some were in the "moss" (Tillandsia) that draped the cypresses, several feet above the water.

134. Neurocordulia yamaskanensis Provancher

Prov. '75, p. 248: Mtk. Cat. p. 123: Walk. '13, p. 161: Howe '19, p. 53: Garm. '27, p. 236.

Length 45 mm. Expanse 65 mm.   **Que. and Me.**

This northern species is similar to the preceding, a little larger in stature and differs in coloration of the wings by lacking the brown spots on the antenodals and nodus, and having less depth and extent of coloration at the wing bases. There are diffuse spots on several cross veins before the level of the triangle. The stigma is a little shorter than in *obsoleta*.

Walker ('08) says that it frequents large lakes or rivers and is unique among our dragonflies in its habit of flying only after sunset, when the mayflies, on which it feeds, are abroad.

135. Neurocordulia virginiensis Davis

Davis '27, p. 155.

Length 49 mm. Expanse 70 mm.   **Va.**

A yellowish brown species, similar to the preceding. Face pale greenish yellow. Thorax rather uniform yellowish brown. Legs pale, with black spines. Wings hyaline with faint isolated yellow clouds surrounding the basal cross veins as far out as the triangles. Cross veins fewer than in *N. obsoleta*, and with none in the (first median) space before the arculus, and with but two cell rows behind Cu_2 in the fore wing. Abdomen, as in *N. obsoleta*. Appendage pale brown.

Male imago and nymph unknown.

29. EPICORDULIA Selys

These are fine large free-ranging Cordulines with beautifully spotted wings. The head is wide, the thorax is hairy. The abdomen is long and slender. The triangles of both wings are divided by a single cross vein. The fore wing subtriangle is divided into 3 cells. The broad brown wing spots occur at base, middle and tip of both wings, and these are so conspicuous that members of this genus are readily distinguished even in flight.

The nymphs are broad, flat, spiny, stiff-legged creatures that inhabit the beds of ponds and slow streams. They sprawl over loose trash or clamber on submerged logs. The head has a low frontal shelf projecting between the antennae, and a pair of obsolete tubercles on top. The hind angles are rounded. The legs are long and widely separated below. There are large, cultriform dorsal hooks on abdominal segments 3 to 9, and lateral spines on 8 and 9, on 8 short, incurved, and on 9 long and slightly outcurved. The female oviposits while flying alone. She descends to touch the water at points wide apart, far out from shore in open water.

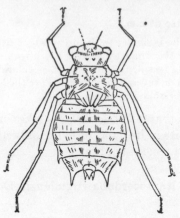

Fig. 34. Epicordulia nymph.

Nymphs

Species	Length	H. fem.	Width of abdomen	Spine of 9	Described by
princeps	23	8	10 mm.	nearly twice as long as segment	Ndm. '01, p. 488
regina	28	10	13 mm.	equals 9	Brtn. '28, p. 33

The genus is indigenous to the eastern United States and includes two species distinguishable as follows:

KEY TO THE SPECIES

1 Expanse of wings 80 mm.; spots of wings light brown covering a fourth or less of the wing area . . . . **princeps**, p. 176

Expanse 100 mm.; spots dark brown covering one half or more of the wing area . . . . **regina**, p. 177

136. Epicordulia princeps Hagen

Hag. '61, p. 134: Mtk. Cat. p. 122: Howe '19, p. 55: Garm. '27, p. 207: Bromley, '28, p. 69.

Length 56 mm. Expanse 80 mm.   **Me. to N. D. and Tex.**

A fine large strong-flying species with long abdomen and conspicuously spotted wings. The face vertex and occiput are pale olivaceous. The thorax is brownish, rather densely clad with tawny hairs, and with only a touch of blackish at the lower end of the two principal lateral sutures. The legs are olivaceous almost to the knees and thence brownish. Wings hyaline with large basal, nodal and apical spots as shown in the figure. Abdomen obscure olivaceous, or brownish, with only a very narrow pale line encircling the apical margin of the 2nd segment. Appendages fuscous.

This species is much commoner in nature than it is in collections for it is difficult to catch. Its flight is swift and well nigh continuous from daylight until dark in midsummer. It flies out of reach of a net, high in the air and often far from water. Still oftener it flies far out from the shore over the open lake or river. Though strong of wing, it is not so agile nor so pugnacious as are some of its congeners. It is often chased all about by the Dog-tail (*Tetragoneuria cynosura*), a species a third smaller than itself.

Its nymph sprawls on the trash of the bottom in shoal waters, and when ready to transform, climbs some distance up the bank, usually several feet from the water.

It shows a marked preference for stumps and logs as a place for transformation.

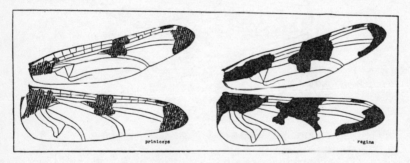

137. Epicordulia regina Hagen

Hag. '71, p. 27: Mtk. Cat. p. 122.

Length 71 mm. Expanse 106 mm. **Fla., Ga.**

This is a very beautiful southern species that seems to differ from the preceding only in much larger size and in the extent of the brown coloration of the wings. This is shown in the accompanying figures.

On the lower Chipola River in Florida the senior author saw this species in flocks of hundreds in early April. They were sailing through the air over the river like miniature biplanes, soaring aloft higher than the great trees of the streamside, volplaning down into the green lane between but not coming very close to the water, and, alas, not at all within reach of the collector's net. Still their effortless, unending flight was beautiful to witness. They seem to be a bit social; for the air would be full of them for a few miles, and then there would be stretches of the river where none were to be seen.

A dilatation of the river known as Chipola Lake was probably the source of these swarms. On the trunks of the cypress trees standing in the lake the cast skins of nymphs of this species were very common hanging to the bark or to the moss often as high as one could reach from a boat.

30. TETRAGONEURIA Hagen

Dog-tails: Wags

These are dragonflies of rather large size. The coloration is brownish, non-metallic with scanty and rather obscure yellowish markings. The thorax is clothed with hoary hairs. The wings are hyaline except for basal subcostal streak and a basal post cubital spot on the hind ones, very variable in extent and in separatiness, according to species and

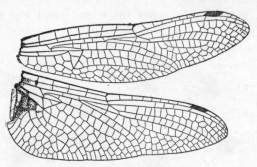

Fig. 35. Wings of *Tetragoneuria cynosura*.

variety. These markings are almost wanting in *T. stella* and they overspread half the wing in *T. cynosura*. The venation is open, being reduced to a minimum and perfected in adjustment, giving excellent powers of flight. The subgenital plate of the female is very long, often longer than the ninth segment, and cleft to the base in two divergent linear lobes.

These dragonflies are very agile. Their flight is rarely straight ahead for any great, continued distance. It is rather a continual succession of dartings and dodgings from side to side. Though they are not shy and will allow one to approach rather near, they are not easy to capture. Hence they are not so common in collections as their great abundance in nature would lead one to expect. They are pugnacious and often pursue larger species about as a kingbird harasses a crow.

The nymphs crawl over the bottom or clamber over loose trash and timbers. They are rather clean and hairless, and show when recently moulted a neat but rather obscure color pattern. The genus is widely distributed over North America. It is often very abundant about the wooded shores of lakes and ponds where cast skins of the transforming nymphs are sometimes found in almost incredible numbers

The species are all about one size and one color pattern of body and are very variable in the markings of brown upon the wings. Many species have been named because of very slight differences. We can find no good use for all these names since our specimens seem to transgress all the boundaries that have been indicated. The last important paper on the genus is that of Muttkowski (1911) in which he endeavors to define eleven species. We recognize five, that are separable as follows:

KEY TO THE SPECIES

Adults

1 Wings with no brown markings...................**stella**, p. 181
  Wings with brown markings...............................2.

2 Frons with a T-spot above; triangle of the hind wings generally
  a cross vein...............................**spinigera**, p. 181
  Frons generally with no T-spot above;......................3.

3 Abdominal appendages of the male straight.....**cynosura**, p. 180
  Abdominal appendages of the male angulated and bent downward
  at the tip..4.

4 Male inferior appendage extends beyond the angulation of the
  superior.....................................**spinosa**, p. 181
  Male inferior appendage does not reach the angulation of the
  superior.....................................**canis**, p. 181

Nymphs

1 Lateral spines of the 9th abdominal segment divergent strongly
  ....**spinigera**.
  Lateral spines of the 9th abdominal segment very slightly or not at
  all divergent..2.

2 These spines distinctly longer than the body of the segment....
  ....**cynosura**.
  These spines distinctly shorter than the segment, and slightly incurved at the tips...................................**canis**.

138. Tetragoneuria cynosura Say

Say '39, p. 30: Mtk. Cat. p. 125: 11, p. 104: Davis '13, p. 23: Whed. '14, p. 97.

Syn: lateralis Burm., *var. basiguttata* Selys, *complanata* Ramb., *costalis* Selys, *Semiaquaea* Burm., *indistincta* Morse.

Length 38 mm. Expanse 58 mm.   **Me. and N. D. to Fla. and La.**

This is a brownish, hairy, non-metallic dragonfly of very great agility. Face yellowish; frons with a black band before the eye, and occasional traces of a T-spot before it on the frons. Thorax brownish, clothed with gray hair; sides with an obsolete yellow stripe. Legs blackish, the front ones darkest. Wings hyaline with brown bases, only the wing roots brown in the fore wing; hind wing brown as far as the triangle, and several droplets of brown at vein conjunctions beyond; the brown area generally fenestrate with hyaline before the arculus and behind the anal crossing.

The aerial prowess of these insects had been noted by all observers:

It is an insect of splendid aerial powers, and on sunny days is seldom seen to rest. (Walker '08, p. 19).

These insects are extremely quick and tireless on the wing. They often dart back and forth across some glade or small clearing near the shores of the larger lakes, keeping at a height of 30 or 40 feet from the ground and at long intervals resting for a moment upon the boughs of a tree. When over the water they fly lower but dart with extreme rapidity along the reedy margins of some promontory (Whedon '14, p. 97).

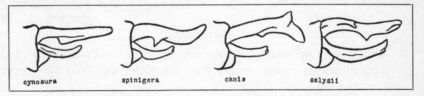

cynosura   spinigera   canis   selysii

———— hovers over the water but rarely alights; very pugnacious, attacking and driving away *Gomphus* and even *Aeschna*. (Wilson '09, p. 656).

On May 28 '10 there was a remarkable gathering of this species, together with an occasional *spinigera* and *semiaquea*, along the road leading from Newfoundland, N. J. to Cedar Pond. The air was full of these dragonflies and on one small dead bush we counted 22 individuals and there were other bushes and stems of plants that also had a great many resting upon them. (Davis '13, p. 23.)

Williamson ('05) has observed the egg laying habits. The female extrudes her eggs and carries them in a pellet underneath the abdomen. The egg mass is held during flight by the long and widely forked subgenital plate. The female carries it for a long time "evidently not looking for a point for ovipositing."

The flight of the female under observation became more deliberate and she approached nearer the surface. Suddenly the tip of the abdomen swept the water as rapidly as though the species were a **Libellula** or **Tramea**. Delay would be fatal here, for the pond is filled with hungry species of the bass family, which all during the day were breaking the water in their efforts to catch Trameas,— always fruitless efforts, so far as I observed. I waded at once to the spot. The strand of eggs, possibly five inches in length, with a specific gravity slightly greater than water, was hung between two horizontal slightly submerged sedge leaves.

139. Tetragoneuria stella Williamson

Wmsn. in Mtk. '11, p. 96.

Length 40 mm. Expanse 66 mm.   Fla.

Similar to the preceding but without brown markings on the wings. The thorax is yellowish clothed with pale hairs. Stripes 3 and 5 of the thorax are widened above and 3 is connected below with a blackish spot at the base of the middle legs. Legs reddish brown, paler at the base.

140. Tetragoneuria spinigera Selys

Selys '71, p. 269: Mtk. Cat. p. 126: Mtk. '11, p. 127: Walk. '13, p. 161: Garm. '27, p. 211.

Length 38 mm. Expanse 58 mm.   B. C. and Wash. to Wis. and Ga.

This species is similar to **cynosura** except that the frons always bears a black T-spot above, and the hair of the thorax is much mixed with brown, and the general coloration is a little darker. It is the most northern of the genus.

141. Tetragoneuria canis McLachlan

McL. '86, p. 104: Mtk. Cat. p. 125: Mtk. '11, p. 96: Garm. '27, p. 211.

Length 40 mm. Expanse 64 mm.   Ont., N. S., Wash.

Similar to *cynosura*, lacking the T-spot on the frons. Hair of thorax grayish giving the body a rather light appearance. Color of wings confined to a few basal spots; membrane often flavescent.

142. Tetragoneuria spinosa Hagen

Hag. '78, p. 188: Mtk. Cat. p. 127: Mtk. '11 p. 96.

Length 40 mm. Expanse 64 mm.   Wis. to Ga.

Similar to the preceding species, differing in the form of the male abdominal appendages as shown in figure. A doubtfully distinct species.

31. HELOCORDULIA Needham

These are small cordulines, that have the antenodal cross veins of the wings prettily spotted with brown. The stigma is narrow and very oblique at its ends with two cross veins touching its rear border. There are six antenodal cross veins in the hind wing. There is a single cross vein in the triangle of the front wing but none in that of the hind wing. The anal loop is rather squarely truncate at the distal end and there are generally two cubito-anal cross veins present.

The genus includes only two species of the eastern United States. *The nymphs* are stocky little fellows with a concentration of sharp dorsal hooks toward the blunt apex of the abdomen, the hooks being longest on segments 7 and 8 and absent from segments 1 to 4. The differences between the two species may be expressed as follows.

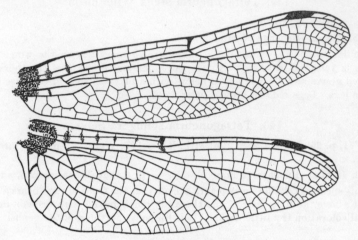

FIG. 36. Wings of *Helocordulia selysi.*

Nymphs

Species	Length	Dorsal hooks	Lateral setae	Lateral spine of 8	Described by
selysii	20	7–9	7	$= \frac{1}{2}$ sp. of 9	Kndy '24, p. 12
uhleri	20	6–9	6	= sp. of 9	Ndm. '01, p. 498

KEY TO THE SPECIES

Adults

1 With a golden fleck in the midst of the brown at base of hind wings
....**uhleri,** p. 182
No golden fleck only brown at base of hind wings . . .**selysi,** p. 183

143. Helocordulia uhleri Selys

Selys '71, p. 274: Mtk. Cat. p. 124: Howe '19, p. 56: Garm. '27, p. 208.
Length 38 mm. Expanse 54 mm.   **Me., Ont., Pa., N. J.**

A pretty bog-loving species with daintily spotted wings. Face, vertex and occiput pale. Thorax brownish olivaceous, hoary, appearing somewhat blackish in the depths of the lateral sutures underneath the hairs. Legs blackish. Wings hyaline spotted with brown, and with a bright golden fleck in the midst of the brown on the base of the hind wings. Dorsum of the abdomen brownish black, except for the basal third of the second segment, which bears a pair of submedian reddish triangles. On the lower side margins of segments 2 to 8 are obscure yellowish spots. Appendages black.

This little species flies swiftly and dodges readily, but is not very hard to capture, for it shows little disposition to avoid the collector's net. It generally flies close in shore and low over the water. It flies in June.

The nymph lives in the trashy places in the edges of the water of upland lakes and ponds and clambers only a few inches upward above the surface to transform

144. Helocordulia selysi Hagen

Hag. '78, p. 189: Mtk. Cat. p. 124: Kndy. '24, p. 1.

Length 38 mm. Expanse 54 mm. **Ga., N. C.**

This species is very similar to *H. uhleri*, lacking the golden fleck in the midst of the black at the wing base, and having the brown more restricted to droplets enveloping cross veins, especially antenodal cross veins, and the cross vein in the anal triangle of the male. This species is southern, and that one is northern in range. This one seems to be much less common.

It is an early spring species (March and April), to be met with in open sunny glades in the woods. Kennedy ('24, p. 1) found its cast skin on the side of a boat-house that stood on the bank of a mud-bottomed artificial pond, at Raleigh, N. C.

32. SOMATOCHLORA SELYS

Ringtails

By Elsie Broughton

This is a genus of 36 described species, 21 of which are represented in North America. They are metallic green or blue in color, with or without lateral thoracic pale spots or stripes. Face is yellowish and the upper surface of the frons and vertex partly or wholly metallic. Legs usually black. Wings hyaline, sometimes with a varying amount of flavescence or even a basal brown tinge. Veins M_4 and Cu_1 of the fore wing are approximated towards the wing margin. The anal loop has a bisector and is asymmetrically by truncate at its distal end.

Although these dragonflies may be abundant locally they are not widespread, and not captured in great abundance. Walker '25 has discussed their habits and their habitat quite fully in his outstanding work on that genus.* He has found that they inhabit rather out of the way places in the wilder districts, preferring well aerated bogs in the uplands or near the sources of the cooler forest streams. The adults have a rather long life of a month and half or so, and are attracted by sunny sheltered spots in the woods, or edges of clearings and lumber roads.

The tenerals of some species "commonly fly at a height of 30–50 feet or more and may be seen on sunny days traveling back and forth, but keeping as a rule within a quite limited area of only a few square yeards or so, for long periods." When in search of prey they doubtless fly lower. The flight of the adult at breeding time is quite different.

They fly low, within a few feet or less of the water or bog. The males often fly back and forth over a bog or pond or skirt the shore of a stream or lake, travelling in a series of rapid forward movements, alternating with periods in which they hover almost motionless, except for the rapid vibration of their wings.

Dr. Walker notes two main methods of oviposition. The first is characteristic of those which have a backwardly directed scoop-shaped ovipositor. These fly low over the water and strike it, or the wet moss, with the end of their abdomen, liberating a large number of eggs at each stroke. They sometimes hover over one place for 2 or 3 seconds, tapping the water at intervals. Those in which the ovipositor projects downward and is pointed, strongly compressed and spout-shaped, always oviposit in flight, in the wet sand, mud or moss near the water's edge, or in the stream bed.

The Known Nymphs

Species	Length	Lat. sp. of 8*	Lat. sp. of 9*	Dorsal hooks	Ment. set.	Lat. set.	Described by
albicincta	22	1/5	1/5	0	11–12	5–6	Walk. '25, p. 170
cingulata	27	1/6–1/5	1/5	0	10–13	6/7	Walk. '25, p. 185
elongata	23	1/7	1/6	4–9	11–12	6–7	Ndm. '03 p. 269
forcipata	20	0	0 or r.	0	12–15	9–10	Walk. '25, p. 138
franklini	18	0	r.	0	13	7–8	Walk. '25, p. 120
hudsonica	24	1/12–1/9	1/10–1/6	0	10–14	7–8	Walk. '25, p. 179
kennedyi	21	0	r.	0	12–13	9	Walk. '25, p. 129
linearis	22	1/5	1/4–1/5	mod. 5–9 r. on 4	11–12	8	Ndm. '03, p. 269
minor	22	1/4	1/3	high 4–9	11–13	6–8	Walk. '25, p. 65
semicircularis	22	0	variable	0	10–13		Walk. '25, p. 149
tenebrosa	20	1/6	1/5	strong 6–9 r. on 4 & 5	11–12	8	Walk. '25, p. 104
whitehousi	21	0	0	0	9–10	6–8	Walk. '25, p. 156
williamsoni	24	1/5	1/4–1/3	low 5 or 6–9	11–12	8	Ndm. '01, p. 500 (as elongata)

* As compared with length of segment bearing them.

* The material incorporated under this genus has been taken almost exclusively from *The North American Dragonflies of the Genus Somatochlora* by E. M. Walker, University of Toronto Studies, Biological Series, No. 26. 1925.

KEY TO THE SPECIES

Adults

1 Labrum yellowish brown or orange, usually with a black border..2.
  Labrum bluish black or metallic green......................7.

2 Tibiae yellow externally; color hardly metallic; side stripes of
   thorax very long and broad. Southern......**georgiana**, p. 186
  Tibiae black externally; metallic..........................3.

3 Lateral thoracic pale stripes entirely wanting....**linearis**, p. 186
  Lateral thoracic pale stripes present.......................4.

4 Second lateral thoracic pale stripe abbreviated below..........5.
  Second lateral thoracic pale stripe continuous..............6.

5 Lateral thoracic pale stripes bright yellow, sharply defined......
  ....**ensigera**, p. 187
  Lateral stripes dull, ill-defined.............**tenebrosa**, p. 187

6 Lateral thoracic pale stripes of equal breadth..**provocans**, p. 188
  Anterior stripe narrower.......................**filosa**, p. 188

7 Middle abdominal segments narrowly ringed with white at apex.8.
  Not so...9.

8 First lateral thoracic pale stripe (at least a spot) present and
   yellow..............**albicincta**, p. 189 and **hudsonica**, p. 190
  First stripe obscure brownish..............**cingulata**, p. 190

9 Both lateral thoracic stripes well developed...............10.
  One or both stripes wanting...............................16.

10 Lateral thoracic pale stripes represented by two round spots....
   ....**minor**, p. 191
  Stripes not round, at least the first one more elongate........11.

11 First stripe narrower than the second but longer....**walshi**, p. 192
  First stripe not narrower than the second..................12.

12 Stripes bright yellow, sharply defined.....................13.
  Stripes dull yellow, ill-defined...........................14.

13 Middle abdominal segments with pale spots..**forcipata**, p. 192
  Middle abdominal segments with no pale spots...**elongata**, p. 193

14 Stripes abbreviated below and roundish...**semicircularis**, p. 193
  Stripes long and parallel sided............................15.

15 Costa black.............................**williamsoni**, p. 194
  Costa yellowish...........................**incurvata**, p. 194

16 With a dark brown spot covering anal triangle of hind wings..17.
  With no such spot...19.

17 First side stripe wanting or obscure brownish; 10 to 22 cells between veins M_1 and $M_{1'a}$..............................**19.**
First side stripe yellow; 6 to 10 cells between veins M_1 and M_{1a} ....**franklini**, p. 195

18 Rear of head with orange brown fringe; male with anal spot in fore wing.............................**septentrionalis**, p. 197
Rear of head with whitish fringe; male with no anal spot in fore wing.....................................**whitehousi**, p. 196

19 First side stripe reduced to a mere dot; 20 to 24 cells between M_1 and M_{1a}...............................**sahlbergi**, p. 195
First side stripe wanting or obscure brownish; 11 to 19 cells between M_1 and M_{1a}........................**kennedyi**, p. 196

145. Somatochlora georgiana Walker

Root '24, p. 320: Walk. '25, p. 98.

Length 49 mm. Expanse 69 mm.   **Ga.**

A small dull species only the female of which is known. Face dull yellow; labrum with a narrow black line on lower margin. Thorax dull brown; lateral pale stripes yellowish, broad, and similar in shape; the first one with its anterior margin nearly straight. Legs brown, paler basally, and externally. Abdomen dark brown with greenish reflections; basal segments dull yellowish. Appendages brownish.

146. Somatochlora linearis Hagen

Hag. '61, p. 137: Mtk. Cat. p. 131: Wmsn. '12, p. 155: Walk. '25, p. 91: Garm. '27, p. 226.

Length 61 mm. Expanse 86 mm.   **Me. to Pa. and Ill., Mo.**

An elongate slender species. Face and occiput brown. Top of frons and vertex metallic blue. Thorax brownish. Abdomen brown; segment 2 with apical

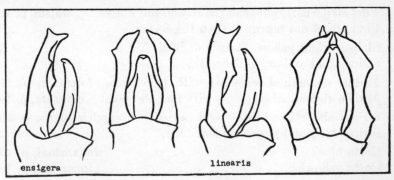

ensigera   linearis

annulus but with the median one very indistinct, though median lateral spot large and conspicuous; 3, pale basally; remaining segments with lateral margins yellowish.

147. Somatochlora ensigera Martin

Mrtn. '07, p. 298: Wmsn. '07, p. 5: '12, p. 153: Walk. '25, p. 86.

Length 50 mm. Expanse 72 mm. **Colo., Mont.**

Syn: charadriae Wmsn.

Labrum orange with a black border and a black median spot. Postclypeus ochraceous. Frons metallic blue in middle, surrounded at side and in front with orange brown. Occiput red brown. Thorax red brown deepening to blue black above. Side stripes well defined, the first broad and parallel sided, the second shorter and convex behind. Legs black, paler basally. Wings hyaline; stigma brownish. Abdomen greenish black, spotted conspicuously with yellow on the three basal segments; middorsal spot on 1, large lateral spots on 2, 2 basal triangular spots on 3, one laterodorsal the other lateroventral.

Williamson '07 quotes concerning this species:

I took it at an altitude of about 8000 feet, July 31, 1898, in Bear Creek Canon, Jefferson Co., Colo. At the place I took it there were 2, but on account of the wariness and the almost inaccessible character of its haunts (on willows overhanging the swift and breakneck dashing Bear Creek), I was unable to secure the other specimen. The one captured was taken with difficulty, as it kept just out of the reach of the net. It appeared a weak flier however, and my opportunity came when an unusually strong gust of wind blew it towards me.

148. Somatochlora tenebrosa Say

Say '39, p. 18: Mtk. Cat. p. 132: Wlsn. '12, p. 194: Walk. '25, p. 100: Garm. 27, p. 227.

Length 48 mm. Expanse 76 mm. **N. H., N. Y. and N. J. to Ill. and Ky.**

A handsome species with brilliant thoracic coloration. Occiput brown. Face ochraceous; top of frons and vertex metallic; labrum yellow with median black spot and sometimes with a black border. Thorax brilliantly metallic bronze and green, the two lateral stripes pale yellow, the first dilated above, the second subovate and shorter. Legs black, femora paler externally. Wings hyaline with a faint basal tinge of amber; veins and stigma dark brown. Abdomen blackish; segment 2 with large ventro-lateral yellow spots; accessory genitalia pale; 3 pale basally with 2 pairs of lateral triangular spots.

Walker ('25) says it is an inhabitant of the small forest streams, and that it seems to be partial to shady places. Other writers speak of it as being distinctly crepuscular and shade loving. Brimley '03 reports it "flying over fields and open ground by the side of small streams and marshes—flies high and is hard to catch." Wilson '12, says:

Ten or a dozen specimens were patrolling back and forth just after sunset in one corner of an old pasture near a small brook at the foot of the mountains. They were strong and rapid fliers and extremely difficult to capture. They moved gracefully up and down and in and out, weaving together their paths of flight like the intricate mazes of an old fashioned dance. But never for an instant could they be caught off their guard. At the first attempt of the net they all retired precipitately, and it was a long time before they returned again. This is a northern species and its presence in Kentucky is probably explained by the high altitude of the region where it was found and the proximity of the mountains.

149. **Somatochlora provocans** Calvert

Calv. '03, p. 39: Mtk. Cat. p. 132: Mtk. '11, p. 176: Walk. '25, p. 109.

Length 54 mm. Expanse 74 mm.   **N. J. and Pa.**

A large slender species conspicuously marked with yellow. Face yellowish below with metallic violet reflections above. Labrum yellow with a black border; postclypeus yellow with two impressed brown dots. Thorax metallic green with violet reflections and rather thin pubescence. Lateral spots well developed,

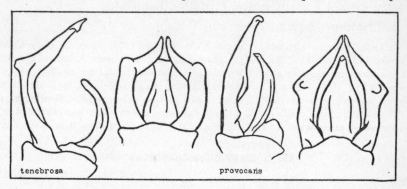

tenebrosa   provocans

yellow, long, straight edged in front with a small additional and intervening pale streak through spiracle. Wings hyaline, costa yellow, stigma brown. Legs black, paler basally. Abdominal segment 1 with posterior lateral edge yellow; 2 with three diverging inferior vertical yellow streaks on side of the segment, the middle one the broadest; 3 with basal dorsal and ventral triangles pointing rearward on sides above and below the midlateral margin. Remainder of abdomen greenish black. Appendages blackish.

Apparently little is known concerning the habits and breeding place of this species. Calvert '03 states that it usually keeps at a considerable distance above one's head, both when in flight and at rest.

150. **Somatochlora filosa** Hagen

Hag. '61, p. 136: Mtk. Cat. p. 130: Walk. '25, p. 112.

Length 68 mm. Expanse 84 mm.   **N. J. and Md. to Fla.**

A fine big southern species. Occiput, top of frons and vertex blue. Face brownish; labrum bordered below with black. Thorax metallic green with the usual 2 lateral stripes and an intervening one, abbreviated above. Legs black, front femora brown. Wings hyaline, stigma tinged with amber. Abdomen black; segments 1 and 2 with apical annuli; 2 with a median one also, dilated to form paired ventral spots; 3 with elongated paired ventral spots, triangularly pointed to rearward.

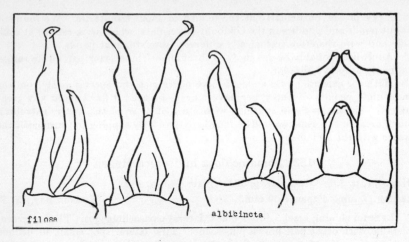

151. Somatochlora albicincta Burmeister

Burm. '39, p. 847: Mtk. Cat. p. 129: Kndy. '17, p. 229: Walk. '25, p. 167: Garm '27, p. 231.

Length 48 mm. Expanse 64 mm.   **Labr. to N. H., Alaska**

Labrum shining black. Frons black with greenish reflections, sides yellow. Occiput brown. Thorax green, metallic, clothed with a thick coat of pale brownish hairs. Pale spot near crest before humeral suture and another behind it. Legs black, paler basally. Wings hyaline, unspotted; stigma brownish. Abdomen bronze black with a metallic luster. Segment 2 with pale spots below and behind the auricles; segment 3–8 with basal lateral dull yellow spots; 10 with a pair of dorsal dull yellowish spots. Appendages blackish.

Walker ('25, p. 175) says:

S. albicincta develops in quiet waters in both sunny and partly shady situations. In Newfoundland and eastern Canada I have found it about slow streams

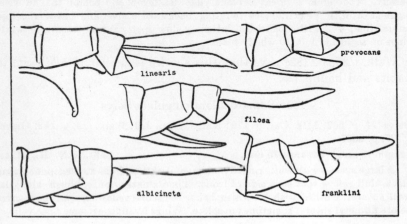

in boggy places, particularly at the mouth of small tributaries. We found it about ponds and puddles in the Godbout River flats, which were refilled at each tide and were therefore ecologically different from stagnant ponds.

Adult life probably begins in June throughout the greater part of its range, probably July in Labrador.

With the exception of a male—I have never seen this species away from the immediate vicinity of water, nor have I ever observed it hawking at any great height. The males fly in sunshine within a foot or so of the water, patrolling small areas in the usual way. The female oviposits by tapping the surface of the water with the abdomen.

152. Somatochlora hudsonica Hagen

Hag. '71, p. 301: Mtk. Cat. p. 131: Walk. '25, p. 176.

Length 52 mm. Expanse 69 mm.   **Hudson Bay, N. F.**

Labrum shining black. Frons black, lateral part ochraceous. Thorax green, metallic, with dense pale brown pubescence. First lateral spot small, ill defined and nearly vertical in position. Wings hyaline, stigma brown. Legs black, paler

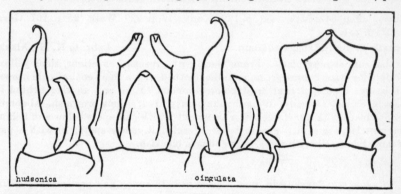

basally. Abdominal segment 2 black yellowish below and behind the auricles; segment 3 with pale triangles pointing backward above and below the mid lateral line; 4–7 with small basal lateral yellow spots; apical transverse white rings on segments 1–9; 10 wholly black.

Walk. ('25, p. 182) says that this species is similar to *albicincta* in habits and haunts.

153. Somatochlora cingulata Selys

Selys '71, p. 302: Mtk. Cat. p. 129: Kndy '17, p. 229: Walk. '25, p. 182: Garm. '27, p. 233.

Length 59 mm. Expanse 76 mm.   **Labr. to N. H., Mass.**

A large species with white ringed abdomen. Labrum, frons and occiput shining black, dull yellow spot each side of frons. Thorax dark bronze, bluish along lateral sutures, clothed with brownish hairs. Obscure yellowish spot near crest before humeral suture; sometimes obsolete. Wings hyaline, extreme base yellowish, veins black, stigma tawny. Legs black. Abdominal segments 3 or 4–8 with small dark yellow lateral basal spots.

"This large robust species is mainly an inhabitant of lakes rather than ponds or streams.—Males were flying here and there over the water, pursuing a rather irregular course, now following the shore line, now wandering out over the water in a manner suggestive of Epicordulia or Tetragoneuria. They were not observed to hover over one spot on the usual manner of Cordulines. Several times males were seen to attempt to capture the females during flight. One or two of these attempts resulted in copulation, the pair immediately flying off into the trees. A pair in copula was also taken on July 24 in the pine barrens a mile or so from any of the lakes." Walk. ('25, p. 189).

154. **Somatochlora minor** Calvert

Calv. '98, p. 97: Mtk. Cat. p. 131: Walk. '25, p. 62: Garm. '27, p. 222.

Length 46 mm. Expanse 68 mm.   **N. H., Me., Ont., Wyo.**

A small slender species. Face blue black except sides of frons and anteclypeus. Thorax steel blue, and reddish brown, obscured by yellowish brown hairs. Lateral stripes reduced to roundish lemon yellow spots. Wings hyaline, slightly flavescent; stigma brown. Legs black, paler basally. Abdomen dull greenish black; segment 2 and 3 each with a small dorsal and a larger ventral lateral spot.

Walk. '25 says:

. . . . They are usually found flying back and forth in small, sheltered, shady opening in woods or along their partly shaded borders. Their flight is generally about shoulder high on an average and I have never seen them flying at a height beyond reach of an ordinary net.

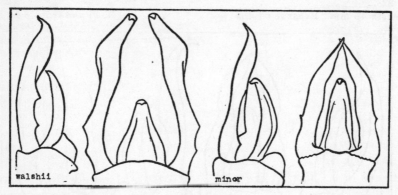

They are characteristic dragonflies of small clear streams, with a gentle current, and do not occur where pond conditions, indicated by the presence of water lilies, Myriophyllum or cat-tails obtain. They seldom occur where the stream flows through dense shade nor are they often seen in open bogs, but are most at home in brooks flowing through the bushy open woods or through deep woods, provided the stream is wide enough to admit the sunlight.

They fly over the brook and alight in the grass occasionally, but are usually balanced over the pools, as wary as hawks, requiring a very swift swing of the net and a sure aim.

155. Somatochlora walshi Scudder

Scud. '66, p. 217: Mtk. Cat. p. 133: Walk. '25, p. 55: Garm. '27, p. 223.

Length 47 mm. Expanse 66 mm.   Alta. and Mich. to Que., Me. and N. Y.

Face brownish yellow with black labrum and black markings on the post-clypeus and front of frons. Vertex black. Occiput brownish or black. Thorax brassy green. Lateral pale stripes sometimes obscured; the first long and straight, the second rather ovoid. Legs streaked with reddish brown. Wings hyaline with an amber tinge, darker about the bases. Second abdominal segment yellow on sides, the paired lateral spots sometimes confluent and continuous with the apical annulus; segment 3 with dorsal and ventral lateral spots anteriorly, and posteriorly with lateral pale streaks; 5, 6 and 7 with small lateral spots; 8 and 9 sometimes with incomplete apical annuli; 10 black, sometimes with a dorsal yellowish spot.

This species inhabits the small quiet streams of boggy places. Walker reports it flying very actively in all parts of the marsh but particularly on the main channel. They flew on the average about waist high, poising frequently in the air with the abdomen slightly flexed, but darting back and forth very rapidly and dodging the net well.

156. Somatochlora forcipata Scudder

Scud. '66, p. 216: Mtk. Cat. p. 130: Walk. '18, p. 370; '25, p. 134: Garm. '27, p. 228.

Length 48 mm. Expanse 66 mm.   N. F. and Ont. to N. H.

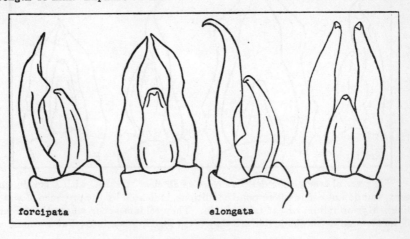

forcipata   elongata

A fine medium sized species. Face brownish; labrum, top of frons, vertex and occiput dark brownish with metallic reflections. Thorax metallic; lateral yellow stripes wide and straight. Legs black, first femora paler externally. Abdomen dark brown; segment 2 with apical and median annuli and pale lateral spot; 3 paler basally with paired dorso- and ventro-lateral triangles (in ♀ continued to segment 7, decreasing in size); 9, 10 and appendages yellow beneath.

157. Somatochlora elongata Scudder

Scud. '66, p. 218: Mtk. Cat. p. 130: Walk. '25, p. 70: Garm. '27, p. 220.

Length 57 mm. Expanse 65 mm.   **N. B. to Mass. and Md.**

A slender, dull greenish, clearwinged species. Face metallic. Anteclypeus and sides of frons yellowish. Thorax dark metallic with a thick coat of whitish brown hairs. Lateral thoracic pale spots light yellow, clearly defined; the first slender and straightish, the second half as long and ovoid. Legs brownish. Wings hyaline with a faint basal yellowish tinge; stigma black. Abdomen brown. Segment 2 with three pairs of lateral pale spots, sometimes more or less confluent, and with an apical annulus; 3 with a pair of small basal dorsal spots; remaining segments greenish black.

158. Somatochlora semicircularis Selys

Selys '71, p. 295. Mtk. Cat. p. 132: Walk. '25, p. 145.

Syn: nasalis Selys

Length 49 mm. Expanse 63 mm.   **B. C. to Calif. and Colo.**

Frons above and in front black with metallic reflections; vertex the same. Labrum and postclypeus black; anteclypeus yellowish. Occiput dark brown. Thorax metallic green with two lateral yellow spots, becoming obscure with age.

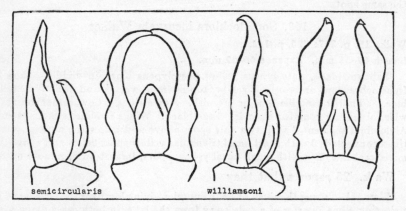

Legs black. Wings hyaline, hind pair with a slight basal flavescent tinge. Abdomen greenish black; segment 2 with two pairs of lateral spots and an interrupted apical annulus; 3 with a pair of basal dorsal spots and a ventral lateral streak; 5 to 8 sometimes with a small lateral spot.

159. Somatochlora williamsoni Walker

Walk. '06, p. 151: Mtk. Cat. p. 133: Walk. '25, p. 78: Garm. '27, p. 224.

Length 56 mm. Expanse 80 mm.   **Me. and Pa. to Ont. and Minn.**

This is a slender, dark colored species with a yellowish face. Anteclypeus and median part of postclypeus darker. Upper part of frons and vertex metallic blue. Labrum greenish black. Thorax dark metallic green and brown with violet reflections. Lateral stripes obscured; the first long and straight; the second ovoid. Legs black, front femora brownish beneath. Wings hyaline, sometimes yellowish at base. Abdomen dark brown; segment 2 with three pairs of lateral yellowish spots, sometimes more or less confluent; 3 with a pair of dorso- and of ventro-lateral yellow spots; 5 to 8 often with small lateral spots.

Walker '25 says:

During the first two or three weeks of adult life it may be seen about the edges of woods or on openings in them, hawking at a height of 30 to 50 feet, or even higher, and usually keeping within an area of only a few square yards for long periods at a time. Sometimes half a dozen may be seen flying together in the same area. From the middle of June to the end of their season though still frequenting the woods, they are more often seen about the watercourses where they breed. They frequent sluggish streams, usually shady but sometimes open and bordered with a zone of standing aquatic plants. Here the males patrol the margins, flying in rapid movements, interrupted by periods of almost motionless suspension in the air. In the sunlight they commonly fly two or three feet or more above the water, while in the dense shade they are generally only a few inches above the surface. Sometimes they may be seen hovering in a dark recess under an overhanging bank, and at such times they may be scarcely visible except for the brilliant green eyes. Frequently they will remain suspended in the air for many minutes, occasionally darting away a few yards and then returning to the same spot.

160. Somatochlora incurvata Walker

Walk. '18, p. 367: '25, p. 142.

Length 49–55 mm. Expanse 66–69 mm.   **Mich.**

Labrum black, anteclypeus yellow, postclypeus black in middle. Sides of frons ochraceous or brownish yellow, top of frons, vertex and occiput metallic blue.   Thorax metallic blue or greenish. Side stripes yellow, rather short and wide, obscurely rounded at ends. Legs black. Wings hyaline, stigma tawny. Abdominal segment 2 with two pale spots above and below the auricle, sometimes connected; 3 with short basal triangular yellow spots below and above the midlateral line; 5–8 with small basal yellow spots, largest on 6, minute on 8.

Walk. '25 reports that they

Were taken along the shore of Lake Superior, flying low over the beach, and in a clearing some quarter of a mile away from the lake, in both cases flying with swarms of Aeshna . . . . . They were found swarming on the beach during the day, when the wind was off shore, and in a clearing at the close of a warm day from about 5 o'clock until sundown or later. If the day were cold they would be entirely absent.

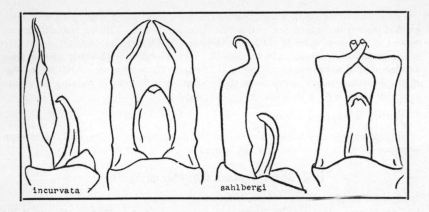

incurvata   sahlbergi

161. Somatochlora sahlbergi Trybom

Trybom '89, p. 7: Mrtn. '06, p. 27: Kndy. '17, p. 229: Whts. '18, p. 2, 9, 13: Walk. '25, p. 163.

Length 48 mm. Expanse 68 mm.   **Alaska**

A small robust, dark colored hairy species. Face metallic greenish black except anteclypeus and sides of frons, which are yellow. Occiput black. Thorax metallic green with long brownish white hairs. Side stripes obsolete except for a minute spot superiorly, the remains of the first stripe. Wings hyaline; stigma tawny. Legs black. Abdomen black with a dull greenish luster. Segment 2 with an apical white ring interrupted middorsally and at sides; 3, with a pale area beneath each side. Appendages black and hairy.

162. Somatochlora franklini Selys

Selys '78, p. 195: Mtk. Cat. p. 131: Walk. '18, p. 374: Walk. '25, p. 117.

Syn: macrotona Wmsn.

Length 44–54 mm. Expanse 53–62 mm.   **Hudson Bay, Sask.**

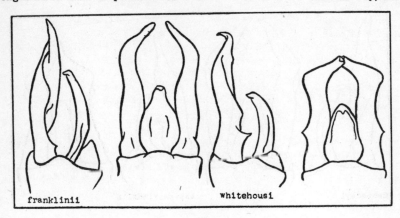

franklinii   whitehousi

Face and frons black with greenish luster except for anteclypeus and spot each side of frons which are yellowish. Occiput black. Thorax metallic green varied with brown, densely clothed with brownish black hairs. Side stripes nearly obsolete, anterior one orate in terminals. Wings hyaline with dark brown spot at base of hind wings covering the anal triangle; stigma brown. Abdominal segment 2 with obscure ochraceous spots above and below; remaining segments greenish black with a dull luster.

Walk. '25 found them:

Flying over mossy bogs at the foot of the mountain. . . . . Several males were seen pursuing their course over the bog at height of 2 or 3 feet.

163. Somatochlora whitehousi Walker

Kndy. '17, p. 234: Walk. '25, p. 154.

Length 47 mm. Expanse 55–61 mm.   **Labr., Hudson Bay to B. C.**

Face black except anteclypeus and sides of frons which are yellowish. Thorax greenish metallic, marked with brown. Side stripes of thorax obsolete, anterior one represented by a pale brownish vertical streak. Hair of thorax brownish, thick and long. Wings hyaline tinged with yellow and with a brown spot on the anal triangle of the hind wing of the male; stigma tawny. Legs black, paler basally. Abdominal segment 2 with apical whitish annulus barely interrupted mid dorsally and laterally, and with obscure yellowish side spots before and behind the auricles; 3, whitish along the ventral margins. Remainder of abdomen metallic blackish green. Appendages black.

Walker' 25 reports this species hawking in the usual manner, over warm, stagnant puddles in a mossy bog, following no definite route and as a rule keeping within 2 or 3 feet of the surface of the bog.

164. Somatochlora kennedyi Walker

Walk. 18, p. 371; '25, p. 125: Garm. '27, p. 230.

Length 51–55 mm. Expanse 61–69 mm.   **N. B., Man. to Mass., Mich.**

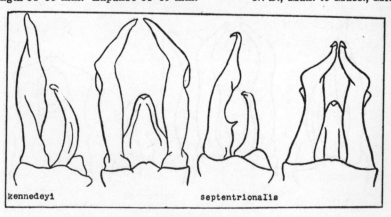

kennedeyi   septentrionalis

A species with dull coloration and very heavy thorax. Face blackish with pale yellowish anteclypeus and sides of frons. Vertex black with greenish reflections. Occiput dark brown. Thorax metallic green varied with reddish brown Side spots obsolete, brownish. Wings hyaline, costa yellow, stigma tawny. Legs black, paler basally. Abdominal segment 2 with large inferior yellow spots before and behind the auricle; 3 with basal spots indistinct; 4–10 greenish black, unspotted; 1–2 densely hairy.

Walker '25 says:

This species . . . . is one of the earliest to appear in the spring. . . . . an inhabitant of cool bogs or shallow bog ponds . . . . kept most of the time a little over 2 feet above the water, just above the tops of the sedges, hovering for a time in one spot but changing their orientation frequently and not remaining long in any one place.

165. Somatochlora septentrionalis Hagen

Hag. '61, p. 139: Mtk. Cat. p. 132: Walk. '25, p. 160.

Length 45 mm. Expanse 59 mm. **N. F. and Que.**

A small somewhat slender species with dark metallic face and vertex. Anteclypeus and sides of frons yellowish. Occiput brown. Thorax bronzy green; lateral stripes obscured, reddish brown. Legs black, front femora brownish beneath. Wings hyaline or slightly flavescent. Basal abdominal segments dull brown; hind lateral margin of 1 yellowish; 2 with a whitish apical annulus; 3 with a pair of obscure yellowish dorsal spots; remaining segments dark metallic green.

33. CORDULIA Leach

These are blackish dragonflies of medium size, clear-winged and with touches of bronzy green color showing on the thorax through a rather heavy coat of gray hair. The triangle of the hind wing is not divided by a cross vein. The inferior appendage of the abdomen in the male is deeply bifurcated, and the arms of the fork are again notched at their tips.

There is one northern species in our fauna, and there is another at similar latitudes in the old world.

The nymphs are thick set and hairy, with no vertical tubercles on the head and no dorsal hooks on the abdomen. The lateral spines of segments 8 and 9 are very short. The nymph of *C. shurtleffi* has been described Ndm. ('01, p. 503).

166. Cordulia shurtleffi Scudder

Scud. '66, p. 217; Mtk. Cat. p. 128: Howe '19, p. 61: Garm. '27, p. 214.

Length 46 mm. Expanse 64 mm. **Alaska, B. C., N. J., Pa. and N. Y.**

A fine greenish, bog-loving, northern species with thorax rather densely covered with whitish hairs. Face olivaceous, tending to a waxy yellowish, overcast above and with a whitish clypeus. Two minute yellowish spots sometimes are apparent toward the apical margin of the dark labrum. Frons above, vertex and occiput metallic green. Thorax of the same color, shining underneath the hoary hairs, only the depths of the lateral sutures appearing blackish. Legs black. Wings hyaline with stigma and costa black. Abdomen blackish green, with only a streak of yellowish on the sides of segments 2 and 3 beneath. Appendages black.

This species frequents the boggy edges of cold upland lakes and ponds. It flies swiftly, a few feet above the water, with occasional haltings, "marking time" in the air. These haltings give the best opportunity for capture with a net. The flight is free and graceful, as the coloration is beautiful. Occasionally one will leave its accustomed beat along the shore and sweep out far away from the water and disappear among the trees.

The nymph (Ndm. '01, p. 503) lives sprawling amid the trash at the edges of the water, and climbs a little way up projecting roots or sticks to transform. June is the time of transformation. Adults fly through July.

34. Dorocordulia Needham

These are elegant little dragonflies with hairy thorax and smooth shiny bronzy green abdomen. The abdomen is constricted in the middle and notably widened toward the tip. These are bog loving species of our Northeastern States and Canada.

The nymphs are similar to those of Cordulia except for the characters stated in the key. Only the nymph of *D. lepida* has been made known (Ndm. '01, p. 505).

KEY TO THE SPECIES

Adults

1 Abdomen with segments 7 to 10 spatulately widened..........
....**libera, p. 198**
Abdomen with segments very moderately widened..**lepida, p. 199**

167. Dorocordulia libera Selys

Selys '71, p. 263: Mtk. Cat. p. 127: Howe '19, p. 54: Garm. '27, p. 238.

Length 42 mm. Expanse 64 mm.   **Me., N. Y., Wis. and Ind.**

A charming little bronzy green species, with spatulately dilated abdomen. Face greenish with yellowish clypeus. Sides of frons obscurely marked with yellowish, top of frons, vertex and occiput metallic green. Thorax green, darkened only in the depths of the lateral stutures, densely clothed with tawny hairs. Legs black. Wings hyaline, with a golden tinge at the extreme base, costa and stigma black; membranule dark gray. Abdomen greenish above, becoming blackish posteriorly; segment 2 yellow at the sides, the pale area being diagonally divided by fuscous 3 yellow at base of sides and along the infero-lateral margin.

This species is common about the boggy borders of small upland lakes, where it flies in midsummer during sunshine, gaily in and out of the little bays and over the shallows. The nymphs inhabit the edges, commonly under the overhanging turf, and clamber up projecting roots and stumps to transform. They usually leave their cast skins less than a foot above the water.

168. Dorocordulia lepida Hagen

Hag. '71, p. 264: Mtk. Cat. p. 127: Howe '19, p. 54: Garm. '27, p. 238.

Length 38 mm. Expanse 62 mm.   **N. Eng., N. Y., N. J. and Pa.**

A small greenish species, similar to the preceding, but with abdomen less spatulate, more nearly cylindric. The face is green but the clypeus is whiter and the yellow spots on the lateral aspect of the frons are larger. The vertex is yellowish at the summit, and the occiput, in the middle. The thorax is green underneath its hoary haircoat, with only the depths of the lateral sutures blackish. Legs black. Wings hyaline, stigma black, costa obscure. Abdomen with yellow basal side spots on the middle segments, and double yellow larger areas on the sides of segments 2 and 3. Segments 8, 9 and 10 and appendages black.

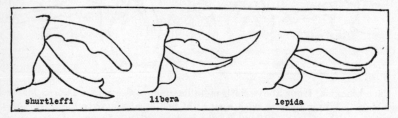

shurtleffi   libera   lepida

35. Williamsonia Davis
(Bull. Brooklyn Ent. Soc. 8: 93, 1913)

Very small Cordulines and very slender. All the triangles are without cross veins. The anal loop is scarcely widened at the tip. The lateral margins of the second abdominal segment in the male are produced backward in a long hairy genital lobe; the auricles are minute, and the inner margin of the hind wing is scarcely notched.

The nymph is unknown.

KEY TO THE SPECIES
Adults

1   Abdomen with segments 2 to 9 ringed with yellow at apex......
....**lintneri,** p. 200

    Abdomen with segments 2 to 9 not with yellow at apex........
....**fletcheri,** p. 200

169. Williamsonia lintneri Hagen

Hag. '78, p. 187: Mtk. Cat. p. 128: Dav. '13, p. 93: Howe '19, p. 53: Wmsn. '23, p. 97: Howe '23, p. 222.

Length 30 mm. Expanse 47 mm.   **N. Y., N. J., Mass.**

A dainty little slender Corduline, the smallest member of the subfamily in our fauna. Face greenish. Labrum yellow. Anteclypeus brown in the middle. Thorax brown, hairy, with some blackish lines on the lateral suture. Abdomen short, narrow, cylindric, swollen at the base, blackish. Segments 2 to 9 ringed with yellow at the apex, and 3 also at the base.

This is an early season (April to June), species concerning which Howe ('23, p. 222) writes:

I always find it a woodland species inhabiting the neighborhood of cold bogs and brook runs, and it alights generally on stones. The orange ring on each abdominal segment makes the insect particularly easy of identification in the field.

170. Williamsonia fletcheri Williamson

Wmsn. '23, p. 96: Howe '23, p. 222.

Length 30. Expanse 47 mm.   **Can.**

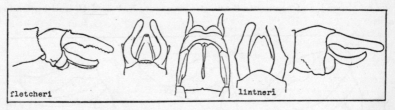

Face blackish; frons above with metallic green reflections. Thorax blackish. Legs black. Wings hyaline with a tinge of yellow at the extreme base. Membranule whitish. Costa yellowish to the nodus. Stigma brown. Abdomen with only obscure paler markings on the sides of segments 2 to 5.

Subfamily LIBELLULINAE

The Common Skimmers

Dragonflies mostly of moderate or large size, generally non-metallic though often of brilliant coloration. Colors in many forms obscured by pruinosity with age. Anal loop generally well developed and foot-shaped, and with a distinct bisector. Triangle of hind wing retracted

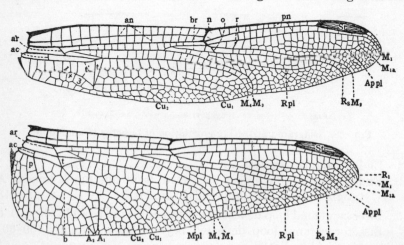

FIGS. 37. Wings of *Orthemis ferruginea*, labelled to illustrate Libelluline venation. Principal veins labelled only at the outer margin. R_1, radius; R_s, radial sector. M_1, M_2, M_3, and M_4, Cu_1 and Cu_2, the branches of media and cubitus respectively. *St*, stigma; *n*, nodus; *an* and *pn*, ante- and post-nodal cross veins; *br*, bridge; *o*, oblique vein; *r*, reverse vein; M_{1a}, apical sector; *Ap. pl*, apical planate; *R.pl.* radial planate; *M.pl*, median planate; *ar*, arculus; *ac*, anal crossing; *t*, triangle; *t'*, subtriangle; *1+3*, number of cells in row subtending subtriangle; *p*, patella; *b*, bisector of anal loop. (From Trans. Amer. Ent. Soc.)

to the arculus. Males with no auricle on the sides of the second abdominal segment, and the adjacent inner margin of hind wings rounded.

KEY TO THE GENERA

Adults

1 Fore wing triangle four sided; anal loop open below............
....**Nannothemis**, p. 204
Fore wing triangle three sided; anal loop closed below and more or
less foot shaped...2.

201

2   Bisector of anal loop nearly straight; wings often highly colored.3.
    Bisector of anal loop strongly angulated at level of heel........4.

3   Fore wing triangle with front side as long as inner side.........
    ....**Perithemis**, p. 205
    Fore wing triangle with front side half as long as inner side.....
    ....**Celithemis**, p. 207
    Fore wing triangle with front side one third as long as inner side
    ....**Pseudoleon**, p. 213

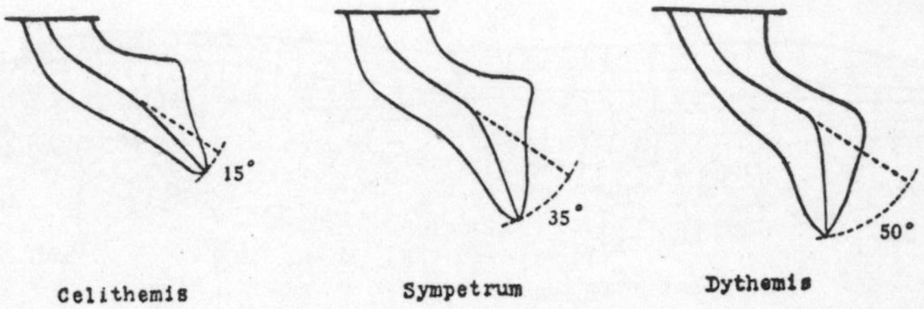

Fig. 38. Diagram illustrating angulation of bisector of anal loop.

4   Ends of stigma parallel.....................................5.
    Ends of stigma convergent backward, front side much longer; A_2
    straight at base with large cells behind it.................18.

5   Bisector of anal loop deflected beyond ankle moderately (30–50).6.
    Bisector of anal loop deflected beyond ankle strongly (50–60);
    spines of legs flattened...................................16.

6   Hind wing Cu_2 rising from hind angle of triangle..............7.
    Hind wing Cu_2 rising from outer side of triangle............14.

7   Base of A_2 distal to Ac.................**Erythrodiplax**, p. 214
    Base of A_2 opposite Ac....................................8.

8   Vein M_2 strongly undulate; stigma long, bordered behind by 3 to 6
    cells..9.
    Vein M_2 smoothly curved; stigma short, bordered behind by 1 or 2
    cells...12.

9   Veins M_{1-3} and M_4 separate almost from the arculus.........10.
    Veins M_{1-3} and M_4 stalked beyond the arculus..**Orthemis**, p. 216

10 Vein M_{1a} rising under proximal fourth of stigma..**Ladona**, p. 217
    Vein M_{1a} rising under middle third or beyond.............11.

11 Wings alike in the two sexes; male with no ventral hooks on seg-
    ment 1...................................**Libellula**, p. 119
    Wings unlike in the two sexes; male with a pair of ventral hooks
    on 1.....................................**Plathemis**, p. 228

Nymphs

7   Length not more than 18 mm.............**Leucorrhinia**, p. 241
    Length more than 18 mm...................**Dythemis**, p. 248
8   Abdomen, smooth...9.
    Abdomen hairy 12
9   Lateral spines very short.................**Paltothemis**, p. 250
    Lateral spines long........................:...........10.
10 Spines of 8 short; of 9 long...............**Pachydiplax**, p. 244
    Spines of 8 and 9 both long and similar....................11.
11 Teeth on inner edge of lateral lobe of labium deeply cut........
    ....**Pantala**, p. 551
    Teeth obsolete...............................**Tramea**, p. 253
12 Lateral setae 6..........................**Nannothemis**, p. 204
    Lateral setae 8–10......................**Erythrodiplax**, p. 214
    Lateral setae more than 10.................**Sympetrum**, p. 231
13 Lateral setae 0–3............................**Ladona**, p. 217
    Lateral setae 5–10.......................................14.
14 Median lobe of labium evenly contoured......**Libellula**, p. 219
    Median lobe of labium crenulate on front border............15.
15 Lateral setae 8...............................**Orthemis**, p. 216
    Lateral setae 10...........................**Plathemis**, p. 229

36. NANNOTHEMIS Brauer

These are the smallest of our dragonflies; dumpy little fellows about an inch long; clear-winged, and with a shape of triangle and of anal loop that at once distinguishes them from everything else in our fauna. There is a single species of local occurrence in the eastern United States.

The nymph (Ndm. '01ᵃ, p. 254) is short, thick set, hairy on legs and rear blunt abdomen. It is an inhabitant of little stagnant pools in marshy places.

Dr. Calvert writes us that he has reared three nymphs from egg to imago; two of them in 23 months with 11 and 12 larval instars respectively, the third in 34 months and 19 days with 11 larval instars.

171. Nannothemis bella Uhler

The Blue Bell

Uhler '57, p. 87: Mtk. Cat. p. 147: Howe '20, p. 75: Ris. '11, p. 388: Garm. '27, p. 260.

Length 19 mm. Expanse 32 mm.   **Me. and Ga. to Ind. and Ont.**

Our smallest skimmer. Face white with a black labrum and a big blackish median spot lying across the front-clypeal stuture. Vertex metallic blue. A broad black transverse stripe includes the middle ocellus. Thorax at first yellow, striped with black, later pruinose blue. Stripes on front of thorax very broad, covering most of area, leaving 2 oblique isolated yellow lines. On the sides the first stripe (2 and 3 fused) is broad and continuous, the 2 other stripes (4 and 5) are interrupted above and irregular, and tend to be confluent with each other at 2 points. Behind the last one there is an additional inferior brown streak. Legs black, Wings hyaline, sometimes broadly tinged with yellow at base, especially in the ♀. Stigma brown, whitish at ends. Abdomen black, broadly cross barred with yellow on the basal segments, becoming wholly pruinose blue with age. Appendage yellow.

Weith ('01) was the first to work on the life history of this species. He says:

Unlike most other Odonata, the imagos do not fly higher than a few feet above the ground, preferring to alight on the marsh grass and bask in the sunshine, where numerous small Deptera suitable for food hover over the little stagnant pools.

On June 22nd I found a number of females ovipositing in the shallow places where I had found the nymphs, in temporary water one to two inches in depth and very warm. The female dips her abdomen to the surface, after the manner of all Libellulines, but only about 3 or 4 times, then rests on the grass a few minutes and then repeats.

37. PERITHEMIS Hagen

Amber-wings

Small dragonflies that lack the usual swelling on the basal abdominal segments and have the middle segments widest. The eyes are large, and for a distance confluent. Prothorax bilobed dorsally, the lobes fringed with long hairs. Thorax densely clothed with short brown hairs. Wings are short and broad with unique venation, the triangle of fore wing being as broad as long, and the bisector of the anal loop in the hind wing being almost straight. Sexes differently colored, wing of the female being very prettily marked with a pattern of brown.

Though a number of names have been applied to the different color forms of this species, we are not able to define them and therefore treat them here as representing a single variable species.

The nymph (Ndm. '01, p. 513) of this genus is rather unique among our Libellulines in possessing a full series of flat, cultriform dorsal hooks the last being on segment 9.

172. Perithemis domitia Drury

Drury 1773: Mtk. Cat. p. 145. Whed. '14, p. 101: Howe '20, p. 75: Ris. '10, p. 331: Garm. 27, p. 258.

Syn: metella Selys, *tenuicinta* Say, *chlora* Rambur, *Var: mooma* Kirby,

seminole Calv., *tenera* Say.

Length 22 mm. Expanse 38 mm.   Mass. and Wis. to Fla., Tex. and Ariz.

A small brownish species with amber tinted and brown spotted wings. Face yellowish, darker above, greenish across the clypeus, brownish at sides and on top of frons. Vertex and occiput brown. Thorax brown, densely clothed with soft brown hairs beneath which appear obscure stripes of yellow, the pair on the front parallel with the carina and wide apart; the 2 on the sides interrupted in the middle portion, the lower ends appearing as roundish spots of considerable size. Legs yellowish with black spines. Wings tinted all over with amber yellow; stigma reddish; a touch of brown at the extreme base and another at the outer angle of the triangles in both wings. In the ♀ there is additional brown spreading forward from the triangle and backward from the nodus, as indicated in the accompanying figure, Abdomen short, stout, a little compressed at base, depressed towards the middle and tapered towards the end; obscure brownish in color, paler laterally and beneath. Appendages yellow, superiorly.

A southern form, doubtfully distinct, having a little more yellow on the thorax where the side stripes are continuous, and much more brown color on the wings, where in the male distinct brown spots surmount the triangles, and in the females, the cross bands of brown are much more extensive, described by Calvert as subsp. *seminole,* has been ranked by Dr. Ris as a separate species; but in a large series of specimens we can find no constant differences.

P. domitia is a "timid, weak species, loving the sunshine." (Mtk. '08, p. 106.)

Tenerals fly in upland fields often resting on the flowers of the ox-eye daisies; adults fly over the pools of standing water. (Brimley '03, p. 154).

On Lake Madison (Wis.) it was present in great numbers about the beds of yellow water lillies and Potamogeton in the quieter bays, now flitting over and now resting upon the lily pads and never far above the surface. (Whed. '14, p. 101.)

Mr. F. G. Schaupp observed this species at Double Horn Creek near Shovel Mount, Texas, perched on sticks fixed in the middle of the creek. They would return repeatedly to the same place after a long, low roundabout flight, often of ten minutes duration.

Our own observations are that this species flies low over the surface of the water, and rests frequently on the tops of low stems and twigs near the shore. It perches horizontally with fore and hind wings often unequally lifted. The female oviposits unattended by the male often on floating masses of partly dead blanket algae, dipping her abdomen to the surface a dozen or more times in rapid succession at points only a few inches distant.

The nymph stands up well on its slender legs and crawls rather actively, and is clean and smooth of body surface. It seems to prefer emergent stumps as a place of transformation. The senior author found one lone oak stump in Benmar Lake near Brewster, N. Y., fairly sprinkled with cast skins, while there were none on the emergent weeds round about.

It appears on the wing about the end of May, and flies through June. Its flight is rather weak, and a bit clumsy and slow. When over water it habitually avoids the altitude of the larger and stronger species, keeping down nearer the surface. It is very sensitive to cloudiness and moisture, being seldom seen in flight except when the sun is shining.

The female is sometimes held by the male while ovipositing, but I have seen her oftener unattended, dropping her eggs on bits of floating dead pond scum by many successive dips made at very nearly the same spot. When a female was taken in hand and "dipped" to the surface of water in a tumbler, 10 to 20 eggs were liberated by her at each descent.

The egg (fig. 8, p. 000) is oblong oval, at first white, turning brownish gray after a few hours; its surface is closely beset with minute tuberculate granulations. The gelatinous envelop is scanty.

The nymphs (Ndm. '01, p. 513) clamber about over trashy submerged vegetation; they climb well, but swim very poorly. They are cleaner and less sprawling than the Libellulas. The nymph goes no farther from the edge of the water to transform than is necessary to find a suitable place—generally but a few inches.

It will be readily distinguished from the other Libellulinae by the possession of a dorsal hook on the 9th abdominal segment. The preceeding dorsal hooks are large, flat and cultriform.

38. CELITHEMIS Hagen

This genus contains a large number of very beautiful species, the wings being richly tinted with brown and gold, and sometimes veined with red. The body is slender, the abdomen being little swollen at the base. The legs are slender. There is considerable variation in the venation of the wings, but the bisector of the anal loop is always nearly straight.

All the species belong to our fauna, and are restricted to the eastern United States. They are common pond and marsh species. Their flight is more fluttering and butterfly-like than that of most dragonflies.

The nymphs are climbers among submerged vegetation. They are rather smooth and usually clean, with slender legs and rather sharp, spine-like dorsal hooks on segments 4 to 7, and long, straight and slender, lateral spines on the end of the abdomen.

The Known Nymphs

Species	Length	Eyes	Lat. Set.	Lat. sp. of 8	Lat. sp. of 9	Described by
eponina	20	rounded	8–9	½ of 8	reaches beyond tip of inferiors	Ndm. '01, p. 515
elisa	17	rounded	7–8	⅓ of 8	reaches tip of superiors	Ndm. '01, p. 515
fasciata	18	pointed	8–9	½–⅔ of 8	reaches beyond tip of inferiors	Brtn. '28, p. 34
ornata	15	rounded	8–9	⅓ of 8	as long as inferiors	Brtn. '28, p. 34

KEY TO THE SPECIES

Adults

Based on Williamson '22

1 Wings with postnodal markings..............................2.
Wings with no postnodal markings; radial planate subtending one cell row..5.

2 Wing membrane yellow; no brown band beyond stigma........
....eponina, p. 209
Wing membrane hyaline; a brown band beyond stigma........3.

3 Fore wing between nodus and stigma, a rounded spot hardly reaching costa..................................elisa, p. 210
Fore wing between nodus and stigma, a brown band spreading along the costa..4.

4 Fore wing antenodal brown band barely reaching Cu$_1$; H. W. pale area in the spot hyaline...........monomelaena, p. 211
pale area in the spot yellowish..............fasciata, p. 211
Fore wing antenodal brown band reaching well beyond Cu$_1$; H. W.

5 Fore wing 2 cell rows beyond the triangle..................6.
Fore wing 3 cell rows beyond the triangle..................7.

6 Hind wing two parallel streaks of brown border the basal space, (cell M$_1$), the rear one covering the triangle......martha, p. 212
Hind wing. The anterior of these basal streaks omitted and the posterior interrupted in its middle portion....amanda, p. 212

7   Hind wing. Two parallel streaks of brown border the basal space, the rear one generally covering the triangle.....**ornata,** p. 212
    Hind wing. Anterior of these omitted and the posterior broken or discontinuous...............................**bertha,** p. 213

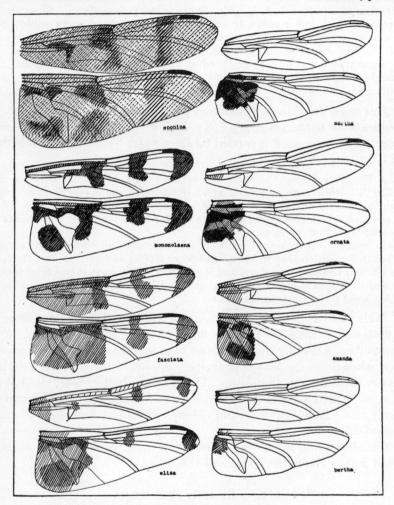

173. Celithemis eponina Drury

Eponina Skimmer

Drury 1773: Mtk. Cat. p. 168: Howe '20, p. 86: Ris. '12, p. 724: Garm. '27, p. 287.

Syn: camilla Ramb, *lucilla* Ramb.

Length 40 mm. Expanse 70 mm.   **Mass. and N. D. to Fla. and Tex**

This is a very pretty slender agile species with yellow tinted wings that bear a pattern of brown bars and spots. Face yellow including top of vertical tubercle. There is a transverse line of black surrounding the middle ocellus in the furrow between the vertex and the frons. Occiput brown. Thorax brown in front, clothed with brownish hairs. Sides with blackish stripes upon the three lateral sutures (stripes 3, 4, 5). Middle stripe incomplete above. Wings tinted throughout with amber yellow and marked with a pattern of brown as indicated in accompanying figure. Stigma yellowish. Legs blackish, the basal segments yellow. Abdomen black with 2 yellow longitudinal streaks, the middorsal one on segment 3–7, narrowly interrupted at apex of each of these segments; one lateral on segment 1–4 composed of double spots diminishing posteriorly. Appendages yellow dorsally.

This beautiful skimmer is abroad from June to early September. It frequents the borders of ponds and neighboring grassy slopes, and sometimes when foraging, it is carried far from water by the winds. Whedon ('14) writes:

A few were taken . . . . along a bay filled with cat tails, bulrushes and sedges . . . . they were present in great numbers on the gravel flats, notwithstanding that the day was very dull and a steady drizzle of cold rain falling. They were covered with glistening rain drops which were shaken from their wings as they fluttered from perch to perch.

In bright weather they were much more agile and quite difficult to capture. When in copulation they would ascend 50 or 60 feet and dart off over the lake for a time. During windy days, and it was very windy when it was bright, they seemed to delight in battling with the gale and in clinging like weather-vanes to tallest weed stalks, their wings half set.

Their flight is not the swiftest or the most continuous, and there is a flutter to it suggestive of the flight of a butterfly. The female in ovipositing is held by the male, and both are apt to be seen on windy days when other species are in shelter, dipping to the crests of foaming waves, far out from the shore. The eggs are better distributed than in most related species, and they seem to be somewhat fewer, and of larger size. Each egg is rotund oblong, whitish at first, soon turning yellowish.

Transformation occurs in the early morning, preferably on stumps about a foot above the surface of the water.

174. Celithemis elisa Hagen

Hag. '61, p. 182: Mtk. Cat. p. 167: Howe '20, p. 86: Ris. '12, p. 725: Garm. '27, p. 285.

Length 35 mm. Expanse 62 mm.   **Me., Wis. to N. C. and Mo.**

A handsome reddish brown species with prettily brown spotted wings. Face red including vertical tubercle, except for a black stripe through the middle ocellus. Occiput brown. Thorax brown, paler at sides and clothed with thin whitish hairs; three black stripes upon the sides follow the sutures (stripes 3, 4, and 5). The middle one incomplete both above and below; the rear one narrowly interrupted below. Legs black, two basal segments paler. Wings yellowish, hyaline basally, clear beyond and marked with brownish spots as indicated in accompanying figure; stigma rufous. Abdomen blackish with segments 3–7 mostly rufous above (black across apical border); this red color spreading forward on the sides of segments 1 and 2. Appendages rufous above.

This species is found on the wing from the last of June to early September. Williamson ('00) wrote of it as follows:

This species may often be found resting on the inflorescence of some of the rushes, preferably the bulrush, *Scirpus lacustris*, growing in the shallow waters of our lakes. So perched on a swinging rush, they have a wide view of what is going on about them and at the same time are inconspicuous, harmonizing well with the dingy brown of the over ripe flowers to which they cling. From this vantage ground they make sudden dashes at passing Diptera and smaller dragonflies, often returning to the identical sedge time and again. Each is the proprietor of a particular locality. When one encroaches on the hunting territory of another, he is quickly hustled away by the rightful and irate owner. . . . . The females are more retired, and are usually found among the sedges back from the water's edge.

175. Celithemis monomelaena Williamson

Wmsn. '11, p. 155: Davis '13, p. 28: Howe '20, p. 87: Ris '12, p. 726: Garm. '27, p. 286.

Length 34 mm. Expanse 60 mm. **Ont., Wis. to Mass.**

A slender blackish species with brown spotted wings. Face metallic bluish or dull yellowish, paler on transverse sutures darker and more metallic on vertex. Occiput brown. Thorax brown, densely clothed with soft brownish hairs. Sides of thorax paler with rather broad irregular stripes on the three sutures (stripes 3, 4, 5) complete and confluent at ends. Legs blackish. Wings hyaline with brownish stigma and a somewhat variable color pattern of the sort shown in the accompanying figure. Abdomen blackish. Young specimens show mid-dorsal diffuse pale spots on segments 2–7 and on infero-lateral margin of segments 3–5. Appendages black.

176. Celithemis fasciata Kirby

Kirby '89, p. 326: Mtk. Cat. p. 168: Ris '12, p. 726.

Length 35 mm. Expanse 64 mm. **N. J. and Wis. to Fla.**

A slender blackish species with wings heavily banded with brown. Face obscure brownish, paler at sides, on the anteclypeus and across postclypeal suture, becoming metallic blue above to match vertex. Occiput brown. Thorax brown becoming blackish with age, thinly clothed with whitish hairs. Teneral specimens show 2 narrow pale stripes on front and sides mostly, yellowish with 3 blackish bands on sutures (stripes 3, 4, 5), the foremost very broad, the middle one unconnected above, the rear one incomplete but narrow below. Legs blackish. Wings tinged with yellowish before the nodus and hyaline beyond except for brown spots shown in accompanying figure. Abdomen in old specimens wholly black. Teneral specimens show diminishing middorsal yellow triangular spots on segments 3–7, and sides of 2–5 yellowish beneath. Appendages black.

177. Celithemis martha Williamson

Wmsn. '22, p. 8: Garm. '27, p. 288.

Length 31 mm. Expanse 57 mm.   **N. Eng.**

Face yellowish, darker above and clothed, especially on the darker portion, with stiff short dark hairs. Edge of labrum and 2 oblique areas within, blackish, an arcuate streak across the postclypeus blackish. Vertex wholly blackish. Occiput very dark brown. Thorax wholly brownish, densely clothed with tawny brown hairs; stripes of thorax similar to those of *amanda* but soon obscured. Legs blackish with paler coxae. Wings hyaline, yellowish at base, with brown spot on hind wings as shown on accompanying figure; stigma tawny. Abdomen black with obscure paler middorsal triangles on middle segments; broad areas below on sides of basal segments. Superior appendages yellowish, inferior black.

178. Celithemis amanda

Hag. '61, p. 183: Mtk. Cat. p. 167: Ris '12, p. 728: Wmsn. '22, p. 108.

Syn: pulchella Burm.

Length 31 mm. Expanse 52 mm.   **Ga., Fla.**

A dainty little dragonfly with a large basal brown spot on the hind wing. Face pale, becoming rufous on labrum and on top of frons and vertex. A black transverse stripe includes the middle ocellus. Occiput brownish. Thorax brownish in front, yellowish on sides, thinly clothed with pale tawny hairs. The usual black stripes of sides are replaced by diffuse spots in deepest portions only of lateral sutures. Legs blackish, 2 basal joints pale. Wings hyaline except at base; stigma yellowish. Color pattern as shown in accompanying figure. Abdomen yellow basally and blackish towards the tip; the yellow overspreads the segments 3 and 4, extends forward on sides of 1 and 2, and backward in dorsal spots on 5, 6 and 7. Appendages yellow above.

179. Celithemis ornata Rambur

Ramb. '42, p. 96: Mtk. Cat. p. 168: Root '24, p. 321: Howe '20, p. 87: Ris '12, p. 727.

Length 32 mm. Expanse 54 mm.   **Atl. Coast, Me. to Fla.**

A very dainty little dragonfly streaked with brown and yellow. Face yellowish. Labrum bordered with brown and with 3 little brown spots in a row along the basal suture. A broad black cross stripe surrounds the middle ocellus. Vertex yellow. Occiput yellowish. Thorax yellow striped with brown. A very broad median stripe covers most of the front but is notched at sides just below the collar; confluent along the collar with the stripes of the sides: three side stripes (2+3, 4 and 5); the foremost, broad, complete; the middle one narrower, incomplete above or confluent rearward at its upper end with the rearmost stripe. Legs blackish with paler coxae. Wings hyaline with a basal tinge of yellow and streaks of brown as indicated in the accompanying figure; stigma tawny. Abdomen blackish, marked with yellow basally in a line of diminishing middorsal triangular spots on 3–7. Sides of 1 and 2 yellow below. Appendages black.

A charming little species that flits about the edges of ponds gaily from one leaf tip of arrowhead or bulrush to another. The clean and light colored nymph climbs among the water weeds.

180. Celithemis bertha Williamson

Wmsn. '22, p. 10.

Length 32 mm. Expanse 53 mm.   Fla.

A pretty little reddish brown species with red veined wings. Face yellowish, becoming rufous with age including the vertical tubercle, and with the usual black cross stripe through the middle ocellus. Occiput brown. Thorax yellowish becoming brown with age, heavily striped with black. A very broad middle stripe widened below at collar and 3 unequal black stripes upon the lateral sutures, the middle one incomplete above but dilated in its middle portion. Legs blackish with paler coxae. Wings hyaline; stigma tawny. Veins reddish, especially before the nodus, and a little area of yellowish brown as shown in accompanying figure. Abdomen blackish with the base yellowish, becoming rufous with age. Segments 3 and 4 mainly yellowish, which color extends rearward in obscure dorsal spots on 5–7 and basalward on sides of 2 and 3. Appendages obscurely paler above.

39. PSEUDOLEON Kirby

These are Sonoran dragonflies of singularly beautiful coloration. The dark thorax is covered with vermiculate lines of dull yellow, and the dorsum of the abdomen bears on its segments a series of V's of the same color. The wings are heavily clouded with brown. The triangle of the front wing is very long and narrow and followed by four or more rows of cells. The post nodal cross veins near the front of the stigma are strongly aslant, simulating brace veins. Vein M_2 is strongly undulate. The heel of the anal loop is very large with a spur vein running out into it. The nymph is unknown.

181. Pseudoleon superbus Hagen

Hag. '61, p. 148: Mtk. Cat. p. 155: Ris '11, p. 528.

Length 42 mm. Expanse 74 mm.   Ariz. and Calif.

A very strikingly colored species with a heavy pattern of brown upon the wings and extensive striping upon the body. Face brown, paler above. Occiput yellow. Eyes with about 8 alternating light and dark stripes of equal width extending vertically across their surface. Prothorax brownish. Wings heavily marked with brown, as shown in accompanying figure; stigmas brown, sometimes bicolored, inner half brown, outer half pale. Legs brownish, darker at the joints and at the spines. Abdomen brownish with paired oblique pale streaks diverging backward on segments 2–7. These form a series of "V's" opening backward; smaller paired pale streaks occur within and without the "V's" on these same segments. Pleural margins of segments strongly serrate, the posterior lateral angles very prominent. Segments 6–9 strongly carinate on middorsal line. Appendages brown.

40. ERYTHRODIPLAX Brauer

These are slender dragonflies of obscure brownish coloration tending to become bluish pruinose with age. The face and frons take on metallic colors above; the thorax, more or less zebra striped in the beginning, becomes wholly obscure. The abdomen is but little swollen at the base. The wings are hyaline with only basal flavescent touches. The base of vein A_2 is situated just a little beyond the anal crossing.

The nymphs are rather thick set and dark colored with no dorsal hooks and with rather sharp, lateral spines. They are known for three of our four species.

The Known Nymphs

Species	Length	Lat. Set.	Ment. Set.	Described by
berenice	14	9-10	10-11	Calv. '04, p. 174
minuscula	12	8	12	Ndm. '04 p. 709
umbrata	18	10–11	13–14	Calv. '28, p. 25

This genus is mainly tropical American. One species ranges far up the Atlantic Coast; three others just enter our borders.

KEY TO THE SPECIES*

Adults

1 Radial planate subtends two rows of cells...................2.
   Radial planate subtends one cell row......................3.
2 Median planate subtends two rows of cells......**funerea**, p. 215
   Median planate subtends one cell row.........**umbrata**, p. 215
3 Expanse less than 45 mm...................**minuscula**, p. 215
   Expanse more than 50 mm..................**berenice**, p. 215

* This key does not include the *E. (Nannophya) maculosa* of Hagen ('61, p. 187) doubtfully recorded from Georgia; a little species (expanse 33 mm.) with a big round, blackish spot covering the base of the hind wing, enveloping the triangle and nearly all the anal loop. In the fore wing the point of the triangle inclines outward, and the subtriangle is divided by a single cross vein (see Ris: de Selys Coll., pp. 526 and 1160).

182. Erythrodiplax funerea Hagen

Hag. '61, p. 158: Mtk. Cat. p. 153: Ris '11, p. 483.

Syn: tyleri Kirby

Length 50 mm. Expanse 70 mm.   Calif.

Adult male black; face brassy black. Legs black except the middle and hind tibiae which are pale externally. Wings blackish, apex and base of front ones hyaline. Abdomen slender, black with yellow appendages. Younger specimens have the thorax yellowish with the front infuscated. The abdomen has the sides washed with brown.

183. Erythrodiplax umbrata Linneus

Linne. 1758, p. 545: Mtk. Cat. p. Ris. '11, p. 484: Calv. '28, p. 25.

Syn: fallax Burm., *flavicans* Ramb., *ruralis* Burm., *subfasciata* Burm., *tripartita* Burm., *unifasciata* De Geer.

Length 40 mm. Expanse 62 mm.   Ga., Fla. to Tex.

Face yellowish becoming brownish with age. Top of frons and vertex lustrous brown, and occiput the same. Thorax brown, scantily pilose with only a suggestion of darker brown lines; 2 narrow straight ones on the front, each side, and 3 irregular ones following the lateral sutures. Legs blackish with most of the femora paler. Wings hyaline with a very variable amount of brown disposed in a broad cross band beyond the nodus and a wash across the apex beyond the stigma, all of which brown color may be entirely lacking. Base of hind wings faintly tinged with yellow out to anal loop. Abdomen obscure brown becoming blackish towards apex. All carinae of middle segments edged with blackish. Appendages yellowish.

184. Erythrodiplax minuscula Rambur

Ramb. '42, p. 115: Mtk. Cat. p. 153: Ris '11, p. 524.

Length 25 mm. Expanse 42 mm.   Ky. and N. C. to Fla. and Tex.

Face yellow, becoming brownish with age especially on labrum and frons above. Vertex darker, becoming metallic blue. Occiput brown. Thorax yellow, becoming pruinose blue with age. Front brownish with a narrow yellowish streak each side the brown carina. Sides paler with only a suggestion of brown lines on the lateral sutures. Legs blackish with paler coxae. Wings hyaline with brownish stigma and a little brown spot at anal triangle of male. Abdomen black with yellow appendages, and in young specimens a double line of yellow spots bordering the middorsal brown streak on segments 3–7, and other yellow spots on sides of 2 and 3 below.

Common about ponds in the south eastern states, where it flits from leaf to leaf about the shores. It is easily taken with a net.

185. Erythrodiplax berenice Drury

Drury 1773: Mtk. Cat. p. 150: Howe '20, p. 77: Ris '11, p. 522: Garm. '27, p. 262.

Syn: lustria Burm., *naeva* Hag.

Length 34 mm. Expanse 54 mm.   Mass. and Pa. to N. C., Fla. and Tex.

A slender clear winged species with a body that shows very great differences in appearance according to age. Face yellow, cross striped with black, or when mature wholly metallic blue. Stripes traverse border of labrum, entire ante-clypeus and the fronto-clypeal suture. Tip of vertex at first, yellow. Occiput black. Thorax yellow traversed by numerous sinuous vertical stripes of brown, later becoming wholly dark pruinose blue. Front of thorax more brown than yellow, a rather wide stripe of which borders the carina and an interrupted one lies in the blue on either side. On the sides are 5 brown stripes of nearly equal width, confluent above and below except on the middle suture. Legs black, coxae paler. Wings hyaline with only a yellowish tinge at base; stigma tawny. Abdomen marked with yellow becoming wholly black with age; the yellow covers the basal segments except for narrow transverse lines of black, and is restricted apically and laterally on segments 5–8; 9 and 10 black. Appendages yellowish at first. Wings of an old female often show a diffuse brownish cloud covering half their breadth at the nodus.

The nymph is an inhabitant of brackish waters.

41. ORTHEMIS Hagen

These are rather large, stout bodied dragonflies of pale brownish color, that assume plumbeous tints with age. The wings are hyaline with very long stigma and with the cross veins behind it elongated crosswise of the wings. The abdomen is parallel sided almost to the tip.

The sections of the arculus are distinctly stalked; the bridge sub-tends but one cross vein; the cells bordering vein M_1 are transversely elongated before the stigma.

Its nymph (Ndm '92, p. 702) is thick-set, hairy, plathemis-like in the bulging hind angles of the head and in the crenate front border of the median lobe of the labium.

A single representative of this neotropical genus is found on our southern border.

186. Orthemis ferruginea Fabricius

Fabr. 1775, p. 423: Mtk. Cat. p. 143: Ris '10, p. 282: Calv. '28, p. 19.

Syn: discolor Burm., *macrostigma* Ramb.

Length 54 mm.   Expanse 88 mm.   **Fla., Miss., Tex. and Ariz.**

This is a large stout bodied species with hyaline wings and a long stigma. Face pale, becoming darker with age on edge of labrum, top of frons and vertex. Occiput shining black. Thorax nearly bare with no long fringe on collar; with no color pattern but only a darker shade in the depths of the sutures; greenish olivaceous when young, becoming plum colored with age. Legs blackish with black spines and claws. Wings hyaline with brown veins and stigma that become rufous with age. Abdomen nearly uniform in color, darkened only narrowly along the carinae. Appendages pale.

According to the observations of Mr. F. G. Schaupp in Texas, this species perches on bushes and stems a little way off from the water and is very shy. It is quicker than a Libellula, and when it is flushed, seldom returns to the same perch. A specimen reared by him transformed September 3d at 5 A.M.

42. LADONA Needham

These are slender dragonflies of moderate size, with stout thorax, tapering abdomen and hyaline wings that have a triangular brown patch across their bases. The colors are obscure brownish, very white pruinosity developing with age upon the front of the thorax and base of abdomen. The apical sector originates under the proximal end of the stigma.

KEY TO THE SPECIES
Adults

1 Expanse less than 60 mm...................**deplanata**, p. 217
  Expanse more than 60 mm...............................2.

2 Dorsum of the thorax pale with a black stripe each side on the humeral suture, no antehumeral stripe of white; the fuscous spot on the base of the hind wing not enveloping the triangle ....**julia**, p. 218
  Dorsum of the thorax blackish brown, with a white antehumeral stripe each side; the fuscous spot of the hind wing envelops the triangle....................................**exusta**, p. 218

The nymphs of this genus are of rather slender form with a long, tapering abdomen, the tenth segment of which is ridged along the side. The setae of the middle lobe of the labium are usually few in number (0–3).

The Known Nymphs

Species	Length	Lateral setae	Mental setae	Dorsal hooks	Described by
deplanata	20?	6	0–0	4–8?	Ndm. '97, p. 146
julia	24	6	3–4	4–8	Ndm. '01, p. 530

187. Ladona deplanata Rambur

Ramb. '42, p. 75: Mtk. Cat. p. 134: Ris '10, p. 259.

Length 30 mm. Expanse 56 mm.   **Fla., Ga.**

A little brownish clearwinged species having some streaks of black at the wing base. Face tawny yellowish; labrum a little darker; frons, and the streak through ocelli brown. Thorax brownish, darker in front with a broad blackish stripe upon the humeral suture (stripes 2 and 3 fused) and a narrow whitish stripe before it. Sides obscure, olivaceous without stripes. Legs pale brown. Wings hyaline with brown streaks in the basal subcostal spaces and with a triangular patch of brown, before the triangle, resting on the hind margin. Membranule white. Stigma brown. Abdomen with a middorsal brown stripe, slowly widened apically and with narrow black lines on all the carinae. Appendages brown.

This little skimmer frequents the borders of ponds and flies about their edges a very little over the open water, flitting mainly from one resting place to another in rather slow, irregular flight. It is quite easy to capture.

188. Ladona exusta Say

Say '39, p. 29: Mtk. Cat. p. 134: Wlsn. '09, p. 656: Howe '20, p. 71: Ris '10, p. 257: Garm. '27, p. 246.

Length 37 mm. Expanse 66 mm.   **N. Eng. and Pa.**

A rather small brownish clear winged species having coloration that varies greatly with age. Face and vertex obscure yellowish brown, with a black stripe between. Thorax whitish in front except for the carina, becoming pruinose (almost snowy white) with age, as do also the basal segments of the abdomen. Sides with a broad stripe of brown, mostly before the humeral stripe; behind this, obscure pale brown. Legs brown, blackening with age. Wings hyaline with brown stigma and with brown streaks in both subcostal and cubital spaces. These more or less confluent basally, the latter in the hind wing spreading rearward in a long point adjacent to the white membranule. Abdomen with ill defined middorsal stripe of black that widens to rearward, and with narrow black lines on all carinae. Appendages brownish.

Muttkowski ('08) reports this species flying over lakes and ponds during June and July. Wilson ('09) writes interestingly of it as follows:

Abundant everywhere with *quadrimaculata* in the undergrowth close to the shore. When it alights it squats like a Gomphus on the rocks, stumps and even on the ground. It is gregarious, as many as 15 or 20 alighting on the same spot; it is also inquisitive and many were caught that actually alighted inside the net as it was being carried. The males are predominant and even pruinose thus early, even the 2 antehumeral stripes showing clear white.

189. Ladona julia Uhler

Uhler '57, p. 88: Mtk. Cat. p. 134: Ris '10, p. 258: Garm. '27, p. 246.

Length 37 mm. Expanse 66 mm.   **N. Y. to Md.**

This species differs from *exusta* in the thoracic stripes as stated in the key. The fuscous spots on the base of the hind wing are smaller, not enveloping the triangle; the eighth abdominal segment of the male is narrower than the seventh; the apex of the inner branch of the genital hamule of the male is directed laterally.

43. LIBELLULA Linnaeus
The Skimmers

These are among the best known of our larger dragonflies for they are familiar figures in the air above every pond in the summer time. The body is stout and more or less pubescent. The abdomen gradually tapers to rearward from somewhat swollen base. The wings exhibit a great variety of color pattern in the different species. The stigma is always rather large, surmounting a number of cells in the first radial space. The sectors of the arculus are not stalked; the bridge subtends several cross veins; vein M_2 is strongly undulate; the anal loop is rather narrow and with a sigmoid curvature.

The nymphs are squat, hairy creatures that sprawl amid the bottom silt. The eyes are very prominent capping the front angles of the head. The border of the middle lobe of the labrum is smooth. Dorsal hooks and lateral spines are small or wanting or well nigh lost in tufts of coarse hairs.

The Known Nymphs

Species	Length	Dorsal hooks	Lat. Set.	Ment. Set.	Described by
auripennis	27	3 or 4–5	5	8–10	Ndm. '01, p. 533
axillena	22	4–8	5	12–13	Ndm. '03, p. 273
cyanea	20	4–8	6	8–9	Ndm. '01, p. 534
flavida	17(?)	4–8	8	12–13	Ndm. '03, p. 224
forensis	24	weak 3–7	6	8	Ndm. '04, p. 706
incesta	21	4–8	5	9	Byers '27, p. 113
luctuosa	25	4–8	10–11	7	Ndm. '01, p. 534
pulchella	26	0 or r	8–9	12–13	Ndm. '01, p. 536
quardimaculata	26	obscure 3–8 r on 8	7	13	Ndm. '01, p. 535
saturata	26	0	9–10	11–12	Ndm. '04, p. 705

This large genus is mainly holarctic with its center of distribution in the United States. Our species may be separated as follows:

KEY TO THE SPECIES
Adults

1 Wings reddish without brown markings (except stigma).......2.
 Wings golden without brown markings (except stigma)........3.
 Wings with broad blackish band covering basal third..........
 ....luctuosa, p. 221
 Wings hyaline, or spotted, or streaked with brown...........4.

2 The reddish color extends to the stigma.........saturata, p. 222
   The reddish color extends to the nodus......croceipennis, p. 222
3 The golden color deepest along costal margin..auripennis, p. 222
   The golden color deepest behind vein *R*........jesseana, p. 223
4 Stigma bicolored..5.
   Stigma uniformly colored.....................................7.
5 Base of wings hyaline........................comanche, p. 223
   Base of wings with a brown streak.........................6.

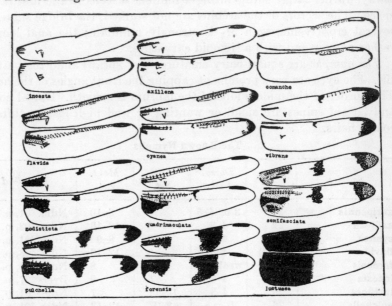

6 Stigma white, dark brown along the front........cyanea, p. 223
   Stigma yellow, dark brown on outer side........flavida, p. 224
7 Wings with a spot or stripe at the nodus...................8.
   Wings with no spot or stripe at the nodus................12.
8 Wing tips brown...9.
   Wing tips hyaline..10.
   Wing spots yellowish...................semifasciata, p. 224
   Wing spots blackish.......................pulchella, p. 224
10 Wings with a broad nodal band or blotch.......forensis, p. 226
   Wings with a small nodal spot.............................11.
11. Hind wing with triangular basal brown spot veined with yellow
   ....quadrimaculata, p. 226
   Hind wing with diffuse broad basal spot.......nodisticta, p. 226

190. Libellula luctuosa Burmeister

The Widow

Burm. '39, p. 861: Mtk. Cat. p. 138: Ris '10, p. 263: Wlsn. '12, p. 194: Howe. '20, p. 71: Garm. '27, p. 248.

Syn: basalis Say, *odiosa* Hagen

Length 47 mm. Expanse 84 mm.   **Me. and N. D. to N. Mex. and Fla.**

A blackish species of moderate size easily recognized by the broad basal bands of the wings. Face obscure yellowish becoming blackish with age. Top of frons and vertex becoming metallic purplish with age. Body brown striped with yellow becoming pruinose blue on dorsal side. Hair fringes on occiput and on collar, yellow. Front of thorax brown with a rather broad middle pale stripe; sides with 2 broad oblique streaks of yellow separated by brown crossing the sutures. Legs blackish, paler at bases and beneath the front femora. Wings marked with brown, as shown in figure; stigma black. Abdomen blackish striped with yellow; stripes broad, the dorsal pair confluent on segment 1 and more widely separated to rearward by the deepening middorsal black stripe; inferior stripes visible at sides of segments 1–3. Appendages blackish.

Fig. 39. The Widow, *Libellula luctuosa.*

This is a common pond species in the Mississippi valley. It flies rather steadily over the ponds resting occasionally on reed tips. It is not very hard to capture. In the cool of the evening adults may be found hanging by their feet to the sloping twigs of nearby shrubbery.

The female usually oviposits unattended. At transformation the cast skins are left most commonly sticking to clustered grass stems a few yards from the pond. Ants kill many of the teneral adults by first biting holes in their newly released wings, preventing their expansion.

191. Libellula saturata Uhler

The Big Red Skimmer

Uhler '57, p. 88: Mtk. Cat. p. 140: Mtk. '10, p. 140: Ris '10, p. 274: Kndy. '17, p. 609: Ndm. '23, p. 129: Smn. '26, p. 34.

Length 55 mm. Expanse 90 mm.   **Mont. to N. Mex. and Calif.**

A large stout-bodied, reddish, southwestern species. Face red, including vertex. Eyes and occiput brown. Thorax reddish brown, clothed with short pubescence of same color, and without stripes. Legs reddish with black spines. Wings broad, dark, flavescent as far as nodus, with a deeper streak out to the triangles, as shown in figure; veins and stigma reddish. Abdomen red, brighter towards apex. Appendages red.

This is a very showy pond species. Its flight is rather heavy and lumbering but well sustained.

The hairy nymph squats amid the black ooze in stagnant ponds and climbs only a little way out of the water to transform.

192. Libellula croceipennis Selys

Selys '68, p. 67: Mtk. Cat. p. 140: Ris' 10, p. 276.

Length 53 mm. Expanse 85 mm.   **Tex.**

Similar to the preceeding species, differing mainly in the following characters: the yellowish brown of the base of the wings does not extend beyond the nodus and is rather uniform in depth of color throughout; there are two cubito-anal cross veins; and there is usually one row of cells subtended by the median planate.

193. Libellula auripennis Burmeister

Golden Wings

Burm. '39, p. 861: Mtk. Cat. p. 135: Ris '10, p. 273: Howe '20, p. 69: Garm. '27 243.

Syn: costalis Ramb.

Length 54 mm. Expanse 86 mm.   **Atl. Coast and Ohio to Fla. and Tex.**

A fine, big species with golden wings and yellow or reddish stigma. Face yellow, becoming reddish with age. Vertex yellowish at tip with a black cross stripe surrounding the ocelli. Occiput yellow, fringed with tawny hairs. Thorax yellow with thin golden pubescence; without stripes save for a suggestion of brown in the hindmost lateral suture (stripe 5). Legs brown, paler to near the knees, front femora reddish below. Wings tinged with yellow or red, more deeply along the radius and at the stigma, without brown markings though there is a shadow of brown sometimes on the extreme tip. Abdomen yellowish, becoming reddish, with the middorsal carina narrowly bordered with black. Appendages rufous.

194. Libellula jesseana Williamson

Wmsn. '22, p. 13.

Length 54 mm. Expanse 86 mm. **Fla.**

This is very similar to *auripennis* differing by the darker metallic coloration of face above and vertex, and by the redder hue of stigma and adjacent veins. Perhaps it is hardly more than a variety of that species.

195. Libellula comanche Calvert

Calv. '07, p. 201: Mtk. Cat. p. 135: Ris '10, p. 272.

Length 50 mm. Expanse 80 mm. **Mont., Wyo. to Tex., Mex. and Calif.**

A large western species, similar to *cyanea*, having the same bicolored stigma (three quarters yellow) and a less development of the basal brown streaks on the wing. Body pattern wholly obscured by pruinosity, with age, as in that species. Face wholly yellow.

According to F. G. Schaupp, dragonflies of this species sit mostly on green bushes at the banks, and fly, mostly over the surface of the water, hunting, and chasing each other, and (to the disappointment of the collector) disturbing other species that might easily be taken but for their continual interference.

196. Libellula cyanea Fabricius

Fabr. '75, p. 424: Mtk. Cat. p. 136: Howe '20, p. 70: Ris '10, p. 272: Garm. '27, p. 244.

Syn: bistigma Uhler, quadrupla Say

Length 43 mm. Expanse 74 mm. **N. H. and Ind. to Ga.**

A slender species with bicolored stigma. Face yellowish becoming shining metallic brown on labrum top of frons and vertex, with age. Thorax thinly clothed with short brownish pubescence; at first pale brownish and yellow, with age becoming pruinose blue all over thorax and abdomen. Front of thorax brown with yellow middorsal stripe, furcate at crest. Sides yellow, except around leg and wing bases, with a single brown stripe on the last lateral suture (stripe 5). Legs blackish, paler at base. Wings hyaline except for short basal subcostal streaks. as shown in figure; stigma yellow over more than basal half, beyond blackish. Abdomen at first pale brown yellowish below on the swollen basal segments; above with a continuous broad line of yellowish that begins high up on dorsum of segment 2 and ends low down on sides of 9 and 10. Appendages brownish, becoming black.

Brimley ('03) found the tenerals occuring "mostly among broom-straw in woods and fields, the adults fly over marshes and standing water."

197. Libellula flavida Rambur

Ramb. '42, p. 58: Mtk. Cat. p. 137: Howe '20, p. 70: Ris '10, p. 271.

Syn: plumbea Uhler

Length 48 mm.　Expanse 78 mm.　　　　　　　Atl. Coast, Pa. and N. J. to Fla.

Face yellowish in the ♀, black in the ♂ and shining, with yellow fronto-clypeal suture and anteclypeus. Occiput brownish with a black cross stripe before it through the ocelli. Thorax brown with middorsal stripe of yellow; becoming wholly pruinose blue above with age. Sides yellow, brown at wing and leg roots and with a single brown stripe (stripe 5) on last lateral suture. Legs blackish, paler to near the knees. Wings broadly tinged with yellow and with diffuse basal brown streaks in subcostal and cubital spaces; stigma tawny. Abdomen brown, becoming black with age; sometimes showing obscure middorsal stripe and a black line on the lateral carina. Appendages brown becoming black with age.

198. Libellula semifasciata Burmeister

Burm. '39, p. 862: Mtk. Cat. p. 141: Ris '10, p. 266: Howe '20, p. 73: Garm. '27, p. 252.

Syn: maculata Ramb., *ternaria* Say

Length 42 mm.　Expanse 74 mm.　　　　　　　Me., Minn. to Fla. and Tex.

This is a fine pale brownish species with prettily spotted and amber tinted wings. Face pale, waxy yellow, shining, paler across the middle. Vertex olivaceous with a narrow black cross stripe through the ocelli, before it. Thorax pale brown in front and yellowish upon the sides with 2 stripes (stripes 4 and 5) upon the sutures. Legs brown, yellowish at base, and with blackish tarsi. Wings spotted as shown in figure; venation richly tinged with yellow as far as triangle and along the region of the radius out to the wing tip; stigma rufous, bordered with black veins, ends pale.

The senior author ('01) has found this species the earliest of the genus to be abroad in the spring, making its appearance in the north before the middle of May. "I have oftenest found the imago about woodland brooks, rarely about ponds." It flies in swift dashes, and in long sweeping curves.

199. Libellula pulchella Drury
The Tenspot

Drury 1773: Mtk. Cat. p. 139: Ris '10, p. 265: Whed. '14, p. 99: Howe '20, p. 73: Smn. '26, p. 33: Garm. '27, p. 249.

Syn: bifasciata Fabr., *confusa* Uhler, *versicolor* Fabr.

Length 52 mm.　Expanse 90 mm.　　　　　　　Me. and N. D. to Tex. and Fla.

A fine, large, strong-flying species. Face obscure brownish, paler in middle and yellowish on top of frons. Vertex brown with a black cross stripe before it, through the middle ocelli. Occiput yellow with brown outer angles. Thorax brown clothed with a thin white pubescence; sides with 2 yellowish stripes well defined inferiorly, very oblique, first crossing the middle suture above the spiracle, the second nearly horizontal and seeming to be continued to rearward by yellow spots underneath the swollen base of the abdomen. Legs blackish, paler at base. Wings spotted with brown as shown in accompanying figure; costa, arculus, and nodal cross veins yellowish; stigma blackish; 10 chalky white spots develop with age, 2 on each fore wing between the brown spots, and 3 on each hind wing, one at anal angle. Abdomen brown with 2 pale stripes upon the sides running the entire length, and a narrow pale streak bordering the middorsal carina on the middle segments. The abdomen of the female tapers all the way to the tip, less strongly than in the male. Appendages brownish, becoming black with age.

This is a beautiful, wide ranging species, a lover of the ponds but a frequent visitor along the "rivers, creeks and roadsides, in woods, fields and open places,"

Fig. 40. *The Tenspot, Libellula pulchella.*

(Muttkowski '08). "Common not merely along the lake but far inland over the potato and corn fields; too wary to be caught easily. . . . . Several individuals . . . . were observed going to roost for the night in the tall iron weed along a dried up overflow bottom. When roosting they flatten back against the vertical stem of the weed instead of holding their bodies horizontal as is done when they alight in the daytime, possibly as a protection against the rain" (Wilson '09).

This is a very familiar dragonfly and a typical skimmer. Wherever it occurs it is sure to be in evidence, flying much and resting little during hours of sunshine. It flies horizontally several feet above the water. The female oviposits unattended, usually over submerged green vegetation in bays and shoals. Striking the water at points wide apart and striking it with a vigor that often sweeps a drop from the surface to fall back with a splash a foot farther ahead. The cast skins are left at transformation several feet from the shore and usually in grass or weeds.

200. Libellula forensis Hagen

Hag. '61, p. 154: Mtk. Cat. p. 137: Ris '10, p. 265: Smn. '26, p. 33.
Length 50 mm.   Expanse 89 mm.   B. C. to Calif., Mont. to Ariz.

The western equivalent of *L. pulchella*, differing from that species most markedly in lacking the brown color on the tips of the wings.

201. Libellula quadrimaculata Linne

Linne. 1758, p. 543: Mtk. Cat. p. 139: Wlsn. '09, p. 657: Ris '10, p. 251: Whths. '17, p. 101: Howe '20, p. 72: Garm. '27, p. 251.
   Syn: maculata Harris, *Var: praenubila* Newman, *quadripunctata* Fabr., *ternaria* Say
Length 45 mm.   Expanse 74 mm.   N. Am.

A handsome slender brownish species of wide holarctic distribution. Face yellow, labrum bordered and traversed with black. Vertex yellow, with black cross stripe, through the ocelli, before it. Occiput yellow with brown outer angles. Thorax tawny, yellow with dense pubescence of same color. Narrow black lines follow the sinuous lateral sutures (stripes 3 and 5), abbreviated below on middle one and confluent beneath 2 obscure yellowish spots. Legs blackish, paler basally. Wings spotted, as shown in figure, the basal triangular brown spot of hind wing traversed by whitish veins; stigma brown. Abdomen hairy at base, olive brown on swollen basal segments; mostly blackish on strongly tapering apical segments, with a narrow streak of yellow running lengthwise just above the lateral margin. Appendages blackish.

This gregarious, typical holoarctic Libellula has been well characterized by many writers in the group. Wilson ('09) reported it,

Everywhere in company with *exusta*; when it alights it does not squat, but perches on a twig, holding its body horizontal even if the twig is vertical. It is gregarious, from 12 to 15 or 20 alighting on the same stalk or twig. It is not wary but neither is it inquisitive like *L. exusta*. . . . . Found by the hundreds in an old lumber yard, ... every stick, stub and bush alive with them. They were very tame, alighting not merely on the net but also on the hand and arm and all over the clothing.

The senior author, on the contrary, has found them ('01) somewhat shy and difficult to capture.

They are common about lakes, rivers, moist woods from May to August, (Muttkowski '08). Of their ovipositing, Whitehouse ('17) writes: "I once observed a female ovipositing with a mate hovering by. Twice they went into copula for short periods between spells of ovipositing—which however she performed alone."

202. Libellula nodisticta Hagen

Hag. '61, p. 151: Mtk. Cat. p. 138: Ris '10, p. 264: Kndy. '17, p. 608.
Length 48 mm.   Expanse 82 mm.   Mont. and Wash. to Calif. and Nev.

A stout heavy western species. Face obscure yellowish, darkened on border of labrum and top of frons. Thorax brownish, becoming whitish on front with age, except carina. Sides with 2 lines of yellowish streaks (equivalent to stripes of other species), the foremost, a row of spots rather widely separated at the middle suture, the second, a horizontal streak low down on the sides, seeming to be continued by the line of spots beneath the swollen base of the abdomen. Legs black. Wings spotted, as shown in figure, with a chalky white area, in old specimens, around the basal brown spots on both wings in the males externally. Abdomen with a line of large ill-defined pale spots upon each side. Appendages blackish.

Kennedy ('17) found this species,

Common on the town drain. In the morning the individuals . . . . were easily captured while seated on brush and weeds in the sunny openings along the stream. . . . . A female observed ovipositing flew about 2 feet above the water and made several quick swings downward, tapping the water with her abdomen just once for each swing.

203. Libellula composita Hagen

Hag. '73, p. 728: Mtk. Cat. p. 136: Ris '10, p. 267: Kndy. '17, p. 625.
Length 42 mm. Expanse 78 mm.   Yellowstone, Utah, Nev., Calif.

Face, frons and vertex white, a small black line across the base of the frons and up to the middle of the ocelli. Thorax in front a clear, violet brown, with a yellowish band across the middle, bordered by a whitish one; antehumeral and humeral stripes well defined (stripes 2 and 3); stripe 4 abbreviated below, and 5 complete but smaller. Legs blackish, the base of the femora yellowish. Wings hyaline; costa as far as stigma white, beyond black; stigma dark reddish brown; base of hind wing yellowish. Abdomen fairly broad, depressed; black with whitish yellow pattern. Wedge shaped lateral spots on 3–7; 8–10 wholly dark.

204. Libellula incesta Hagen

Hag. '61, p. 155: Mtk. Cat. p. 137: Ris '10, p. 270: Davis '12, p. 68: Brim. '20, p. 138: Howe '20, p. 69: Byers '27a, p. 113.
Length 54 mm. Expanse 90 mm.   Me. and Wis. to Mo. and N. C.

A slender clear-winged species with dull yellow thoracic and abdominal stripings that entirely disappear, becoming dark pruinose blue with age. Face obscure yellowish, becoming metallic, shining, on labrum and on top of frons. Frontal tubercle acutely double pointed, dark colored. Occiput brown. Thorax clothed with very short, dark pubescence, when young showing narrow median pale spots on the brown front; 2 blackish spots below the yellowish sides and very diffuse discolorations along the lateral sutures, especially the hindmost (stripe 5). Legs blackish, paler at base. Wings hyaline except for brown tips of variable extent, generally restricted to margin beyond stigma; stigma blackish. Sometimes there is a brownish streak in the base of the subcostal space. Abdomen very slender in both sexes, blackish with a broad yellow stripe each side, becoming wholly purplish black with age. Appendages blackish.

Found about the shores of lakes from June to September (Muttkowski '08).

205. Libellula vibrans Fabricius

Fabr. 1793, p. 380: Mtk. Cat. p. 141: Ris '10, p. 268: Howe '20, p. 70: Garm. '27, p. 253.

Syn: leda Say

Length 60 mm. Expanse 100 mm.   **Me. and Mass. to Mo. and N. C.**

A very large species with long slender wings and abdomen. Vertex brown or purple. Face yellow. Occiput fringed behind with white hairs. A longer fringe of white hairs encircles the collar. Body brown and yellow, becoming wholly pruinose blue with age. Front of thorax brown with narrow middorsal yellow stripe; sides yellow with an interrupted brown stripe (stripe 5) on last suture and the rudiment of another one (stripe 4) just before the spiracle beneath. Legs yellowish to middle of femur, thereafter blackish. Wings marked with brown, as shown in figure, with black stigma. Abdomen yellowish on the slightly swollen basal segments, brownish beyond with broad lateral yellow obscure stripes; these extend forward dorsally on segments 2 and 3 and beneath the brown of the sides there are confluent yellow spots below on these same segments. Appendages blackish.

Called by the senior author ('01) "Another handsome, graceful, well proportioned insect of very swift flight," and reported by Brimley ('03) as ". . . . flying over marshes and standing water, the largest and most sluggish of the Libellulas." Found about lakes and ponds from June to September (Muttkowski '08).

206. Libellula axillena Westwood

Wstwd. '37, p. 47, fig. 1: Mtk. Cat. p. 136.

Length 57 mm. Expanse 90 mm.   **Pa. to Fla. and La.**

A fine large species with slender abdomen. Face obscure yellowish, darkening with age (except at sides) and becoming rich metallic purple on labrum and top of frons. Bilobed tip of vertex yellow. Occiput olivaceous. Thorax brown and yellow, becoming pruinose blue above with age; front, brown with median yellow stripe; sides brown rather extensively above the legs and below the wing roots; with yellow extending along the middle from the collar to and upon the abdomen. There is a half stripe of brown (stripe 5) on the last lateral suture above. Legs black with yellow bases. Wings spotted with brown, as shown in figure; stigma black. Basal abdominal segments with middorsal, midlateral and midventral stripes of brown, the 2 former narrowly connected by brown lines on the carinae. Segments 4–8 or 9 with a broad pale stripe above, bordering the lateral margin. Appendages blackish.

44. PLATHEMIS Hagen

White-tails

In this genus the sexes are very differently colored. The males having but two, the females three brown patches on the wings, and these differently proportioned. The male has a pair of hooks on the ventral side of the first abdominal segment. There are three yellow spots in a vertical row on the occipt behind the eyes. The genus is otherwise similar to Libellula.

The nymph (Ndm. '01, p. 536) is like that of Libellula except that the head is widest behind the eyes, and the front border of the median lobe of the labium is crenulate.

KEY TO THE SPECIES

Adults

Male with a median cross band on the wings of a uniform brown color....................................**lydia**, p. 229

Male with a median cross band on the wings divided by a paler area.....................................**subornata**, p. 230

207. Plathemis lydia Drury

Drury 1773: Mtk. Cat. p. 142: Ris '10, p. 261: Howe '20, p. 74: Garm. '27, p. 255.

Syn: trimaculata De Geer.

Length 47 mm. Expanse 68 mm.   **N. F. and B. C. to Ark., N. C. and Calif.**

A very common and widely distributed species in which the wings of the two sexes differ markedly in coloration. Face and vertex yellowish brown, shining, with a broad black stripe between. Occiput brownish.

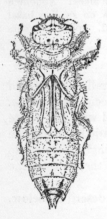

Thorax obscure brownish, clothed with short pubescence; sides blackish inferiorly and marked by two very oblique yellowish white streaks that are very variable in distinctness and some times interrupted where they cross the suture, best defined at their lower end and tapering upward. Legs brownish, darkening with age; tarsi and spines blackish. Wings with a conspicuous pattern of brown, differing in the two sexes, as shown in the figures on p. 200. Behind the broad basal spot of the hind wing of the male, a large chalky white triangle develops with age. Abdomen brown, slowly tapering beyond segment 3 in the male, parallel sided to 8 in the female, showing a row of oblique pale spots low down on sides of segments 3–9. These are less distinct in the male and become wholly obscured with age by pruinosity.

FIG. 41. The nymph of the White-tail skimmer, *Plathemis lydia.*

"Common from April to October, having the longest seasonal range of any of our dragonflies" (Brimley '03, p. 157).

"This species is a constant companion of *L. pulchella.* Often they have a definite beat along some bend in the shore or around beds of bulrushes where they race up and down the banks, now and then meeting with a rustle of wings" (Whed. '14, p. 100).

This is a most familiar skimmer. It divides its time between hovering over the water surface and perching on shore. The males are much in evidence. They rest with head low and tail elevated, and move the wings forward and downward into a drooping position by a succession of jerks. When old and pruinose they seem to prefer whitish perches, and will sometimes settle upon the rim of a collector's white net or on his shirt sleeve or straw hat. They search ordinarily for the females and fly after them with great swiftness when discovered.

The females slip in and out of sheltered places along shore, finding with difficulty a little freedom from molestation while laying their eggs. They hover low over the water, marking time, dipping down to the surface many times in nearly the same place, liberating 25 to 50 eggs at each descent.

208. Plathemis subornata Hagen

Hag. '61, p. 149: Mtk. Cat. p. 142: Ris '10, p. 263: Ndm. '23, p. 130: Smn. '26, p. 35.

Length 45 mm. Expanse 70 mm.   **Kans. and Utah to Tex. and Calif.**

Face obscure brownish. Labrum, vertex, and cross stripe through ocelli, black. Thorax brownish with pale pubescence; the dark sides bear yellowish oblique stripes that are composed each of rows of 2 or 3 yellowish spots. Legs black. Wings as shown in accompanying figure; entire area before broad brown cross bands becoming pruinose around basal spots; stigma black. Abdomen blackish with lateral yellowish spots both above and below on swollen basal segments. These pale spots narrow and disappear to rearward. Apical segments and appendages black.

45. Cannacria Kirby

Slender and elongate dragonflies with abdomen laterally compressed on the three basal segments, scarcely widened as seen from above. Legs slender, hind femora spineless and thinly fringed with soft white hairs. Venation as indicated in key to the genera. Radial and median planate unusually well defined at outer end where strongly attached to veins; the upper of the 2 rows of subtended cells twice the width of the lower.

Includes one South American species and the one described below. Habits and nymph unknown.

209. Cannacria gravida Calvert

Calv. '90. p. 35: Mtk. Cat. p. 170 (as *Brachymesia*): Ris '12, p. 735.

Length 50 mm. Expanse 82 mm.   **Md. to Fla. and Tex.**

A slender brownish species having usually a brownish spot on the middle of the wing. Face black and white. Labrum and frons black; sides of postclypeus white; intervening area variable, more or less spread over with brownish. Vertex and occiput blackish clothed with thin brown hairs. Thorax and the swollen base of the abdomen rusty brownish, darker about the bases of the appendages and in the depths of the lateral sutures, but without stripes. Legs brown, paler basally. Wings hyaline, shining, slender, tinged with amber yellow beyond the nodus and generally bearing a large brownish spot of very variable extent which extends from the nodus well out towards the stigma and fades out towards the edges. The costal strip, amber yellow when stripe not developed; stigma whitish or pale yellow; veins brown. Abdomen long and slender, the paler basal segments compressed; 2 and 3 carinate; middorsal band of black on 3 to 9, dilated at apex of each segment. In old specimens these segments appear entirely black; 10 and appendages paler.

46. SYMPETRUM Newman

Syn: Diplax; Brachymesia

Topers

These are rather small, autumnal dragonflies of brilliant red, mature coloration. The teneral color is usually olivaceous. Stripes of white (reduced sometimes to inferior spots) often appear upon the sides of the thorax, and sometimes, narrower ones upon the front, in teneral specimens; but these are apt to wholly disappear with age, the entire thorax becoming reddish brown. Only in *S. danae* (of our species) is it conspicuously striped with black. The sides of abdominal segments 3 to 9 bear a line of black triangles which tend to overspread the dorsum with black, most widely on segment 8. The wings are hyaline, with flavescent tinge at the base, of very variable extent,

FIG. 42. Nymph of *Sympetrum rubicundulum*.

The Known Nymphs

Species	Length	Lat. sp. of 8	Lat. sp. of 9	Dorsal hooks	Lat. set.	Ment. set.	Described by
assimilatum	16		1/3 of 9	4–8	9	12	Ndm. '01, p. 524
corruptum	19	0	rud.	0	13–14	17	Ndm. '03, p. 271
costiferum	14 1/2	1/2 of 8	2/3 of 9	sharp 6–8	10–12	13–18	Ndm. '01, p. 520
danae	14			low r or 0 on 8	11–12	13–15	Walk. '17, p. 417
illotum	18	0	rud.	0	9	13	Ndm. in Byers '27, p. 71
madidum	14 1/2		equals 9	low 5–8 r on 8	12	12	Ndm. '04, p. 707
obstrusum	16	1/5 of 8	1/3 of 9	moderate 4–8	9	12	Ndm. '01, p. 524
pallipes	16–18	1/4 of 8	2/5 of 9	sharp 4–8	10–11	12–15	Walk. '14, p. 373
rubicundulum	17	1/6 of 8	1/3–1/5 of 9	low 4–8 r or 0 on 8	9	12	Ndm. '01, p. 525
semicinctum	14 1/2	1/3 of 8	exceeds 9	large 6–8	9	12	Ndm. '01, p. 524
vicinum	13	2/3 of 8	equals 9	large 6–8	9	12–13	Ndm. '01, p. 523

varying from almost none at all to half the wing extent, and the veins are often red.

These are the latest of our dragonflies in season. One of our species *S. corruptum* is sometimes taken in early spring, having hibernated as an adult. They are pond species and the swales adjacent to the shoals are the best places to find them. They fly moderately and rest frequently on the low vegetation and are not very hard to capture.

The females of some species lay their eggs upon floating masses of "blanket algae" where, exposed more or less to the air, they become infested with minute Hymenopterous parasites.

KEY TO THE SPECIES

Adults

1 Fourth abdominal segment with a median encircling ridge (in addition to the apical ridge)................................2.
  Fourth abdominal segment with only the apical ridge.........3.

2 Fore wing, antenodals 7; sides of thorax with two white stripes ....**corruptum**, p. 233
  Fore wing, antenodals 8 to 10; sides of thorax with two white spots......................................**illotum**, p. 233

3 The radial planate subtends two rows of cells...**madidum**, p. 234
  The radial planate subtends but a single row of cells..........4.

4 Expanse more than 70 mm...................**furcatum**, p. 234
  Expanse less than 60 mm.....................................5.

5 Male superior appendages with a prominent median inferior tooth; female subgenital plate bifid..............................8.
  Male superior appendages with no prominent inferior tooth (with only denticles); female subgenital plate entire or only a little emarginate...6.

6 Tibiae yellow externally.....................................7.
  Tibiae black externally....................................10.

7 Abdomen with black markings..............**ambiguum**, p. 235
  Abdomen with yellowish brown markings........**pallipes**, p. 235

8 Male bifid for a third of its length, the outer branch twice as stout as the inner..9.
  Male hamule bifid for not more than a fourth of its length, the outer branch four times as stout as the inner..**obtrusum**, p. 236

9 Wings yellow only at the roots...........**rubicundulum**, p. 236
  Wings with basal half yellow...............**assimilatum**, p. 237

10   Wings yellow only at the roots............................11.
      Wings yellow to the nodus...............**semicinctum,** p. 237

11   Legs more or less yellow................................12.
      Legs black...13.

12   Tibiae entirely yellow.....................**vicinum,** p. 238
      Tibiae striped with black on the sides........**costiferum,** p. 239

13   Male superior abdominal appendages black........**danae,** p. 239
      Male superior appendages yellow or red.........**atripes,** p. 240

210. Sympetrum corruptum Hagen

Hag. '61, p. 171: Mtk. Cat. p. 160: Ris '11, p. 678: Whed. '14, p. 101: Bethel '15, p. 119: Kndy. '17. p. 620: Garm. '27, p. 270.

Length 41 mm. Expanse 65 mm.   **B. C., N. Y. to La. and Tex.**

Face and vertex yellow with a black stripe between. Occiput tawny. Thorax tawny, with whitish pubescence; front with 2 parallel whitish stripes, and sides with 2 very much broader oblique stripes behind the 2 principle sutures, both

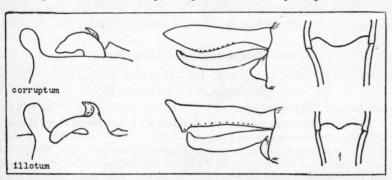

bordered with blackish at their lower ends. Legs blackish, lined externally with yellow, and with the 2 basal segments yellow; tarsi black. Wings hyaline with reddish veins and tawny stigma, darker in the middle. Abdomen olivaceous with the spots on the sides of segments 3–9 forming a diffuse blackish line, and with middorsal black spots on segments 8 and 9. Appendages black.

It squats on the bare earth of path or roadway much of the time, often with the abdomen elevated and the drooping wing tips touching the ground.

"It is one of the first dragonflies to appear in the spring, having been repeatedly taken in April" (Whed. '14, p. 101).

211. Sympetrum illotum Hagen

Hag. '61, p. 172: Mtk. Cat. p. 161: Ris '11, p. 676: Kndy. '17, p. 609: Ndm. '23, p. 130 (as *onustum* by error): Smn. '26, p. 37: Byers '27, p. 71.

Var: giluum Selys

Length 38 mm.   Expanse 62 mm.   Pac. Coast, Nev.

Face and vertex yellowish, becoming rufous above with black cross line between. Occiput tawny. Thorax reddish, clothed with tawny hairs; sides with 2 oval white spots (lower end of stripes behind the 2 principle sutures). Legs rufous with black tarsi. Wings hyaline with red veins and stigma; fuscous stripes in the base of subcostal (in the hind wing) and cubital spaces. The golden tint extends to or beyond the nodus and rearward; on the hind wing it envelopes most of the anal loop. Abdomen red, only the apical carinae of the middle segments darker. Appendages rufous.

"Usually the female of this species oviposits unaccompanied by the male but here I observed a pair working together. These copulated on the wing, then rested half a minute in copulation on a branch, when they flew about over the water, the male holding the female by the prothorax, the pair making tentative dives from an elevation of about 2 feet. After a half a minute they dropped 2 inches above the water when with a swinging motion the female dipped her abdomen in the water about 30 times, after which they made a sudden upward flight and separated, each to seat itself on a twig." (Kndy. '17, p. 609.)

212. Sympetrum madidum Hagen

Hag. '61, p. 174: Mtk. Cat. p. 162: Ris '11, p. 679: Kndy. '15, pp. 337, 345.
Syn: flavicostum Hag., *chrysoptera* Selys

Length 42 mm. Expanse 62 mm.   B. C. to Calif., Mont., Wyo. and Colo.

A fine reddish species, both wings streaked with flavescent along the radial vein. Face and vertex red with the usual black stripe, enclosing the middle ocellus and widened at the ends to enclose also the lateral ocelli. Occiput red. Thorax reddish to olive brown, with 2 whitish side stripes behind the 2 principle lateral sutures, distinct below and obsolete above. Legs black beyond the extreme base of the femora. Wings hyaline traversed lengthwise by a yellowish streak that leaves the basal costal interspaces clear, and in the hind wing spreads rearward beyond the anal triangle; stigma rufous. Abdomen rufous, paler basally, and with all carinae narrowly lined with black. Appendages reddish.

Kennedy ('15, p. 337, 345) has observed that the male and female of this species are practically never found associated together.

213. Sympetrum furcatum Hagen

Hag. '61, p. 169: Mtk. Cat. p. 170: Ris '12, p. 737 (as *Brachymesia furcata*).
Syn: australis Kirby, *smithii* Kirby

Length 45 mm. Expanse 78 mm.   Fla., Mo.

A tawny brownish species with red abdomen. Face red with margin of labrum, sides of frons, extreme apices of notched vertex, and occiput, all yellowish. Thorax obscure pale brownish, densely clothed with soft hair of same color;

without stripe. Legs blackish, paler basally. Wings hyaline, extreme base of fore wings and a slightly broader area of the hind wing (extending out to anal crossing). Costal and basal antenodals yellow; stigma tawny, between black hairs. Abdomen reddish more deeply red on the middle segments, only the extreme apices of the middle segments transversely lined with black. Appendages reddish, yellowish within, tips of forked inferiors black, thinly clothed with blackish hairs.

214. Sympetrum ambiguum Rambur

Ramb. '42, p. 106: Mtk. Cat. p. 160: Ris '11, p. 689: Howe '20, p. 83.

Syn: albifrons Charp.

Length 37 mm. Expanse 58 mm.   Mass. and Ill. to Mo., Tex. and Ga.

Face and vertex yellowish with a narrow black stripe between. Thorax olivaceous at the sides, rufous above, bright red on the wing roots; lateral sutures and carina in teneral specimens obscurely striped with brown (interruptedly on the sides). Legs pale to knees, brownish beyond, claws blackish. Wings hyaline with brown stigma, paler at ends, with scarcely any basal flavescence. Abdomen rufous, the side spots on segments 3-9 increase in extent and overspread the dorsum on the last 2 segments. Appendages yellowish.

215. Sympetrum pallipes Hagen

Hag. '74, p. 589: Mtk. Cat. p. 163: Ris '11, p. 688: Walk '14, p. 373: Byers '27, p. 71.

Length 37 mm. Expanse 61 mm.   B. C. to Colo.

Face and vertex yellow with a narrow black cross stripe between. Occiput and thorax tawny to rufous brown, scantily pubescent, darker in the depths of the sutures and on the crest, and with broad, pale oblique stripes more or less evident on the sides behind the 2 principle sutures. Legs olivaceous, becoming blackish at the joints and on the tarsi. Abdomen olivaceous to rufous with the apical carinae of the middle segments narrowly blackish. Appendages pale.

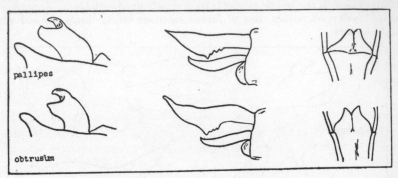

216. Sympetrum obtrusum Hagen

Hag. '67, p. 95: Mtk. Cat. p. 162: Ris '11, p. 685: Wmsn. '14, p. 456: Howe '20, p. 80: Garm. '27, p. 275.

Length 31 mm. Expanse 50 mm.   **N. H. to B. C.**

Like rubicundulum in all respects except as shown in the figures, but smaller and with the abdominal appendages tending to be black on the apical half.

Found about "lakes and rivers June to October" (Mtk. '08, p. 110).

217. Sympetrum rubicundulum Say

Say '39, p. 26: Mtk. Cat. p. 163: Ris '11, p. 682: Wmsn. '20, p. 103: Howe '20, p. 79: Ndm. '27, p. 20: Garm. '27, p. 272.

Length 33 mm. Expanse 54 mm.   **Me. and Pa. to N. D. and Wyo.**

A dainty reddish species of wide distribution. Face reddish yellow. Vertex darker, with a conspicuous black cross stripe that includes the middle ocellus.

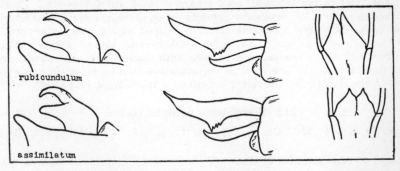

Occiput rufous. Thorax reddish brown clothed with tawny pubescence; unmarked, paler beneath. Legs black beyond base. Wings hyaline with a tinge of yellow at the extreme base (or sometimes throughout the membrane) and with a brown stigma. Abdomen reddish with a row of lateral black triangles on segments 4–9 forming a marginal stripe. Appendages reddish yellow.

Pale teneral yellowish specimens of this species begin fluttering up out of the grasses that fill the shallow waters in the upper reaches of most ponds about the latter part of June. A month later when they have assumed their brilliant red and black coloration and have become more numerous, we find them scattered everywhere. They seem most numerous however about wet meadows, where they delight to go foraging.

The female in ovipositing is accompanied by the male. He seems to direct the course and to assist in the flight. Together they descend to touch the water many times in rapid succession in nearly the same place; then a short flight, and many more descents together in a new place.

218. Sympetrum assimilatum Uhler

Uhler '57, p. 88: Mtk. Cat. p. 160: Ris '11, p. 682.

Length 40 mm. Expanse 62 mm. **N. Y. to B. C. and Neb.**

A rather large species with hyaline wings flavescent at base. Face and vertex yellowish with a black cross stripe through the middle ocellus. Occiput brown. Thorax olive brown clothed with a thin brown pubescence and sometimes obscurely striped, in which case a narrow pair on the front, and 2 broad stripes behind the principle lateral sutures all abbreviated above, appear. Legs fuscous, paler basally and beneath the front femora. Wings hyaline, flavescent to a very variable degree over the basal half; stigma brown, paler at ends. Abdomen reddish with lateral black triangles on middle segments, widened toward the apices of these segments and forming a continuous black lateral line. Appendages obscure reddish yellow.

The senior author (Ndm. '01, p. 524) found that this species at Old Forge, N. Y. "could be seen any clear morning climbing up the Sparganiums tems and transforming."

"July to September in marshes and woods." (Mtk. '08, p. 110.)

219. Sympetrum semicinctum Say

Say '39, p. 27: Mtk. Cat. p. 164: Ris '11, p. 690: Kndy. '17, p. 623: Howe '20 p. 82: Garm. '27, p. 274.

Length 31 mm. Expanse 52 mm. **Me. and Pa. to B. C.**

A very pretty reddish brown species with broad flavescent bands of variable depth of color covering more or less of the basal half of the wings. Face yellow, reddish above, narrowly cross striped with black through the middle ocellus. Thorax reddish brown clothed with brown pubescence, usually without pattern but sometimes showing narrow black lines on sutures below. Legs black beyond basal femora. Wings hyaline beyond the very broad flavescent cross band which varies in tint, especially towards the outer margin from pale yellow to brown. Abdomen reddish brown, paler basally; black at sides of apical segments, the black spreading upward on segment 8, blackest middorsally. Appendages rufous.

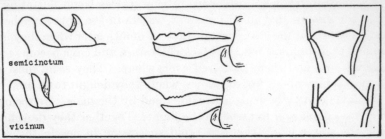

Whedon ('14, p. 101) says it is "Usually found among the low shrubs and brushes at the margins of woods near streams and ponds."

Kennedy ('17, p. 623) says it is "Common in the fields along the river. The males of this species sometimes go to sleep while seated in the sunshine, when they can be picked up by hand."

220. Sympetrum vicinum Hagen

Hag. '61, p. 175: Mtk. Cat. p. 164: Ris '11, p. 693: Davis '13, p. 27: Howe '20, p. 82: Garm. '27, p. 275.

Length 32 mm. Expanse 52 mm.   **Me. and N. C. to B. C.**

This late season species is at first yellow but later it becomes bright red. Face reddish yellow or brown with pale, short pubescence, and without color pattern. Legs pale brown with yellow tibiae. Wings hyaline with extreme base flavescent, stigma rufous. Abdomen rufous obscured with blackish at sides of middle segments. These sometimes become wholly black, but not in a distinct pattern. Appendages pale.

Davis '13 says, "We have seen them in copulation on Staten Island on Nov. 8. They are much attracted to anything bright colored, like a newspaper lying on the ground, and several may often be seen sunning themselves on such a situation. They will light on your hat if you keep quiet, and will show no inclination to fly away provided you walk about quietly."

This pretty little yellow legged autumnal species is likely to be found about every marsh-bordered pond within its range. It flits about the shore vegetation and is not at all difficult to capture with a net. The female oviposits on wet mats of club rush and blanket algae, sometimes alone, but more often held by the male. The male seems to direct the course. The pair descends swiftly and the female is swung downward, the tip of her abdomen striking the surface like a whiplash, to brush off her eggs. They fly backward a little bit as they rise. Thus they swing obliquely, up and down, many times in the same place.

Some eggs obtained in September at Ithaca hatched the following January, having been kept the while in a laboratory of the normal temperature. Doubtless under normal conditions they do not hatch before spring.

Dr. Calvert ('26, pp. 185–190) has studied the disappearance of this species in autumn at a pond in the Botanical Garden of the University of Pennsylvania. He says that "The bright red abdomen of the male lends a brilliant touch of color on sunny days of September and of the two following months. The duller brown of the female renders her less conspicuous." Observations made over 20 years give the latest data for the appearance of this species on the wing as ranging from October 17th to November 23rd. It survived minimum daily temperatures, once as low as 29°F, twice as low as 32°F.

Mr. F. R. Nevin has raised *vicinum* from eggs, laid on October 1 by females from this same pond, which hatched, in doors, from Nov. 28 to Jan. 4 and yielded imagos on May 3 to May 10, after 11 larval instars.

The nymphs are rather daintily colored with bands of black across the head including the eyes, around the femora, and across the middle of the abdominal segments. They clamber about amid the aquatic vegetation.

221. Sympetrum costiferum Hagen

Hag. '61, p. 174: Mtk. Cat. p. 161: Ris '11, p. 692: Wmsn. '14, p. 456: Howe '20, p. 81: Garm. '27, p. 271.

Length 37 mm. Expanse 60 mm.   **Me. and N. Y. to B. C. and Kans., Ga.?**

Another reddish species with blackish abdomen. Face, vertex and occiput reddish, the black cross stripe before the vertex includes both lateral and middle ocelli. Thorax olivaceous brown or rufous. without pattern, clothed with pale short pubescence. Legs pale to knees and on tibiae externally; spines and tarsi black. Wings hyaline with a faint flavescent tinge across extreme base and a long radial vein; stigma tawny with black bordering veins. Abdomen olive brown or rufous, suffused with black along the sides to form an inferior lateral stripe, and sometimes along the dorsum also of segments 4–9. Pattern very obscure. Appendages obscure reddish.

Kennedy ('15) says "I have seen thousands of this species on a telephone wire for a stretch of a mile and all facing the same way."

222. Sympetrum danae Sulzer

Sulzer 1776, p. 169: Mtk. Cat. p. 163 Ris '11. p. 646: Howe '20, p. 80: Garm. '27, p. 271.

Syn: scoticum Donovan

Length 40 mm. Expanse 50 mm.   **N. H. to B. C.**

A short blackish species with hyaline wings and a thick stigma. Face yellowish sometimes suffused with black. Cross stripe through ocelli very broad, overspreading part of vertex and frons. Thorax blackish in front and yellowish with anastomosing black stripes upon the sides; the foremost on the humeral suture

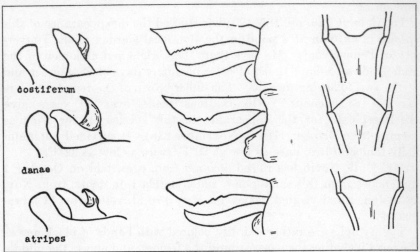

costiferum

danae

atripes

(stripe 3) and the others on the 2 lateral sutures, usually more or less confluent; from the hindmost a black streak extends to the abdomen below. Legs black. Wings hyaline with blackish stigma, sometimes with flavescent area at extreme base. Abdomen mainly black but with paler spots above and below on segment 2; a large divided one above on 3, and smaller dorsal ones on 4–7, 8. Appendages black.

223. Sympetrum atripes Hagen

Hag. '73, p. 588: Mtk. Cat. p. 160: Howe '21, p. 80.

Length 36 mm. Expanse 56 mm.   **Yellowstone**

Face and vertex reddish with broad black stripes through ocelli. Thorax olivaceous or rufous with thin tawny pubescence and lateral sutures more or less distinctly marked with narrow black lines. Legs black. Wings hyaline with a variable amount of flavescence at base (sometimes reaching nodus of hind wing); stigma reddish, bordered with black veins. Abdomen reddish, the spots at the sides of the segments forming a black stripe, the black sometimes spreads upwards and envelopes the apical segments. Appendages obscurely colored, yellowish to black.

47. Leucorrhinia Brittinger
The White-faced Skimmers

These are rather small dragonflies with blackish bodies and clear wings, with short, broad stigmas. The face is white and shining, often with the whiteness of porcelain. The thorax is blackish, with something of a pattern of blackish stripes on the paler sides when recently emerged. The abdomen is pale at base where striped with black, becoming wholly black at the end. There is little enlargement of the basal segment. The anal loop is short and broad, the heel being developed about as long as the toe.

The nymphs are smooth bodied, greenish in color and clamber in beds of submerged vegetation. There are dorsal hooks on segments 2 to 6 or 8, and lateral spines on 8 and 9, the latter never very long. The lateral setae are 10 or more, and the mental setae are still more numerous.

The Known Nymphs

Species L.	Dorsal hooks	d. h. of 7*	d. h. of 8*	Lat. sp. of 8**	Lat. sp. of 9**	Described by
frigida	2–8	=7	=8	=1/2 of 8	=9	Walk. '13, p. 168
intacta	2–8	=2/3 of 7	=2/3 of 8	=2/5 of 8	=3/5 of 9	Ndm. '01, p. 517
glacialis	2–8	=1/2 of 7	=1/3 of 8	=1/3 of 8	=1/2 of 9	Ndm. '01, p. 518.
proxima	2–8	=1/4 of 7	=1/5 of 8	=1/4 of 8	=1/3 of 9	Walk. '16, p. 420
hudsonica	2–6	0	0	=1/3 of 8	=1/4 of 8	Walk. '14, p. 275
borealis	2–6	0	0	=1/2 of 9	=1/3 of 9	Walk. '16, p. 416

* Dorsal hooks in relation to length of segment bearing them.
** Lateral spines in relation to length of segment bearing them.

This holarctic genus is represented in our fauna by half a dozen species that may be separated as follows:

KEY TO THE SPECIES (exclusive of borealis)
Adults

1 Middle abdominal segments (4–7) with pale middorsal triangles
. . . . hudsonica, p. 241
  Middle abdominal segments black. . . . . .2.
2 Abdominal segment 7 with twin dorsal spots of yellow intacta, p. 242
  Abdominal segment 7 with no twin dorsal spots of yellow. . . . .3.
3 Sides of thorax heavily clouded, not streaked. . . .glacialis, p. 243
  Sides of thorax with at least 1 distinct fuscous stripe (stripe 5)
. . . . .4.
4 Length 30 mm. . . . . .frigida, p. 243
  Length 35 mm. . . . . .proxima, p. 244

224. Leucorrhinia hudsonica Selys

Selys '50, p. 53: Mtk. Cat. p. 166: Ris '12, p. 718: Howe '20, p. 84: Garm. '27, p. 282.
Length 27 mm. Expanse 46 mm.   **N. B. to Alask., B. C. and N. H.**

This is a little brownish species with yellow costa and spotted abdomen. Face pale, vertex black except at pale tip. Occiput brown. Thorax hairy, tawny on front and a little paler on sides with only a suggestion of two broad brown stripes that widen below toward the leg bases. Legs black. Wings hyaline, costa and outer veins of stigma yellow. Basal brown streaks of both wings well developed; the broader stripe of the hind wing extending beyond the membranule. Abdomen black with sides of swollen basal segments yellow, and yellowish triangular spots on dorsum of segments 4–7. Apical segments and appendages black.

This species which according to Muttkowski ('08) is found about marshy places and Kennedy ('15) in more or less open sloughs, is described by the latter as spending "most of their time seated on the tops of aquatic plants. They copulated on the wing, the male picking up the female as she sat on some plant. The flight was short, after which the male dropped the female but hovered near, while she deposited by tapping the tip of her abdomen repeatedly on the surface of the water."

225. Leucorrhinia intacta Hagen

Johnny White-face

Hag. '61. p. 179: Mtk. Cat. p. 167: Ris '12, p. 716: Howe '20, p. 83: Garm. '27, p. 218.

Length 32 mm. Expanse 48 mm.   **Me., Pa. to Wash. and B. C.**

A fine little blackish species with a very white face and twin spots of yellow on the seventh abdominal segment. Face pale, becoming pearly white with age, up to the very black streak that envelopes the frons. Occiput yellowish in middle with black edges and a fringe of long tawny hairs that is continued behind the eyes. Thorax villous with tawny hairs which hide a very obscure pattern of stripes; becoming wholly black with age. Carina at first pale and sides yellowish with diffuse blackish streaks following the 3 lateral sutures. Legs black. Wings hyaline with a short broad stigma and a whitish touch on the costa just beyond. Extreme base of both wings with 2 short blackish streaks in the subcostal and cubital spaces; the latter, in the hind wing, spreading rearward along the membranule. The moderately swollen basal segments of the abdomen mostly pale with 2 brownish streaks each side twice connected on the carinae; segments 3–10 black with a rather conspicuous pair of yellow spots on the dorsum of 7. Appendages black.

Wilson ('12) found this dragon fly "familiarly known as 'Johnny White-face' . . . . around freshwater ponds or on side creeks; there were none on the river."

Whedon ('14) says: "they are usually very alert and agile, floating before the collector like a host of jet black ivory centered balls. When resting, the wings are thrown forward, the abdomen held high in the air and the head is kept turning watchfully from side to side."

The senior author observed the females ovipositing in two quite different ways: descending and striking the water with the tip of the abdomen while in flight after the manner most common among the Libellulidae, and at rest on some vertical stem at the surface of the water, plying with the tip of the abdomen just below the surface. In both cases the female was unaccompanied by the male.

The nymph is an alert sprawler, rather prettily marked in an intricate pattern of green and brown. Paired dots of brown underneath the abdomen are rather distinctive. Transformation commonly occurs in the forenoon, usually within a few inches of the surface of the water.

226. Leucorrhinia glacialis Hagen

Hag. '90, p. 234: Mtk. Cat. p. 166: Ris '12, p. 719: Howe '20, p. 84: Garm. '27, p. 281.

Length 36 mm. Expanse 58 mm.   **N. H. and N. Y. to Wis. and Nev.**

A dainty little species with reddish thorax and black abdomen. Face pale, greenish white, including top of frons. Vertex and occiput black. Thorax pale reddish brown and black in a clouded portion that covers the whole of the sides and is expended on the base of the abdomen. There is a pair of broad rufous bands on the front bordering a stiff broader median black tract, around which they are dilated and attingent at their upper ends. The darker streaks on the sides do not conform to the sutures; the middle one crosses them. Legs black. Wings hyaline with tawny or rufous stigma. The short brown basal streaks little developed except for the one at the anal angle of the hind wing, which is large and conspicuous. Abdomen pale on the more convex portion of the swollen basal segments. Elsewhere black, including appendages.

The senior author has written of this species ('01):

During the first week or two of adult life, before age and pruinosity have obscured its remarkably fine coloration, it is a singularly beautiful insect. One who sees only preserved specimens would not suspect this however, for then faded browns have replaced the ruby red color of the males and the brilliant yellow of the females. I well remember with what delighted surprise I greeted my first specimen. It was a young male, with a brilliant red body phalerate with jet black, a flavescent tinge beyond the basal markings of the wings, a rich red brown stigma, with a touch of yellow on the costa either side of it, and a face with the whiteness and subopaqueness of fine china. That specimen was captured the last week of June; soon afterward I found plenty of them—females as well—about a bog pond. They were flying with *Cordulia shurtleffi*, *Dorocordulia libera*, and *Lestes eurina*—a group of rare beauties.

227. Leucorrhinia frigida Hagen

Hag. '90, p. 231: Mtk. Cat. p. 166: Ris '12, p. 719: Walk. '13, p. 161: Howe '20, p. 84: Garm. '27, p. 280.

Length 30 mm. Expanse 48 mm.   **Mass., Pa., Ont., Dak. to B. C.**

A dainty little white-faced species with black abdomen the base of which becomes pruinose blue with age. Face pale, including the whole of the frons. Vertex and occiput blackish, bare, shining. Thorax thinly clothed with pale hairs, obscurely colored, blackish in front, olivaceous on sides with darker color in depths of the first and third lateral sutures (vestiges of stripes 3 and 5). Legs black. Wings hyaline with short brown stigma and yellowish costal margin, conspicuously paler just beyond the stigma and on a few adjacent longitudinal veins. Basal black markings as in *intacta*. Slightly swollen basal abdominal segments yellow, narrowly ringed with black on carinae, becoming wholly pruinose blue with age. Abdomen beyond, wholly black, including appendages.

228. Leucorrhinia proxima Calvert

Calv. '90, p. 38: Mtk. Cat. p. 167: Wlsn. '09, p. 656: Ris '12, p. 720: Walk. '00, p. 420: Howe '20, p. 85: Calv. '23, p. 88: Garm. '27, p. 284.

Length 35 mm. Expanse 56 mm.   **Me. and N. H. to B. C.**

This is a dainty little white faced species with obscure brownish hairy thorax and black abdomen. Face white with margin of labrum black. Vertex and occiput blackish with tawny hairs. Thorax densely clothed with similar longer hairs; obscure brownish in front and paler at sides with indistinct markings, only the hindermost of which (stripe 5) conforms to a lateral suture. A broad blackish area covers the lower end of the humeral suture and extends below the thorax. Legs black. Wings hyaline with tawny stigma followed by the usual pale streaks on veins and with the hinder of the basal brown streaks on the hind wing well developed to rearward along the membranule. Basal half of abdomen white hairy; the swollen basal segments mostly paler on sides, narrowly crossed with black on sutures, beyond which all is black, including appendages.

229. Leucorrhinia borealis Hagen

Hag. '90, p. 231: Mtk. Cat. p. 166: Walk. '16, p. 416: Ris '12, p. 716.

Length 38 mm. Expanse 64 mm.   **Hudson's Bay**

This species was described by comparison with the European *L. rubicunda* from which it is said to differ by having a large red spot on the dorsum of abdominal segment 8. In that species spots are present on the preceding segments only. The species is unknown to us.

48. PACHYDIPLAX Brauer

Dragonflies of medium size, olivaceous in color and striped with brown, becoming wholly pruinose blue with age.

There is a wide space without cross veins before and beneath the stigma. The space beyond the fore wing triangle is strongly narrowed toward the wing margin. Vein Cu_1 springs from the outer side of the triangle in the hind wing. There is but one species.

The nymph of Pachydiplax (Ndm. '01, p. 527) is smooth and depressed of body with wide head. It has no dorsal hooks. The superior abdominal appendages are one third shorter than the inferiors.

230. Pachydiplax longipennis Burmeister

The Blue Pirate

Burm. '39, p. 850: Mtk. Cat. p. 165: Ris '11, p. 619: Kndy. '17, p. 628: Howe
'20, p. 78: Ndm. '23, p. 130: Smn. '27, p. 36: Garm. '27, p. 277.

Length 38 mm. Expanse 64 mm.   **U. S. generally**

This is a common and widely distributed species of moderate size, striped
of body when young but becoming wholly pruinose blue with age. Face pale,
but with top of frons and vertex shining metallic green. Occiput shining brown.
Thorax nearly bare, brown in front with a pair of divergent narrow yellow stripes
abbreviated above and a pair of cross streaks below the crest which join 2 very
irregular narrow yellow antehumeral stripes; sides yellow with 3 brownish stripes
(stripes 3, 4, 5) diminishing in breadth from front to rear, and confluent above
at wing roots. Legs black, paler basally. Wings hyaline or tinged with smoky
brown before the stigma, often broadly flavescent at base with brown streaks
sometimes present in subcostal and cubital spaces of the hind wing; stigma
brown. Swollen basal abdominal segments mostly pale at sides; dorsum of
segments 2–8 with a pair of parallel pale streaks abbreviated at ends. 8–10 and
appendages blackish.

Old pruinose blue specimens look quite like old *Mesothemis simplicicollis*
but are at once distinguishable by the long space without cross veins behind
the stigma, in this species.

Adults of this species are swift of wing and somewhat difficult to
capture with a net. The males hover near the surface of the water,
darting hither and thither, meeting every newcomer, perching on a
twig and immediately quitting it; and, when 2 males meet in combat,
they have the curious habit of facing each other threateningly, then
darting upward together into the air and flying skyward, often until
lost from view.

The females are less in evidence. They rest habitually, except when
foraging or ovipositing on trees back from the shore. When ovipositing
over open water, they have a curious habit which I have not observed
in other dragonflies: they do not rise and descend again between
strokes of the abdomen against the surface of the water, but fly horizontally close to the surface and from time to time strike downward
with the abdomen alone, presumably washing off eggs. In the midst
of vegetation, however, they fly down and up again, as do other species.

The nymphs clamber about among the trash, and when grown, transform within a few inches of the margin of the water, if suitable place
be found so near; otherwise they may go a distance of several feet.
They are smooth, generally of dark color, with little pattern of color
showing, except in the transverse banding of the femora.

Williamson says ('00), "This species will frequently rest on some
twig or stem with the wings drooping and the abdomen pointing

straight up. The object to be gained by such a position is not evident, for the abdomen makes a favorite mark for passing Libellulas to nip at."

49. MESOTHEMIS Hagen*

These are clear winged dragonflies of moderate size and striking coloration. The recently emerged adults have bodies of bright green color, with the abdomen ringed with black. Old specimens become wholly hoary, pruinose blue, only the head colors remaining unchanged. The first named species is of wide distribution and, sometimes, locally, it is very abudnant. It inhabits the weed beds of clear ponds and is to be sought about their borders, where it flies intermittently, resting much on the low vegetation, or on the bare earth of some open path. It is not very hard to capture. It flies through the summer season, having a rather long period of emergence.

The nymph of this genus (Ndm. '01, p. 527) is easily recognizable among allied forms by the strongly decurved inferior abdominal appendages and by the very short, thick, stocky body with prominent green eyes.

KEY TO THE SPECIES

Adults

1   Wings hyaline; abdomen stout.............**simplicicollis**, p. 246
    Wings with a basal brownish spot; abdomen slender...........
....**plebeja,** p. 247

231. Mesothemis simplicicollis Say

Green Jacket

Say '39 p., 28: Mtk. Cat. p. 157: Whed. '14, p. 102: Ris. '11, p. 598: Howe '20, p. 77: Smn. '27, p. 35: Ndm. '23, p. 120: Garm. '27, p. 264.

Length 44 mm. Expanse 68 mm.   **U. S., Ont. to B. C.**

A clear winged species of medium size, having a body of bright green when young, the abdomen ringed with black, becoming wholly pruinose blue with age. Face and vertex green with a transverse black stripe covering the middle ocellus. Thorax green, with crest and the depths of the lateral sutures narrowly lined with blackish. Legs black beyond coxae, front femora greenish below. Wings hyaline with tawny stigma. Abdomen with a middorsal line, and an apical transverse line that widens towards the apical segments, and an inferior lateral marginal line, black. Abdomen yellowish.

This is a vigilant, if somewhat sedentary species. It squats on the bare ground, or on some floating logs or trash; or if on a twig, it

* United with Erythemis Hagen, under the latter name by some authors.

generally selects a low perch, then it waits for suitable prey to come along, and darts out upon it. Many a damsel-fly is thus snapped up unawares. At night it hangs up among the foliage of pondside or roadside weeds. The female oviposits unattended making descents to touch the surface at points wide apart.

Whedon says ('14): "One usually meets with it along the shores of lakes and ponds where it perches upon weed stems or flattens itself against a path, a dock or an old boat. Its voracious appetite keeps it continually active." This habit of squatting, Gomphus-like, was suggested by the senior author ('01) as the possible explanation of the long spines found on the hind femora.

Mr. F. G. Schaupp observed at Double Horn Creek near Shovel Mount Texas that young (teneral) specimens of this species were commonly found 500 to 600 yards distant from the stream sitting on the ground or on bushes, while the old (pruinose) specimens were always found near the water and rested on projecting stones in the stream bed.

This species abundant southward, is often of local distribution, as shown by the following observations, of Wilson ('09, p. 667).

In passing up the river . . . . 2 distinct colonies of E. simplicicollis were found. The first was 10 miles above Grafton (Ill.) where the east bank of the river was covered with hundreds of this species, including both sexes, while many were flying across the river. The other colony was 4 miles up the river, at the head of an island. Here the island seemed to be the headquarters from which the dragonflies flew out in every direction.

Williamson ('00) notes a peculiar aerial performance:

Two males . . . . flutter motionless, one a few inches in front of the other, when suddenly the rear one will rise and pass over the other, which at the same time moves in a curve downwards, backwards and then upwards. so that the former position of the two is just reversed. These motions kept up with rapidity and regularity give the observer the impression of two intersecting circles which roll along near the surface of the water.

232. Mesothemis plebeja Burmeister

Burm. '39, p. 856: Calv. '98, p. 78: Mtk. Cat. p. 158 (as *verbenata*): Ris '11, p. 603.

Length 45 mm. Expanse 70 mm. **Tex.**

A yellowish green species that becomes almost black with age. Thorax of teneral specimens yellowish with a broad black antehumeral stripe (stripe 2 of fig. 00) each side. Hind wing with a dark brown basal spot reaching the anal crossing. Stigma yellowish, membranule black. Abdomen yellowish with black carinae. Apical half of segments 4–7 and all of 8–9 black. Appendages yellowish.

50. Lepthemis Hagen

These are very elongate bright green clear winged dragonflies with the swollen base of the abdomen very much compressed, then constricted, then parallel and slender. The head is broad with bulging frons. The thorax is high and almost without color pattern. The legs are long, blackish and spiny. The stigma is large, surmounting little more than a single cell. Dr. W. T. M. Forbes reports that this big green fellow attacks other insects viciously, taking butterflies and other dragon-flies in flight almost at the mouth of the collector's net.

The single Neotropical species barely transgresses our southern border.

The nymph is unknown.

233. Lepthemis vesiculosa Fabricius

Fabr. 1775, p. 421: Mtk. Cat. p. 158: Ris '11, p. 607.

Length 57 mm. Expanse 86 mm. **Fla. Keys, Tex.**

A slender greenish species with long spinous hind legs. Face yellowish, including vertex. Thorax green, thinly clad with short tawny hairs; without stripes but with slightly darker shade of color about wing roots and leg bases. Legs black, brownish at base. Distal half of hind femur bares several extremely long, slender inferior spines. Wings hyaline, with tawny stigma between black veins. A few cells of the hind wings adjacent to membranule tinged with brown. The strongly swollen base of abdomen green, and a very slender portion posterior to it blackish with paler areas across the dorso-basal half of the middle segments. Appendages yellowish.

51. Dythemis Hagen

These are slender and graceful dragonflies having the dark thorax striped with green and brown and the abdomen blackish.

The wings are tinged with brown at base and apex. There are many antenodal cross veins, and there are but two widely separated cross veins under the stigma. South western species.

The nymphs (Ndm. '92, p. 699) are smooth, mottled green and brown, with spine like dorsal hooks on abdominal segments 3–9.

KEY TO THE SPECIES

Adults

1 Wings with only touches of brown at base and tip..**velox**, p. 249
Wings with a broad brownish basal area reaching the triangle...
....**fugax,** p. 249

234. **Dythemis velox** Hagen

Hag. '61, p. 163: Mtk. Cat. p. 172: Ris '13, p. 841: Smn. '27, p. 38.

Length 45 mm. Expanse 70 mm.   **Tex., N. Mex. and Calif.**

A slender blackish species with striped thorax and half ringed abdomen
Face yellowish darkened across labrum, postclypeus and top of frons and vertex.
Thorax brown, sinuately striped with yellow and covered with a very short,
close, brown pubescence. Collar with a fringe of longer, paler erect hairs. Front
of thorax with three nearly parallel pale stripes, the median one on carina narrowest. Sides of thorax alternately brown and yellow in streaks, a foremost pale
streak obscure and interrupted; the next two, entire and rather broad; the rearmost pale stripe nearly divided by a backward spur from the dark stripe on the
last lateral suture (stripe 5). Legs blackish, paler only at base. Wing hyaline
with a variable touch of brown on both extreme base and tip; stigma blackish.
Abdomen moderately swollen on paler basal segments, blackish and slender
beyond. Sides of 1 and 2 with narrow vertical pale stripes; side of 3 with a broad
basal pale stripe narrowed above; dorsum of 4–7 with paired pale spots, largest
and plainest on 7; 9, 10 and appendages blackish.

At Double Horn Creek near Shovel Mount Texas Mr. F. G. Schaupp
observed the habits of this species. He says of it (*in litteris*):
"It sits on tall dry stems, perching, with the hinder half of the abdomen lifted high into the air. It deserves its name (*velox*, swift) by
full right (it might be *velocissima*). It flies off before you are near;
but it invariably returns to the same place, even after several attempts
have been made to catch it. It may take ten minutes for returning,
coming into the collector's neighborhood frequently, but keeping always at a safe distance."

235. **Dythemis fugax** Hagen

Hag. '61, p. 163: Mtk. Cat. p. 171: Ris '13, p. 839.

Length 48 mm. Expanse 75 mm.   **Texas**

A fine brownish species with half ringed abdomen and basally brown-spotted
wings. Face pale, becoming reddish with age, including frons. Thorax nearly
bare, pubescence very short except for long, erect, pale fringe on collar. Front of
thorax with scarcely a trace of pale stripes; sides brown, with 3 obscure pale
stripes of which the middle one is broader, and the rear one dilated at upper
end. Legs blackish, paler at base. Wings hyaline except for a rich brown cross
band that extends just beyond the arculus in both wings, and a touch of brown
on the extreme apex. Stigma black. The slightly swollen basal abdominal segments are mostly yellow, ringed with black on the carinae; remainder of abdomen
blackish with yellow spots. Paired pale spots of dorsum in fours on segments
3–6; single on 7, and larger and more conspicuous. 9, 10 and appendages
black.

52. BRECHMORHOGA Kirby

Large dragonflies of hoary appearance due to a short grayish pubescence that covers head and body. A single Sonoran species enters our southwestern border. Its nymph is unknown.

236. Brechmorhoga mendax Hagen

Hag. '61, p. 164: Mtk. Cat. p. 174: Ris '13, p. 861: Kndy. '17, p. 605, 627.
Length 57 mm. Expanse 88 mm.   **Tex., Calif.**

A rather stout grayish species with clear wings and a half ringed abdomen. Face yellow, including vertex, clothed with short whitish pubescence. Thorax clothed with a similar longer pubescence and with the erect fringe of white hairs on the collar. Front of thorax with 2 broad brown stripes beside the pale carina, abbreviated above. Sides with a broad brown stripe upon the humeral suture (stripes 2 and 3) and 2 additional stripes on the succeeding suture (4 and 5), confluent above, all on a yellow ground. Legs brown, paler at base and on front femora to knees externally. Wings hyaline with a short black stigma and a tinge of brownish on extreme base, broader on hind wings. Abdomen mostly pale on moderately swollen basal segments, blackish beyond; 2 and 3 narrowly annulate with black on carina; 3 and 7 with large diffuse, dorsal, paired spots, largest on 7. There is a touch of yellow at sides of 8 and 9. 10 and appendages black.

Kennedy ('17) says of them: "These usually had short beats in the shade of the occasional large willow trees that grew on the gravel beaches."

"The males were taken while flying on short beats over the stream. The female was captured while cutting S's and figure 8's through a swarm of small Diptera. She was indifferent to several passes I made at her before I succeeded in netting her. This species is the most graceful on the wing of any odonate with which I am familiar. Frequently they fly with a swinging mayfly-like motion. In the heat of the day they floated around among the tree tops."

53. PALTOTHEMIS Karsch

Large rusty red dragonflies with strongly tapered abdomen. The wings are very broad at the base and pointed at the apex. The stigma is rather small, its outer end a little more oblique than the inner. The triangle of the fore wing points inward, vein Cu being strongly bent. The toe of the anal loop is long and narrow.

The nymphs (Ndm. '04, p. 699) are very smooth and very dark colored. There are low dorsal hooks on abdominal segments 2 to 6, diminishing in size to rearward. The lateral spines on 8 and 9 are short, sharp and straight. The teeth on the front border of the lateral lobes of the labium are separated by deep notches.

237. Paltothemis lineatipes Karsch

Karsch '90, p. 362: Mtk. Cat. p. 173: Ris '13, p. 846.

Length 50 mm. Expanse 90 mm.   **S.W. States, Tex.**

This is a fine large reddish, broad-winged species. Face pale, becoming reddish with age, including the vertex, especially in the male. Frons bare, shining. Thorax thinly clothed with short pale pubescence; collar with erect fringe of long whitish hairs. Front of thorax brown; sides with roundish spots of deeper brown in front of humeral suture above and below. Rearward on the olivaceous sides there are three stripes of brown of very irregular outline, two on the lateral (stripes 4 and 5) and a third (confluent below with 5) on the infero-lateral margin, abbreviated above. The slightly swollen basal segments of the abdomen are pale or rufous dorsally, and blackish ventrally, with narrow cross lines of black on the carinae; the slowly widened segments beyond are more extensively blackish with basal and apical cross streaks of deeper black; diffluent to front and rear towards middle of segments. Segment 10 narrower, partly pale. Appendages obscure yellowish brown.

54. PANTALA Hagen

These are large strong flying dragonflies of brownish coloration with an overcast of red when fully mature. The face is pale. The thorax is thinly hairy without color pattern. The wings are broad at base and pointed at apex with trapezoidal stigma; the markings are restricted to the base of the hinder pair. The abdomen is moderately swollen at base and there are extra transverse carinae upon segments 2–5. The wings are extremely broad at the base and pointed at the apex. Veins M_2 and R_s are very strongly undulate. Vein M_4 at its outer curvature bends sharply towards M_3. The straight portion of vein M_2 at the base is very strong and borders a long patella cell, and the adjacent anal border is richly veined.

The nymphs of this genus are smooth and depressed with very wide head and laterally prominent eyes. The abdomen has long, lateral spines and no dorsal hooks. The superior abdominal appendages are as long as the inferiors.

Nymphs

Species	Length	Lateral setae	Mental setae	Described by
hymenea	28	15	16	Kndy. '23, p. 37
flavescens	26	12–14	15	Cabot '90, p. 43,

KEY TO THE SPECIES
Adults

1 Wings with a brown spot at the anal angle.....**hymenea**, p. 252
   Wings with no distinct brown spot at the anal angle...........
   ....**flavescens**, p. 252

238. Pantala hymenea Say

Say '39, p. 19: Mtk. Cat. p. 178: Ris '13, p. 921: Wlsn. '12, p. 194: Kndy. '23
p. 36: Garm. '27, p. 294.

Length 50 mm.   Expanse 90 mm.   **Pa. to Wis. to Fla. and N. Mex.**

A handsome brown species with conspicuous basal brown spots on the hind
wing. Face pale, becoming reddish with age, including most of frons. Occiput
brown, bare. Thorax tawny with short pubescence of same color; no pattern of
stripes. Legs brown except inferiorly. Wings hyaline with rufous stigma bordered
with black veins, extreme tips touched with brown and a brown basal spot of
form shown in figure 00. Abdomen brown narrowly cross lined with black on
supernumerary sutures of segments 2–5, then becoming blackened on sides of
6 and 7, and broadly so on dorsum of 8, 9, and 10. Appendages pale.

239. Pantala flavescens Fabricius

The Globe-skimmer

Fabr. 1798, p. 285: Mtk. Cat. p. 177: Ris '13, p. 917: Howe '20, p. 89: Garm.
'27, p. 293.

Length 52 mm.   Expanse 92 mm.   **N. Am.**

This is a fine strong flying cosmopolitan species. Face pale, including vertex,
with a narrow black cross stripe through the middle ocellus. Occiput shining
yellow. Thorax tawny yellow without stripes but with 3 black crescentic spots
above leg bases. Clothed with short tawny golden pubescence. Legs yellow at
base, black lined beyond to the wholly black tarsi. Wings hyaline with yellowish
stigma and reddish veins; the base of the broad hind wings close veined with
yellow. Abdomen yellowish, cross lined on the carinae of 2–5, becoming obscure
on 6 and 7, appearing as black middorsal spots on 10. Appendages brown.

This cosmopolitan species is reported not only from all parts of the
globe but from nearly all varieties of habitat. Muttkowski ('08) has
found it flying from July to September near rivers, lakes, ponds, in
woods, and in open places. Davis ('13) has seen it flying in great
numbers over an oat field, and has even observed a female ovipositing
in a ditch of brackish water by the roadside.

55. MACRODIPLAX Brauer

This is a tropical genus of two species, one old world and one American, the latter barely within our southern limits. The venation is
open. Triangles open; cross veins few; antenodals seven, and a long
vacant space before the stigma. Reverse vein extremely oblique. Two
rows of cells beyond the triangle. Radial and median planate subtend
one cell row in a well circumscribed series.

240. Macrodiplax balteata Hagen

Hag. '61, p. 140: '90, p. 383: Mtk. Cat. p. 183: Ris '13, p. 1038
Length 37 mm.   Expanse 67 mm.   **Tex., Fla. Keys**

This is a clear winged species that has the extreme bases of the wings spotted with dark brown. Face olive brown with the labrum darker. Thorax reddish, golden brown clothed with long, thick yellowish gray hairs with traces of black on the humeral suture, below the spiracle, and in the depths of the third lateral suture. Legs obscure red brown, paler basally. Wings broad at the base and pointed at the apex, with dark brown spots on the extreme base, the spot on the hind wing larger, rounded externally, reaching almost to the triangle. Abdomen reddish brown also, with a diffuse blackish middorsal band on segments 2 to 7, greatly widened on 7. 8 to 10 and appendages black.

56. TRAMEA Hagen

The Raggedy Skimmers

These are elegant strong flying dragonflies with conspicuous irregular bands of brown across the base of the hind wings. The eyes are very large; the face is pale. The thorax is nearly uniform brown in color. The abdomen is much swollen on the basal segments where ringed with extra transverse carinae. It is strongly tapered beyond the base and blackened dorsally, terminating with long slender appendages. Wings are externally broad at base, pointed at apex. Some of the cells bordering vein M_1 before the stigma are transversely elongated. The triangle of the fore wings is very narrow and followed by four rows of cells. The anal loop is long, narrow and sinuous.

The nymphs are smooth and broadly depressed with wide heads, laterally prominent eyes and very long spines at the end of the abdomen. There are no dorsal hooks. The teeth on the lateral lobes of the labium are hardly more than crenulations of the border.

The nymphs of North American forms seem to be lacking in good specific characters. Three of them were rather inadequately characterized by Cabot ('90, pp. 45 and 46). Recently they have been carefully studied by Dr. Calvert, ('28, p. 29).

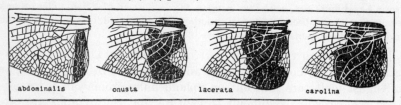

abdominalis onusta lacerata carolina

KEY TO THE SPECIES

Adults

1 Brown band of hind wing covering the triangle..............2.
   Brown band of hind wing not covering the triangle............
   ....**abdominalis, p. 256**

241. Tramea virginia Rambur

Ramb. '42, p. 33: Mtk. Cat. p. 181: Ris '13, p. 978.
Length 53 mm.   Expanse 104 mm.   **Va.?**

Reddish brown in front above, and top of vertex brassy purple. Thorax obscure brownish. Legs black, paler basally. Wings hyaline with a touch of yellow at extreme base of front wings and basal fourth of hind wings blackish brown, veined with yellow and the brown surrounded with yellow and with a large yellowish hyaline spot upon the middle of the hind margin. Stigma brownish, membranule white.

This species is doubtfully included here. Dr. Ris thinks the label "*Amer. sept.*" on the type specimen was in error.

242. Tramea lacerata Hagen

Hag. '61, p. 145: Mtk. Cat. p. 180: Ris '13, p. 998: Dav. '13, p. 28: Kndy. '17, p. 628: Howe '20, p. 88: Ndm. '23, p. 130: Smn. '27, p. 31: Garm. '27, p. 291.
Length 52 mm.   Expanse 94 mm.   **N. Y. and S. Dak. to Calif. and Fla.**

This is a very handsome broad winged, blackish, strong-flying species. Face pale, darker on labrum, metallic violet on top of frons and whole of vertex and occiput also metallic. Thorax scantily clothed with short whitish pubescence; obscure brown without distinct pattern; sides somewhat paler. Legs blackish. Wings hyaline, broad at base and pointed at apex with trapezoidal stigma and brown basal markings, as shown in figure 00. Abdomen blackish, paler on basal segments with an obscure yellowish middorsal spot on middle segments, plainest on 7. Apical segments and appendages black.

It flies through the greater part of the season. The pairs are often seen coursing the borders of ponds and ovipositing in early spring, and in August males are seen out on upland miles from water, foraging. They are exceedingly difficult to capture; but the nymphs are often found quite abundantly and are easily reared.

243. Tramea onusta Hagen

Hag. '61, p. 144: Mtk. Cat. p. 181: Ris '13, p. 996: Smn. '27, p. 31: Byers '27, p. 72.
Length 45 mm.   Expanse 80 mm.   **Ohio and Ill. to Fla. and Calif.**

A fine brown species with reddish face and black spotted tip of abdomen. Face, including vertex, pale, becoming reddish with age; a distinct black cross stripe between, enclosing middle ocellus. Occiput brown. Thorax thinly hairy with uniform darker brown front and paler sides that show dark streaks only in the bottom of the lateral sutures (stripes 3 and 5). Legs brown beyond yellowish bases of femora; front femora pale to knees. Wings hyaline with reddish veins and stigma, and a brown basal, jagged spot, of form shown in figure 00. Abdomen pale brown with large black middorsal spots on segments 7-10; on 10 extended below. Appendages yellow with blackish tips.

This is the species whose very pretty aerial egg-laying performances are described in our introductory chapter (see p. 26). The senior author had repeated opportunities for observing these at a pond near Laguna Beach in Southern California. Between egg-laying flights the adults flew constantly about the shores of the pond, in and out among the bulrushes, often almost, but never quite, within reach of the collectors net. Floating along on the planing surfaces of its broad hind wings its flight is swift and sure and very graceful.

244. Tramea carolina Linneus

Linne. '63, p. 28: Mtk. Cat. p. 179: Davis '98, p. 197: '13, p. 28: Ris '13, p. 997: Howe '20, p. 88: Garm. '27, p. 290.

Length 48 mm. Expanse 84 mm.   **Mass. to La. and Fla.**

A handsome reddish brown species with black tipped abdomen. Face pale, becoming darker on labrum, top of frons and vertex, with age. Occiput brown, hairy. Thorax rather densely clothed with pale pubescence; uniform brown in color, without stripes; sutures of sides indistinct. Legs brown, reddish to middle of femora. Wings hyaline with reddish veins and stigma, and a broad basal brown spot on the hind wings, of form shown in figure 00. Abdomen reddish brown, without color pattern basally, segments blackened towards apex, 8, 9 and 10 being mostly black. Appendages pale, slightly darkened at tips.

". . . . a male *Tramea carolina* was flying over one of the . . . . ponds. Soon a female came and commenced dipping her abdomen into the water. In a moment she was seized by the male and they flew away. In half an hour they were back and went flying about together, the male now and then suddenly letting go his hold and with equal rapidity catching the female again by the neck. Other male dragonflies flew after them and when the female stopped to lay eggs, they annoyed her considerably. The chief among the disturbers was a *Libellula basalis*. After a time the male Tramea left his mate and she was quickly seized by the aforesaid *Libellula basalis*, after which they flew about together for a considerable time. After letting go his hold once and flying down the pond, the *L. basalis* returned and seized the Tramea a second time." (Davis '98, p. 197.)

245. **Tramea abdominalis** Rambur

Ramb. '42, p. 37: Mtk. Cat. p. 179: Ris '13, p. 994: Howe '20, p. 88: Garm. '27, p. 290.

Length 47 mm. Expanse 92 mm.   **Tenn. to Fla.**

This is a rather slender species with tawny thorax and red abdomen and a basal brown streak across the hind wing. Face pale except for a very narrow edging of black on the labrum, becoming reddish above. Vertex reddish. Thorax obscure, densely clothed with tawny hairs, without distinct color pattern. Legs slender, black except at base. Wings hyaline with reddish brown stigma and veins; the brown cross band of the hind wing extends from Cu to the hind margin; it is bounded externally by vein A_2 and it is emarginate internally by an oval clear spot on the inner wing margin. Abdomen reddish, suffused with blackish on dorsum of segments 8, 9 and 10. Appendages black with reddish bases.

SUBORDER ZYGOPTERA

Damselflies

Insects of slender stature. Head transversely elongated. Eyes wide apart, separated on the top of the head by more than their own horizontal diameter, and directed laterally. Fore and hind wings similar in form, folded vertically above the back when at rest (held obliquely upward in Lestes). Wing with a simple quadrangle instead of triangle and supra-triangle, and the vein *Cu* not sharply bent between the arculus and its fork. Middle lobe of labium deeply cleft. Male with four terminal abdominal appendages, there being a pair of inferiors. Female with a well developed ovipositor.

The nymphs have three caudal gills that are more or less plate like, appended to the end of the abdomen, and the slender body tapers from the head backward.

KEY TO THE FAMILIES

Adults

1 Antenodal cross veins numerous; wings not stalked............
....**Agrionidae**, p. 258
  Antenodal cross veins two; wings stalked.**Coenagrionidae**, p. 267

Nymphs

1 Basal joint of antenna very long; labium with a deep and wide
    median cleft.............................**Agrionidae**, p. 258
  Basal joint of antenna short; labium entire, or nearly so........
...................................**Coenagrionidae**, p. 267

Family AGRIONIDAE

These are broad winged damselflies. The wings are not stalked (i.e. the membranous area behind the anal vein extends to the wing base). The quadrangle is long, parallel sided, and traversed by a number of cross veins. There are numerous antenodal cross veins. There is no brace vein to the stigma. The colors of the body are highly metallic.

The nymphs are very long legged, stream inhabiting, slender creatures that cling to roots and trash in the edges of the current. The basal joint of the antenna is longer than the six succeeding segments taken together. The deep median cleft of the labium is diamond shaped. The gills are thick and ridged longitudinally. There are no raptorial setae on the labium.

The adults of this family have been called the "Birds of Paradise amongst Odonata." In our fauna there are but two genera, separable as follows:

KEY TO THE GENERA

Adults

1 The space before the arculus free from cross veins..**Agrion**, p. 259
   The space before the arculus with cross veins...**Hetaerina**, p. 262

Nymphs

1 Middle lobe of labium cleft far below base of lateral lobes......
   ....**Agrion**, p. 259
   Middle lobe of labium cleft only to base of lateral lobes........
   ....**Hetaerina**, p. 263

57. AGRION Fabricius

Syn: Calopteryx

Black Wings

These are elegant bronzy green damselflies with broad wings, variously cross banded with brown. The bodies are wholly metallic green; the legs are long and black and spiny. There is no color pattern except on the wings. The stigma is wanting in the male and very irregular in the female, being traversed by irregular cross veins. The wings have abundant venation with many short intercalated sectors between the principal veins towards the wing margin. The quadrangle is long and narrow and traversed by many cross veins. The two branches of the median vein are fused with R_1 after their departure from the arculus.

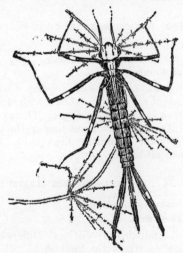

FIG. 43. Nymph of *Agrion maculatum*.

The flight of these damselflies is slow and wavering, butterfly-like, fluttering from one resting place to another, by the waterside. The female oviposits unattended.

The nymphs (Ndm. '03, p. 224) cling to roots and stems swaying in the current. They are long legged, stiff, awkward creatures that move but little from place to place. Two of our species have been reared: *A. maculata*, which has the basal segment of the antennae as long as the head is wide; and *A. aequabile*, which has it a third longer. Another, *A.*

angustipenne supposition, differs strikingly in having the middle gill but three fourths as long as the lateral gills, and broadly dilated toward the tip.

KEY TO THE SPECIES

Adults

1 Wings hyaline, not banded with brown.....**angustipenne, p.** 260
   Wings with apices only, banded with brown...............2.
   Wings all brown..........................**maculatum, p.** 261
2 Apical brown bands on hind wing only..........**amatum, p.** 260
   Apical brown bands on both wings.........................3.
3 Apical brown bands of two wings of equal width.............4.
   Apical brown bands wider on hind than on fore wing..........
   ....**aequabile, p.** 260
4 Apical bands covering one fourth of wing.....**dimidiatum, p.** 261
   Apical bands covering one sixth of wing.........**apicale, p.** 261

246. Agrion angustipenne Selys

Selys '53, p. 9: Mtk. Cat. p. 28.
Syn: elegans Hag.
Length 56 mm. Expanse 80 mm.   **Pa. to Ga.**

An elegant bronzy green species with shining wings faintly tinted with yellowish. Face green except for a yellow labrum with black front border. There is an oblique yellow streak below each antenna. Thorax shining metallic green in front, yellowish beneath, the yellow extending up the third lateral suture and covering the junction with the abdomen. Legs black. Costa green, stigma of female yellow. Abdomen all bronzy green.

247. Agrion amatum Hagen

Hag. '90, p. 244: Mtk. Cat. p. 28: Garm. '27, p. 111.
Length 56 mm. Expanse 80 mm.   **N. H. to N. C.**

Similar to the preceding; doubtfully distinct. Differs by having a pale brown patch covering the apical fourth of the hind wing. The green of the dorsum changing to brilliant irridescent blue in certain lights.

248. Agrion aequabile Say

Say '39, p. 33: Mtk. Cat. p. 27: Ckll. '13, p. 173: Kndy. '15, p. 338: '17, p. 484: Garm. '17, p. 467: Kndy. '18, p. 406: Garm. '27, p. 109: Walk. '18, p. 410.
Syn: virginiana Selys, *Var: hudsonicum* Hag., *yakima* Hag., *coloradicum*
Ckll., *californicum* Kndy.
Length 50 mm. Expanse 66 mm.   **Ont. and Iowa to Me. and N. Y.**

This is a broad winged species of metallic green hue with wing tips unequally covered with brown. Face greenish with black labrum. Antennae black. Thorax metallic bluish green with narrow black lines on all sutures and lines of paler about the wings roots and behind the leg bases. Legs black. Wings with the brown areas of the tip covering one fourth of the length of the fore wing and one third of that of the hind wing; inner margin of the brown diffuse. Costa black; stigma of female white. Abdomen metallic bluish green with black appendages.

"While often found in company with *maculata*, *aequabilis* prefers the larger streams, and is considerably warier and swifter of flight than its congener." (Walk. '08, p. 3.)

This species "oviposits by inserting the eggs under the water in willow roots. She is unaccompanied by the male but remains indifferent as various males hover over her." (Kndy. '15, p. 338.)

249. Agrion dimidiatum Burmeister

Burm. '39, p. 829: Mtk. Cat. p. 28.
              Syn: cognata Ramb., *syriaca* Ramb.
Length 46 mm. Expanse 54 mm.   **Mass., Del. to Ky., Fla. and Mich.**

A dainty little metallic greenish blue species with black wing tips. Face metallic with gray hair fringes and black antennae. Thorax metallic with all the sutures black. Venter black. Legs black. Wings with blue costa; apical fourth brownish black with straight, well defined inner margin; stigma of female white.

250. Agrion apicale Burmeister

Burm. '39: p. 827: Mtk. Cat. p. 29: Garm. '27, p. 111.
Length 46 mm. Expanse 54 mm.   **Mass., Pa. to Mich.**

Similar to the preceding species, appearing to differ only in that the brown spot at the tip of the wings covers only about a sixth of their length.

251. Agrion maculatum Beauvais

Beauv. '05, p. 85: Mtk. Cat. p. 29: Walk. '07, p. 1: Davis '13, p. 13: Whed. '14, p. 90: Garm. '17, p. 469: Holl. '22, p. 117: Garm. '27, p. 112.
    Syn: virginica Westwood, *materna* Say, *opaca* Say, *holosericea* Burm., *papilonacea* Burm., *virgo* Drury.
Length 42 mm. Expanse 64 mm.   **Ont. and Me. to Fla. and Tex.**

This is the common widespread species that has the wings wholly suffused with blackish, lustrous, shining black in the adult male, and the body wholly metallic green, including face and top of head. The thoracic sutures are black. The wings show variable small basal areas that are subhyaline. The costal edge is metallic; the stigma of the female is white and the general coloration paler.

Whedon ('14, p. 90) says: "This very conspicuous damselfly is to be found along streams, generally the smaller ones, weakly fluttering over the ripples at the water's edge or perching on the vegetation within a foot or two of the surface. Not infrequently numbers of them rest among the taller grasses of the shady flood plains some distance from the water. Though sometimes taken about ponds they are usually much less plentiful there.   They are especially fond of small streams over-shadowed by willows and wild cucumber vines."

The flight of this familiar species is halting and irregular, butterfly-like, with frequent shiftings of level, up and down. Adult males resting on the green foliage of some drooping streamside leafy spray in the sun, slowly open their elegant wings, and then quickly snap them closed, displaying all their gorgeous reflections, as if in ecstasy. The females back down into the water only the length of the abdomen in laying their eggs, and insert them into either green herbage or soft rotten sticks, always where the water is flowing.

Davis ('13) writes that it is

Common along brooks in June, July and August. and generally distributed. This dragonfly will fly from a twig or low plant by the brookside, catch a tiny insect and return to the same station again. They often come back to the same resting place many times in succession where they remain until some small insect

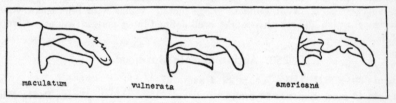

maculatum   vulnerata   americana

attracts their attention and they sally forth to catch it. In this respect they resemble the insect-catching phoebe bird and its relatives. Though usually a slow flyer this species often indulges, when two males happen to meet, in a very rapid aerial dance and at such times their bright colors show to the best advantage. They will advance against each other, dodge or recede, with remarkable rapidity and grace, but neither of the combatants ever appears to be injured. It seemed to be more of an endurance test.

58. HETAERINA Hagen

Ruby Spots

These are beautiful, slender, bronzy brown damselflies, conspicuously marked in the male sex by a broad red spot at the wing base. The entire dorsum is bronzy brown with metallic reflections. The sides show narrow pale lines upon the sutures conjoined ventrally with the paler under side of the body. The legs are slender and spiny. Wings are long and narrow with the stigma well developed but small. The arculus is strongly aslant its sectors rise from before the middle; the quadrangle is arcuate convex anteriorly and vein Cu_2 begins with a reverse curvature. The females differ by generally paler coloration, better developed stripings upon sides of thorax, little development of ruby color upon wing bases, and by a shorter and stouter abdomen.

One species, *H. americana*, is wide ranging and variable. Four other Sonoran species occur on our southern border.

The nymph (Ndm. '03, p. 227) is a long legged, sprawling creature that clings to the trash in the edges of the current in slow streams. The median lobe of the labium is cleft only to the level of the bases of the lateral lobes. The lateral margins of abdominal segments 7-9 end in small flattened lateral spines. The dorsum of the prothorax has two angulate teeth each side.

KEY TO THE SPECIES (after Calvert)

Adults (Males)

1 Basal spots red..2.
    Basal spot of fore wing red, of hind wing brown.............4.

2 Labrum partly yellow; inferior appendage equal one half of superior..3.
    Labrum wholly black; inferior appendage equals one third of superior.................................**sempronia**, p. 263

3 Wings with only a small basal median spot black.**vulnerata**, p. 263
    Wings with black across whole base..........**americana**, p. 264

4 Red spot of wing not bordered with brown......**tricolor**, p. 265
    Red spot bordered with brown....................**titia**, p. 265

252. Hetaerina sempronia Hagen

Hag. '53, p. 45: Mtk. Cat. p. 32.
Length 46 mm. Expanse 60 mm.   **Atl. Coast, Tex.**

Face metallic. Thorax dull bronze with narrow pale lines on the three lateral sutures conjoined below with the yellow of the under side. Wings hyaline, stigma black. Apex of hind wing with a large brown spot; basal spot of fore wing short, commencing at median vein, ending a little beyond the quadrangle; that of the hind wing still smaller, does not go past anal vein. Legs black. Abdomen black.

253. Hetaerina vulnerata Hagen

Hag. '53, p. 40: Mtk. Cat. p. 34.
Length 48 mm. Expanse 66 mm.   **Ariz.**

This is a black and brown and copper bronze species with bright red wing bases. The face is blackish above on postclypeus and in middle of labrum at base; else yellow. Basal segments of antennae yellow ringed with black. Prothorax copper bronze with black bordered carinae. A pale streak narrowly bordered with black upon the humeral suture; another on the midlateral suture, behind which is a pale area divided by an oblique line of brown. Legs brown, paler beneath the femora and on the outer face of the tibiae. Wings hyaline with big red basal area behind the radius and beyond the quadrangle, on the hind wing strikingly veined with white beneath. Abdomen brown or coppery, blackening toward the tip, narrowly ringed on the base of segment with the pale color of the under side.

254. Hetaerina americana Fabricius
Common Ruby Spot

Fabr. 1798, p. 287: Mtk. Cat. p. 30: Whed. '14, p. 90: Garm. '17, p. 471: Wlsn. '12, p. 196: Smn. '27, p. 9: Garm. '27, p. 114.

Syn: basalis Say, *scelerata* Walsh, *pseudamericana* Walsh, *californica* Hag., *texana* Walsh

Length 44 mm. Expanse 58 mm.   **N. Am. Generally**

A beautiful copper bronze and metallic green species with brilliant spots of ruby red covering both wing bases. Labrum bordered with yellow. Bases of antennae same color. Thorax coppery bronze with short brownish pubescence. Sutures black edged. Thorax beneath grayish, this color extending up the third lateral suture. Legs blackish with the femora beneath and the tibiae externally pale chocolate color. Wings hyaline with the red spot of the base covering an area behind the radius well out beyond the quadrangle. Stigma brown. In old specimens the veins of the hind wings are white beneath. Abdominal segments bronzy green, darkening toward the tip with narrow basal rings of gray and a longitudinal gray streak each side beneath.

The female differs by having the bright color of the wing base amber yellow instead of red, and diffusely extended outward, and by the yellow of the sides of the thorax which is more extensive.

A southern variety described by Walsh as *H. texana* seems to differ by having the pale color of the under side of the thorax extended upward along all lateral sutures and the red color of the wing bases much more extensive, covering the entire width of the wing and extending almost to the nodus.

This charming damselfly haunts the riffles in small, clear flowing streams. Males are frequently seen resting on stones or on little islands of sand in the riffles or on drooping sprays of white grass close to the water's edge, furtively opening their wings now and then as if to give just a tantalizing glimpse of the crimson spot on their bases within.

The long-legged twig-simulating nymphs crawl up the trash only a few inches above the surface of the water for transformation.

It is a late season species. Kellicott ('95, p. 198) says of it:

It is abundant along rivers and smaller streams, especially where grasses and shrubs overhang the water rippling over bars of pebbles and among boulders.

I have not seen adults until the middle of July, but they are often numerous until the middle of October, and may ordinarily be found as late as the beginning of that month. . . . . It seems it is peculiarly restricted in its range of flight. I have never observed one so far as a few rods away from the accustomed habitat —the water's edge. Another notable habit is that of congregating, sometimes in companies of hundreds. These assemblies commence in the afternoon, and do not disperse until the warmth of the following day awakens them to activity. Both sexes assemble, and they rest so compactly that I have captured seventy-five by one sweep of the net. The slender, drooping twigs of the willow, loaded with these beautiful insects, like a string of gems, present a beautiful picture. . . . . I have seen the female unattended by the male, resting on a half sub-merged log, or algal-laden rock, or water-weed, and thrusting the abdomen beneath the water, place her eggs, one by one, in the soft substance.

One of the senior author's earliest collecting trips was made to the Sangamon River in Illinois. He chased the wary ruby spots up and down the bank with a net of pink mosquito bar, with which he was equipped, capturing each one with great difficulty and labor. Then while standing, wearied, with the net under his arm, he chanced to look backward over his shoulder, and there was a fine male sitting placidly on the rim of the net! Was the pink color a lure? He held the net still in front of another and lo it promptly settled on the rim. After that collecting was easy. The males would come and perch, almost inviting capture.

255. Hetaerina tricolor Burmeister

Burm. '39, p. 827: Mtk. Cat. p. 33: Wmsn. '12, p. 101: Wlsn. '12, p. 196.
    Syn: rupinsulensis Walsh, *rupamnensis* Walsh, *Var: limbata* Selys.
Length 47 mm. Expanse 54 mm.   **Ill. and Pa. to Tex. and Fla.**

This is a dainty little brownish species with red spots on the fore wing and brown ones on the hind. Face brown, blackening upward. Thorax coppery with black middle carinae and sides obscurely and diffusely paler. Legs blackish with the tibiae paler externally. Wings subhyaline with a red spot on the base of the fore wing behind the radius extending outward well beyond the quadrangle and reaching the hind border for most of its length. Hind wing with a brown spot extending from the costa rearward beyond the anal vein and outward beyond the quadrangle, prolonged along the radius almost to the nodus. A wash of brown borders the wing tip. Abdomen blackish brown, darkening on the apices of the middle segments and on the entire dorsum of the apical segments. Sutural pale rings very obscure.

256. Hetaerina titia Drury

Drury 1773, II p. 83: Mtk. Cat. p. 33: Garm. '17, p. 474.
    Syn: bipartita Selys
Length 51 mm. Expanse 62 mm.   **Tex. and Fla.**

This is an elegant brownish slender species. Face black. Thorax bronzy black with narrow pale lines on the three lateral sutures, confluent below with the paler color of the under sides. Legs wholly black. Wings with the diffuse crimson spot covering the area about the arculus, quadrangle in the fore wing, the red surrounded by brown which extends two thirds of the way to the nodus behind the subcosta. On the hind wing only the veins of this same region are red; the membrane is brown in an irregular and variable band that extends outward beyond the nodus along the costa, and after a clearer portion, is diffuse over the entire wing tip. Tip of fore wing also is brown beyond the stigma. Abdomen in old species is wholly blackish.

Family COENAGRIONIDAE

These are narrow winged damselflies. The wings are stalked at the base, the anal vein for a distance forming the hind border. The quadrangle is trapezoidal, its anterior side shortened, its outer hind angle pointed, and it is not divided by a cross vein. There are but two antenodal cross veins and there is generally a well developed brace vein to the stigma.

The nymphs are slender creatures with bodies that taper to the three thin plate-like caudal gills. The basal segment of the antenna is not longer than some of the succeeding segments. The labium is entire; or if cleft, the cleft is short and closed. It is armed with raptorial setae. They are climbers on submerged vegetation and are among the commonest inhabitants of all still waters.

In our fauna we recognize two subfamilies, separable as follows:

KEY TO THE SUBFAMILIES

Adults

1 · Vein M_3 rises nearer the arculus than the nodus; between veins M_3 and adjacent principal veins there are short intercalary sectors running to the wing margin..........**Lestinae,** p. 268

Vein M_3 rises nearer the nodus than the arculus; no such intercalary longitudinal veins present......**Coenagrioninae,** p. 280

Nymphs

1 Gills multiarticulate, parallel sided; labium with a median closed cleft....................................**Lestinae,** p. 268

Gills simple with curved margins; middle lobe of labium entire..
....................................**Coenagrioninae,** p. 282

Subfamily LESTINAE

These are rather large, clear winged damselflies of very elongate form. The quadrangle is rather strongly inclined to rearward, and is so very pointed at its outer angle as to be almost triangular. Vein M_3 rises near to the arculus. The stigma is large and well braced and surmounts two or more cells. On both sides of vein M_3 there are intercalated sectors in the interspaces. The colors run to browns and bronzy greens.

The nymphs are slender climbing forms, with legs, antennae and labium of unusual length and slenderness, and with pedunculate, nearly parallel sided, blunt-tipped gills, that show axial subsegmentation. The median lobe of the labium has a short closed median cleft, and the lateral lobe is trifid. There are raptorial setae in both, two of these springing from the end hook of the lateral lobe on its dorsal side.

In our fauna there are but two genera, separable as follows:

KEY TO THE GENERA
Adults

1   Vein M_2 rises about one cell beyond the nodus . **Archilestes**, p. 268
    Vein M_2 rises several cells beyond the nodus . . . . . . **Lestes**, p. 270

Nymphs

1   In the trifid lateral lobe of the labium the upper notch is simple
    . . . . **Archilestes**, p. 269
    In the trifid lateral lobe of the labium there is a serrated border
    within the upper notch . . . . **Lestes**, p. 273

59. ARCHILESTES Selys

These are large damselflies with rather stout bodies and rather broad wings. The quadrangle has the front side so greatly shortened as to be almost in line with the outer, making an almost triangular enclosure. Vein M_2 rises hardly more than a single cell beyond the nodus.

This is a small genus of two southwestern and western species. Their habits have been observed by Kennedy and his account of *A. californica* is quoted under that species.

KEY TO THE SPECIES
Adults

1   Color metallic green or brown; expanse 82 mm. . . . **grandis**, p. 269
    Color dull grayish brown or grayish blue; expanse 62 mm. . . . . . .
    . . . . **californica**, p. 269

The nymphs clamber among submerged vegetation in still waters. They have broad, oblong, blunt-pointed gills that show indistinct segmentation along their axis, and 2 bands of obscure, darker color, one before the middle and one broadly covering the tips.

Nymphs

Species	Length	Length of gills	Lat. Set.	Ment. Set.	Described by
grandis	40	12	3 or 4	7–7	Ndm. '92, p. 712
californica	30	10	3	6–7	Kndy. '15, p. 268

257. Archilestes grandis Rambur

Ramb. '42, p. 244: Mtk. Cat. p. 36.
Length 62 mm. Expanse 82 mm.   **Wash. and Calif.**

This is a fine, brownish species with yellow side stripes upon the thorax. Face and occiput shining brown. Top of head with scanty, hoary pubescence. Front of thorax black with a median, rather narrow pale stripe narrowly divided by the black of the carina. Another broader pale brown stripe covers the humeral suture. Sides black with two broad, yellow pale stripes, one behind the middle suture and one at the rear below. Wings hyaline or faintly tinged with brownish with very long stigma. Legs blackish, yellow externally and paler at base. Abdomen greenish black narrowly and obscurely ringed with paler at base of segments 2–7 and paler on sides below. Apex blackish, 9 and 10 becoming pruinose in age. Appendages black.

258. Archilestes californica McLachlan

McL. '95, p. 20: Mtk. Cat. p. 35: Kndy. '15, p. 260: Smn. '27, p. 9.
Length 48 mm. Expanse 62 mm.   **Calif.**

This species seems not to differ in any constant structural characters from the preceding. The only differences noted by us are those stated in the key.

This species was carefully studied by Kennedy in Oregon. He says of it ('15, p. 266):

Females that possess an ovipositor insert their eggs generally in soft plant tissues, such as green herbaceous stems or rotten wood. The genus Archilestes, however, uses the stems of woody plants, such as willows and alders, and places her eggs high above the water.

During August, or until active breeding began, the individuals of this species with wings held loosely open were usually found hanging on the leaves and stems on the sunny side of willow and alder bushes. Here each appeared to have its favorite position, from which it would fly up and out a distance of 6 to 10 feet from time to time to take passing insects, returning each time to its resting place. On being disturbed none ever hesitated to dart into the densest portion of the bush on which it rested. Many, especially tenerals, rested on grass, and such when attacked flew into the nearest bush.

Even fully developed imagoes were never on the wing for any great length of time, seldom at any time flying more than 20 or 30 feet; but in spite of their apparently weak flight they were not easily taken, because a single stroke of the net would send all the nearby individuals into the bushes.

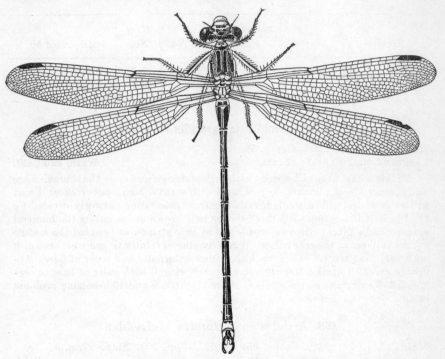

Fig. 44. *Archilestes californica* (drawn by Kennedy).

In capturing the female the male flies toward her while she is on the wing; or if she is alighted, as is the usual case, she flies up to meet him, when he first seizes her head with his feet, then, bending his abdomen forward, seizes her prothorax with the claspers on the tip of his abdomen.

While ovipositing the pair are remarkably indifferent to enemies, as both can be easily picked up by the hand.

Though I watched carefully I found only one place along the creek where ovipositing took place. This was in the alders and willows along a scum-covered stagnant pool of the creek. This was fringed by a thick growth of Juncus and Scirpus, on the smooth stems of which were found many exuviae of Archilestes.

60. Lestes Leach

ese are elongate damselflies of rather large size. The wings are held obliquely upward and backward in repose, and are hyaline with a large stigma which has a good brace vein. Vein M_2 rises several cells beyond the nodus. The abdomen is very long and slender.

This is a cosmopolitan genus well represented in our fauna. The adults fly little over open water but seek the seclusion of marshes or the closer vegetation of reed choked streams. In the midst of their shadowy environment they are difficult to see when at rest but they are easy to capture when they are discovered. Our species are closely allied. The males are separable as follows:

KEY TO THE SPECIES*

Adults

1. Males

1 Inferior appendages longer than the superiors...**inequalis,** p. 275

 Inferior appendages shorter than the superiors...............2.

2 Inferiors less than one-half the length of the superiors.......3.

 Inferiors more than one-half the length of the superiors......4.

3 Wings flavescent. Dorsum of thorax metallic green............

 ....**eurinus,** p. 275

 Wings clear. Dorsum of thorax dark brown....**congener,** p. 275

4 Inferiors sigmoid, roughly S-shaped; their apices curved in an opposite direction to the superiors........................5.

 Inferiors not sigmoid; their apices curved, if at all, in the same direction as the superiors................................6.

5 Inferiors stout. Superiors with the mesal margin roughly denticulate, following the basal tooth. Dorsum of thorax dark brown ....**unguiculatus,** p. 276

 Inferiors slender. Superiors with mesal margin not visibly denticulate following the basal tooth. Dorsum of thorax pale with metallic green spots on either side, or entirely dull black in old age.......................................**sigma,** p. 277

6 Superiors with a distinct basal and apical tooth on the mesal margin...7.

 Superiors with a distinct basal tooth only, followed by a serrated margin of greater or less development....................10.

7 Basal tooth of the mesal margin of the superiors, longer than the tooth of the apical third.............................8.

 Basal tooth of the mesal margin of the superiors as long as or distinctly shorter than the tooth of the apical third.........9.

* Prepared by C. Francis Byers.

8   Superior appendages smooth, at least part way between the teeth ....**vidua,** p. 277

     Superior appendages serrated between the teeth.............. ....**forcipatus,** p. 277

9   Metapleural suture with a black stripe. Length 32–37 mm...... ....**disjunctus,** p. 278

     Metapleural suture without a black stripe. Length 50–52 mm... ....**rectangularis,** p. 278

10 Inferior appendages boot shaped, little expanded at the base. Serrations of the mesal margin of the superiors in approximately a straight line.................................**11.**

     Inferior appendages not boot shaped, sides nearly parallel, base noticeably expanded. Serrations of the superiors expanded near the apical third, or absent in *vigilax*.....................**12.**

11 Color metallic green, abdomen 26–28 mm. long...**uncatus,** p. 278

     Color black, abdomen 30–34 mm. long...........**stultus,** p. 279

12 Dorsum of thorax and abdomen metallic green. Inferiors long and very slender. Mesal border of superiors undulating but not serrated................................**vigilax,** p. 279

     Dorsum of thorax black or pale blue with metallic green spots or stripes on either side. Mesal border of superiors deeply serrated **13.***

13 Rear of head black, yellow around the occipital foramen. Dorsum of thorax black..............................**alacer,** p. 279

     Rear of head yellow, dorsum of thorax pale blue with green spots ....**forficula,** p. 280

2. Females

1   Dorsum of thorax metallic green or with metallic green spots or streaks on a pale background............................**2.**

     Dorsum of thorax black or dark brown....................**7.**

2   Wings flavescent...........................**eurinus,** p. 275

     Wings clear...**3.**

3   Rear of head (occiput and postgenae) pale..................**4.**

     Rear of head black.......................................**6.**

4   Dorsum of the thorax metallic green. Abdomen 38–40 mm. long, hind wings 28 mm. long....................**inequalis,** p. 275

     Dorsum of thorax pale with a metallic green stripe or black spot on either side. Length of abdomen 32–35 mm., of hind wings 22–24 mm...**5.**

* *L. simplex* doubtfully recorded from Texas (Calv. '01, p. 48)is not included in this book (near *alacer*).

5   Each mesepisternum with a small, superior, antehumeral black
    spot (young), or entirely black (old age)........**sigma, p. 277**
    Each mesepisternum with a metallic green stripe one-fifth to one-
    eighth as wide as the mesepisternum itself.....**forficula, p. 280**

6   Basal half of the first abdominal segment yellow. Stigma always
    surmounting less than three cells. Length approximately 35
    mm......................................**uncatus, p. 278**
    Basal half of the first abdominal segment black. Stigma usually
    surmounting three or more cells. Length 43–47 mm.........
    ....**vigilax, p. 279**

7   Metepimeron with a black spot on its lower anterior edge, just
    above and sometimes below the latero-ventral carina.......8.
    Metepimeron not so marked.............................9.

8   A black spot on the lower apical angle of abdominal segments
    3–8, which is not connected with the dorsal black............
    ....**stultus, p. 279**
    Lower apical angles of abdominal segments 3–8 pale, without
    black spots, or if present broadly connected with the black of
    the dorsum..............................**congener, p. 275**

9   Rear of head yellow. Abdomen with a greenish tint...........
    ....**unguiculatus, p. 276**
    Rear of head black or dark brown. Abdomen never with a greenish
    tint..10.

10 Tarsi black above.......................................11.
    Tarsi with more or less pale yellow above. Length 47 mm......
    ....**rectangularis, p. 278**

11 Southern species...............................**alacer, p. 279**
    Eastern and Northern species..........................12.

12 Length approximately 41 mm...............**forcipatus, p. 277**
    Length approximately 35 mm...............**disjunctus, p. 278**

13 Unknown...................................**vidua, p. 277**

3. Nymphs*

1   Lateral setae 4–5. Mentum of labium broad at its proximal end;
    its narrowest width equal to about one-third its width at the
    bases of the lateral lobes.........................**congener.**
    Lateral setae normally three. Mentum of labium narrow at its
    proximal end; its narrowest width equal to about one-fifth to
    one-eighth its width at the bases of the lateral lobes........2.

* Based in part on illustrated key of Howe ('21, p. 107).

2   Lateral spines present on abdominal segments 2–, or 3–9. Gills not sharply pointed............................**vigilax.**

    Lateral spines present on abdominal segments 4–, or 5–9......3.

3   Lateral spines present on segments 4–9. Mentum from five and one-half to five and three-fourth millemeters long. Mental setae 7 or 8. Hind femora 6 mm. long, outer wing pad 6.5 mm. long..**eurinus.**

    Lateral spines on segments 5–9. Mental setae usually 5–6, often 7. Hind femora less than 6 mm. long, outer wing pads 5.5 mm. long or less...4.

4   Mentum of labium more than 4.2 mm. long, reaching generally to the apex of the hind coxa or beyond. Ovipositor extending beyond hind margin of segment 10......................5.

    Mentum of labium 3.7–4.2 mm. long, rarely reaching beyond the middle of the hind coxa. Ovipositor just reaching the hind margin of 10..6.

5   Mentum of labium 4.3–5.1 mm. long, reaching the apex of the hind coxa or slightly beyond. Ovipositor 3–3.5 mm. long, extending just beyond the basal joint of the gills........**uncatus.**

    Mentum of labium 4.75–5.5 mm. long, reaching beyond the apex of the hind coxa often to the apex of the trochanters. Ovipositor 2 mm. long, and extending very little beyond the hind margin of 10...**disjunctus.**

6   Mental setae Normally 5.....................**rectangularis.**

    Mental setae Normally 6–7......................**forcipatus.**

Nymphs*

Species	Length†	Lat. spines‡	Lat. Set.§	Ment. Set.§	Described by
congener	20+9	5–9	4–5	7	Walk. '14, p. 191
disjunctus	19+9	5–9	3	5–6	Walk. '14, p. 196
eurinus	25+11	4–9	3	7–8	Walk. '14, p. 192
forcipatus	17+9	5–9	3	6–7	Walk. '14, p. 196
rectangularis	20+9	5–9	3	5	Ndm. '03, p. 231
stultus	22+12	5–9	3	7	Kndy. '17, p. 487
uncatus	23+9	5–9	3	5–6	Walk. '14, p. 195
unguiculatus	23+8	5–9	3	7	Ndm. '03, p. 233
vigilax	22+10	2 or 3–9	3	5	Walk. '14, p. 198
* forficula: 18+9		5–9	3	5	Calv. '28, p. 8.

† Length of body + gills..

‡ Of abdomen on segments.

§ Of labium.

7   Segment 9 with 8–13 spinules on lateral carina (Cosmopolitan)..
....unguiculatus.

Segment 9 with 12–13 spinules on lateral carina (Western)......
....stultus.

259. Lestes inequalis Walsh

Walsh '62, p. 385: Mtk. Cat. p. 38: Garm. '17, p. 487 and '27, p. 102.

Length 50 mm. Expanse 58 mm.   **Me. to Ill. to Tenn. and N. C.**

This is a fine big metallic green species with a bright yellow labrum, the external edge of which is black, fringed with white hairs. Top of head shining green as is the front of the thorax except for the black carina. Sides of thorax yellow below the mid-horizontal line, with only the third lateral suture faintly darker. Legs blackish, lined with yellow externally. Abdomen bronzy green above, and yellow at sides of basal segments; 8 and 9 becoming pruinose. Appendages black; inferiors remarkably long, incurved and tufted with tawny hairs.

260. Lestes eurinus Say

Say '39, p. 36: Mtk. Cat. p. 37: Garm. '17, p. 482 and '27, p. 99.

Length 47 mm. Expanse 58 mm.   **Mass. and Pa. to Ill. and Wis.**

This is a handsome bronzy green species with bluish reflections. Face pale green below the interclypeal suture; metallic blue green above. Front of thorax metallic with only the carinae black. Sides of same color above, but with a row of five yellowish spots below, separated by blackish. Venter yellow. Legs blackish externally lined with yellow; paler basally. Tarsi blackish. Wings hyaline, a little tinged with yellowish. Abdomen bronzy green, yellowish at extreme base and on side of 2, and with a narrow basal ring dilated below on some of the middle segments. Apex darker. Appendages black.

261. Lestes congener Hagen

Hag. '61, p. 67: Mtk. Cat. p. 37: Kndy. '15, p. 339: Garm. '17, p. 479 and '27, p. 97.

Length 37 mm. Expanse 43 mm.   **B. C. and Tex. to Ont. and Del.**

This is a rather small blackish brown species. The front of the thorax is blackish with metallic reflections and with a narrow, median line and a narrow stripe each side of obscure yellow. Sides yellow with a blackish stripe that is dilated at the wings. Under surface yellow. Legs yellowish; femora and tibiae with lateral line of black. Abdomen blackish with a yellowish crescent upon the base of each segment.

"A pair was seen ovipositing . . . . . The male was holding the female and she had her abdomen looped up as does the female of Archilestes and was placing eggs in a small willow stem about 2 inches above the surface of the water." (Kndy. '15, p. 339.)

Montgomery ('25, p. 383) writes:

Williamson and I observed a pair ovipositing in a stem of *Scirpus fluviatilis*. The pair moved down the stem depositing eggs at short intervals. The female was observed to straighten out her abdomen after each egg was inserted in the

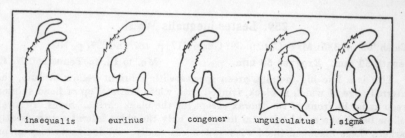

tissue of the plant. After the pair had moved down the stem several inches in this manner, they walked up the stem about a foot and began the process over again. This move was carried out in perfect unison; . . . . A section of the plant containing eggs was brought to the laboratory and examined under the microscope. The eggs were inserted at intervals of 1½–4 mm. and pointed downward at an angle of about 45 with the surface of the stem. Most of them were inclined either slightly to the right or to the left, from the plane passing through the line of punctures and the center of the stem.

262. Lestes unguiculatus Hagen

Hag. '61, p. 70: Mtk. Cat. p. 40: Davis '13, p. 14: Whed. '14, p. 91: Garm. '17, p. 494 and '27, p. 105.

Length 36 mm. Expanse 40 mm.   **N. S. and N. J. to N. D. and Calif.**

Labrum yellowish; the face blackish above. Front of thorax brassy black, yellow on carinae with an isolated stripe, abbreviated both above and below, bordering the humeral suture in front. Sides of thorax yellow with a very broad stripe covering and extending rearward from the third lateral suture, and widened upward. Before its lower end there are some black spots about the leg bases. Legs black, lined with yellow externally on femora and tibiae. Abdomen greenish black with yellow side margins on all middle segments: apical segments becoming darker: appendages black at tip.

This species is oftenest seen sitting on the vertical stems of bulrushes, from whence it makes sudden dashes at passing Diptera. It eats them, sitting.

(Whedon '14, p. 91) says "It is an inhabitant of pond and small lake regions and is very seldom seen about streams . . . . . It seems clear that great numbers of this species migrate from pond to pond or lake to lake during the breeding period; ovipositing for a day or so at each stopping place. Incomputable myriads."

263. Lestes sigma Calvert

Calv. '09. p. 96: Mtk. Cat. p. 39.
Length 41 mm. Expanse 44 mm.   **N. Mex. and Tex.**

A rather pale southern species of medium size. Face pale, becoming black above with age. Thorax yellowish with a small superior metallic green spot and an isolated green stripe, becoming pruinose black with age. Femora pale lined with black; tibiae pale externally; tarsi black. Abdomen greenish, blackening with age. Middle segments with basal blue rings interrupted on the middle line. Side margins of 3–7 blue. Apical segments and appendages black.

264. Lestes vidua Hagen

Hag. '61, p. 69: Mtk. Cat. p. 40.
Length 39 mm. Expanse 45 mm.   **La.**

This is a small blackish species. The face is a drab color below the interclypeal suture, plainly clothed with long white bristles. Head black above. Front of thorax black with a narrow brown line on the carina and a broader one at the humeral suture, widest in the middle. Sides of thorax blackish above, yellow beneath with a stripe on the third lateral suture that is confluent above with the black about the wing roots. Legs brownish, paler basally. Interalar area densely pruinose. Abdomen obscure blackish with greenish reflections on middle segments. Pale side margins on basal segments. Appendages black-tipped and scantily clothed with short, tawny hairs.

265. Lestes forcipatus Rambur

Ramb. '42, p. 246: Mtk. Cat. p. 37: Garm. '17, p. 485 and '27, p. 100.
Syn: hamatus Hag.
Length 37 mm. Expanse 47 mm.   **N. D. and B. C. to Me. and Ga.**

This is a blackish species of moderate size. The face is greenish below the interclypeal suture; blackish above. The front of the thorax is black with carinae narrowly yellow; narrow yellow humeral stripes interrupted above. The sides are blackish above to the roots of the fore wing; yellowish below with a rather broad and irregular stripe broadly overspreading the third lateral suture. Legs blackish paler at base and lined with yellowish externally. Abdomen blackish above with greenish reflections; yellowish on sides of three basal segments inferiorly, and to a less extent on some of the middle segments. Apical segments black; 9 and 10 becoming a little pruinose with age. Appendages blackish.

Common about "rivers and small lakes" (Mtk. '08, p. 70).

The flight of this species is weak, low halting and indirect. It keeps to the cover of the sedges and tall grasses and perches on the sides of bare vertical stems and leaves. The female, attended by the male, oviposits commonly in submerged grass blades. Transformation occurs just above the water, mostly on vertical green stems.

The nymph perches lightly on its long stilt-like legs with gills outspread, but is singularly hard to see because of its protective coloration.

It darts aside and dodges with the utmost agility, aided by side strokes of the broad gills. It undergoes extensive color changes with age and with ecdysis. Its food seems to be mainly the larger entomostraca and mayfly nymphs.

266. Lestes disjunctus Selys

Selys '62, p. 302: Mtk. Cat. p. 37: Garm '17, p. 482 and '27, p. 98.
Length 34 mm. Expanse 40 mm.   **N. S. and N. C. to Wis. and Calif.**
This is a small blackish species with greenish face and greenish stripes upon the thorax. Front of thorax black with carina narrowly green and a broader greenish humeral stripe. Sides black becoming pruinose below with age, with an oblique "?" in green upon the middle. Legs yellowish with blackish stripes

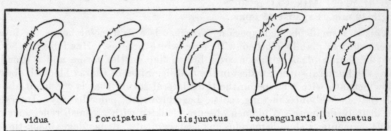

vidua.   forcipatus   disjunctus   rectangularis   uncatus

and with black lines on sides of tibiae and tarsi. Abdomen blackish with the sides of the middle segments greenish, the pale color extending upward on the extreme base of each of these segments. Apical segments blackish becoming pruinose with age. Appendages black-tipped with a few whitish apical and basal hairs.

267. Lestes rectangularis Say

Say '39, p. 34: Mtk. Cat. p. 38: Garm. '17, p. 489 and '27, p. 103.
Length 49 mm. Expanse 49 mm.   **Me. and N. C. to N. D.**
A rather elongate, slender species. The labrum is green, fringed with long bristling hairs. The thorax is black in front with carinae yellow and an ante-humeral stripe that widens downward and is confluent around the isolated lower end of a broad, black stripe. A yellow figure 7 interrupts this stripe above, just below the wing roots. Some blackish marks follow the wing crest to rearward, but the sides beneath are wholly yellow, the second stripe of the sides being wanting. Legs yellow; sides of femora and front of tibiae lined with black. Abdomen very long and slender; brown above with black apical saddle marks on segments 1–6, becoming diffuse rearward; 8–10 mostly black above. Side margins of 1–8 yellowish; 9 with two included yellow spots and 10 mostly yellow. Tips of appendages black, tufted with golden hairs.

268. Lestes uncatus Kirby

Kirby '90, p. 160: Mtk. Cat. p. 39: Kndy. '15, p. 324: Garm. '17, p. 492 and '27, p. 104: Ndm. '27, p. 20.
Syn: hamata Selys
Length 40 mm. Expanse 42 mm.   **N. S. and Pa. to Calif. and B. C.**

This is a metallic green species with sides of the body yellow. Labrum yellowish. Face and top of head blackish. Front of thorax brilliant metallic green with black carina. Sides of thorax metallic green above, yellowish beneath with an obscure blackish stripe (that becomes pruinose with age) bordering the third lateral suture. Legs blackish, lined with yellow externally; tarsi black. Abdomen metallic green, becoming black on the third apical segment; the middle segments very narrowly ringed with yellowish. Appendages black.

"Common about stagnant alkaline pools." (Kndy. '15, p. 324.)

269. Lestes stultus Hagen

Hag. '61, p. 67: Mtk. Cat. p. 39: Kndy. '17, p. 484.

Length 40 mm. Expanse 46 mm.   **Calif.**

This is a blackish species with yellowish sides. The labrum is pale blue. The top of the head is black. The front of the thorax is black except for a narrow pale line on the carina. There is a narrow pale stripe bordering the humeral suture in front. The sides of the thorax are pale with an irregular blackish line on the third lateral suture and isolated spots below it on the inferior margin. Legs pale with external black stripes to the knees and internal black stripes on the tibiae; tarsi black. Abdomen black above with greenish reflections; yellow at sides, less broadly on the terminal segments. Superior appendages black; inferiors pale.

270. Lestes vigilax Hagen

Hag. '62, p. 306: Mtk. Cat. p. 40: Whed. '14, p. 91: Garm. '17, p. 496 and '27, p. 107.

Length 47 mm. Expanse 54 mm.   **Mass. and Pa. to N. D.**

This is a fine, metallic green species of medium size. Face is obscure yellowish, black above. Front of thorax bronzy green with the narrow pale line on the carina and another on the humeral suture. Side green above, pale beneath, becoming densely pruinose with age. Legs blackish; darker towards the joints paler basally. Abdomen bronzy green dorsally, and yellowish at sides; more broadly towards the base. Segment 1 pruinose; terminal segments blackish. Appendages black-tipped.

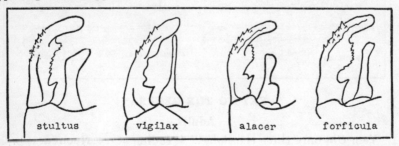

stultus   vigilax   alacer   forficula

271. Lestes alacer Hagen

Hag. '61, p. 67: Mtk. Cat. p. 36.

Length 39 mm. Expanse 42 mm.   Tex., N. Mex. and Ariz.

This is a blackish damselfly of the southwest. The front of the thorax is black; the sides are paler, obscure, with a broad brownish middle band. The legs are yellowish with blackish tarsi. Femora and tibiae with black lines upon the sides. Appendages blackish with sides yellow inferiorly. Appendages black.

272. Lestes forficula Rambur

Ramb. '42, p. 246: Mtk. Cat. p. 38.
Length 40 mm. Expanse 39 mm.   Tex.

This is a blackish southern species. Face pale inferiorly. Front of thorax bluish each side of the bronzy green stripe that is margined with black. Sides blackish becoming pruinose with age. Legs yellowish with black lines on femora and tibiae. Abdomen brassy black, middle segments ringed with paler at their joinings; end segments becoming pruinose. Appendages black.

Subfamily COENAGRIONINAE

These are the smallest of the damselflies. They are mostly clear winged forms, and not very long legged. Vein M_3 rises nearer the nodus than the arculus. The stigma is short, surmounting hardly more than a single cell. There are no intercalary sectors in the spaces either side of vein M_3. The colors run to black and blue and red.

The nymphs are slender, mostly greenish forms that clamber among submerged vegetation. The middle lobe of the labium is entire. The lateral lobes have not more than two end hooks, oftenest but one with a serrated margin above it. The gills are non-segmented in form, generally lanceolate, pointed, with raptorial setae, but with none springing from the movable hook. The genera and species are numerous and closely allied. They may be separated as follows:

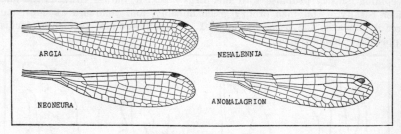

KEY TO THE GENERA*

Adults

1   Vein Cu_1 only three cells long; Cu_2 rudimentary.**Neoneura**, p. 283
    Veins Cu_1 and Cu_2 well developed.........................2.

* Omits the South American genus Oxyagrion, one species of which was once reported from the coast of California. (Mtk. Cat. p. 53)

2   Spines of the tibiae long, generally twice as long as the intervening
spaces...3.

Spines of the tibiae short, hardly longer than the intervening
spaces...5.

3   Two rows of cells between vein Cu_2 and the hind margin........
....**Hyponeura**, p. 284

One cell row between vein Cu_2 and the hind margin..........4.

4   Vein Cu_2 four or five cells long.............**Argiallagma**, p. 302

Vein Cu_2 ten or more cells long...................**Argia**, p. 286

5   No pale post ocular spots on head............................6.

With pale post ocular spots on head.......................10.

6   Body (mature) black and red, at least in the males; rather short
and stout..7.

Body not black and red; more slender......................9.

7   Hind wing with the costal side of the stigma shorter than the
radial side.............................**Hesperagrion**, p. 303

Hind wing with the costal side of the stigma not shorter than the
radial side..8.

8   No ventral spines on abdominal segment 8 of female; male superior appendages bifid.................**Amphiagrion**, p. 304

With a ventral spine on abdominal segment 8 of female; male
superior appendages entire.................**Telebasis**, p. 305

9   Body metallic green above; very slender; length about an inch
.....................................**Nehalennia**, p. 306

Body blue and black above; larger and more robust............
.....................................**Chromagrion**, p. 309

10 Stigma in fore and hind wing of male similar...............11.

Stigma in fore and hind wing of male dissimilar.............15.

11 One or both wings generally stalked to the anal crossing; abdomen
very long (32–36 mm.)...................**Teleallagma**, p. 309

Wings not stalked as far out as the anal crossing............12.

12 Costal side of stigma shorter than the radial side..............
.....................................**Hesperagrion**, p. 303

Costal side of stigma not shorter than the radial side........13.

13 No ventral spine on abdominal segment 8 of female............
.....................................**Coenagrion**, p. 310

With ventral spine on abdominal segment 8 of female........14.

14   Last abdominal segment of male with no bifid process..........
    ....**Enallagma**, p. 311
    Last abdominal segment of male with a bifid dorsal process.....
    .... **Zoniagrion**, p. 342

15   Fore wing stigma of male bordered by the costa; hind tibia of
    female with external black stripe............**Ischnura**, p. 342
    Fore wing stigma of male removed from costal margin; hind tibiae
    of female wholly pale .... **Anomalagrion**, p. 357

Nymphs*

1   Gills half as broad as long: no mental setae.................2.
    Gills not more than one third as broad as long: mental setae
    present..3.

2   Lateral setae 1–4...............................**Argia**, p. 286
    Lateral setae 0 (occasionally 1) ....**Hyponeura**, p. 284

3   Hind angles of head angulate...............................4.
    Hind angle of head rounded................................5.

F<small>IG.</small> 45. The nymph of Amphiagrion.

4   Gills widest in middle, one third as broad as long..............
    .... **Amphiagrion**, p. 304
    Gills widest toward the distal end, one sixth as broad as long ...
    .... **Chromagrion**, p. 309

5   Mental setae 1 or 2...6.
    Mental setae 3 or more....................................7.

6   Mental setae 1—......................... **Nehalennia**, p. 306
    Mental setae 2..8.

* From *Guide to the Study of Fresh-water Biology*, by James G. Needham
and Paul R. Needham.

7   Lateral setae 6–7...........................**Telebasis**, p. 305

     Lateral setae 4–5.......................... **Enallagma**, p. 313

8   Lateral setae 6–7...9.

     Lateral setae 4–5...12.

9   Gills tapering to a slender point...........................10.

     Gills rather bluntly pointed...............................11.

10   Length without gills 18 mm................ **Teleallagma**, p. 309

     Length without gills 11–13 mm.............. **Ischnura**, p. 342

11   Tip of gills obtusely angled................. **Coenagrion**, p. 310

     Tip of gills rounded..................... **Hesperagrion**, p. 303

12   No lateral spines on terminal abdominal segments............

     .... **Anomalagrion**, p. 357

     With lateral spines on terminal abdominal segments.........13.

13   Gills tapering to a slender point...........................14.

     Gills ending in an acute angle............... **Enallagma**, p. 313

14   Side of abdomen fringed with long hairs...... **Zoniagrion**, p. 342

     Sides of abdomen not fringed with long hairs... **Ischnura**, p. 342

61. NEONEURA Selys

These are slender blackish damselflies rather strikingly marked with reddish yellow, the amount of blackening increasing with age. They will be instantly recognized by the brevity of the branches of the cubital veins, Cu_1 being but 3 cells long and Cu_2 a rudiment.

The nymph is unknown. These are tropical American damselflies of which the following species enter our borders.

273. Neoneura aaroni Calvert

Calv. '03, p. 139: Mtk. Cat. p. 72: Wmsn. '14, p. 446: Kndy. '17, p. 289.

Length 29 mm. Expanse 36 mm.   **Tex.**

This single member of a large tropical genus has been taken as yet only in southern Texas. Face pale with blackish dots on the postclypeus and labrum. Top of head brown becoming red with age. Front of thorax with a pair of narrow blackish stripes bordering the middorsal carina, narrow and interrupted in younger specimens; a broad blackish area covering the humeral region that varies with age from a shadowy line to a broad, dark band. Legs yellowish with black lines on femora and tibiae, the blackish portion becoming pruinose with age. Abdomen blackish above, yellowish beneath with lateral basal, narrow rings at joinings of segments 3–6. 8 and 9 obscure.

Williamson ('14, p. 446) writes of it as follows: "a small lot of drift debris on one side of a relatively deep pool in a small stream on the right bank of the river . . . . . From the drift the *Neoneura* flew out to hover motionless above the deep water of the pool. As the collector approached they would disappear, leaving him to guess at the direction of their flight. I have collected several species of *Neoneura* and the flight and actions of all have been similar. Their agility must be seen to be appreciated. And almost invariably they have been found about deep pools in small streams with drift or overhanging bushes near at hand."

62. HYPONEURA Selys

Rather large and heavily built, clear winged damselflies with stout spiny legs. The thorax is strongly bulged above the bases of the fore legs. The stigma of the wings is rather large, surmounting two entire cells. The quadrangle is very short and broad, especially in the fore wing.

The nymph is a rather large, dark colored climber with very thick gills; the paired ones with heavy midlateral external ridges. The labium generally lacks raptorial setae; occasionally there is a single lateral one.

This Sonoran genus which enters our southwest border is represented by the following species:

274. Hyponeura lugens Hagen

Hag. '61, p. 95: Mtk. Cat. p. 44: Smn. '27, p. 11.

Length 42 mm. Expanse 64 mm. **N. Mex. and Ariz.**

This is a stout bodied bluish species that varies very much in depth of coloration. Face in young specimens is of a light tan color, paler in labrum, becoming wholly black with age. Thorax bluish green with a black carina, developing, when a little older, narrow black stripes as follows; a narrow pale pair on the front, rather close to the carina; a very narrow line on the humeral suture; a broader but incomplete one on the yellow area behind it, narrowly connected below with the black spot above the base of the fore leg; a short stripe on upper end of midlateral suture and a complete line on the third lateral suture, these connected at the wing roots. Thorax, in old males, wholly black, pruinose. Legs yellowish, blackish about the knees, darkening with age. Abdomen stout; two submedian, dorsal, black streaks are narrowly connected near apex of all middle segments. Paler color more extensive on end segments. Appendages pale.

63. ARGIA Rambur.

By C. Francis Byers

Argia is a very complex genus, found chiefly in the American tropics but represented in our limits by 18 species. Unlike most of the damselflies, they seem to have a pronounced distaste for vegetation. The imagoes are to be found commonly flying very low above hard clay roads, or in the open spaces of fields and woods that are devoid of vegetation. They thus frequently wander far inland from water and are to be found in and around houses in towns and villages. The author saw his first *Argia fumipennis* on a pipe organ in a Church in a small Florida town. The females in ovipositing seem to prefer floating chips, boards, etc., to vegetation. Many females will congregate on such floatsam and, clinging to the edges of it, will deposit their eggs by thrusting the ovipositor as far under water as possible. The emerging nymphs seem also to have this marked distaste for vegetation. For when they leave the water to transform they will, when ever possible crawl up the hard surfaces of stones, piers, logs, bare banks, etc. rather than green plants.

In some species the male accompanies the female in ovipositing and when she submerges he goes with her. A few species of Argia are to be found in the deep vegetation along the banks of rivers and streams. All Argias are extremely nervous. They remain but a little time at rest, and are continually darting hither and yon, seemingly never content to remain inactive.

The males divide sharply into two general color groups: One, the "light group," having the body predominantly pale in color (gray, blue, violet or purple) with the black reduced to spots, streaks, or narrow bands. The other, the "dark group" having the body predominantly black or dark brown, the pale colors being yellow or light brown. *Argia bipunctulata* is however, an intermediate between these two groups, having the abdomen light and the thorax and the head dark. The females of Argia do not fall into this same grouping, almost all of them have the pale colors predominating on some part of the body at least.

The postocular spots are either well defined in the dark group, or broadly merged into the general pale color of the head in the light group. The color pattern of the abdomen is of some value in the separation of species. The coloration of the thorax is of special interest in Argia, especially in the males, varying as it does according to age, geographic distribution, and, probably, climate and altitude. In general there are six types of thoracic color patterns, (all with their various modifications), as shown in the accompanying figure.

Structurally, Argia can be separated from the other genera of the Coenagrioninae, by the long spines on the tibia, which are at least twice as long as the spaces separating them; and by the larger number of them (10 or more).

The male superior and inferior abdominal appendages are very small and hard to observe, but of very great importance taxonomically as are also the mesostigmal plates (laminae) of the females. Figures of both are given with the descriptions that follow.

The nymphs of Argia are usually recognizable at a glance by reason of their thick set bodies and the dark colored, short, broad gills. If this is not sufficient, the entire absence of mental setae will serve to separate the members of this genus from all the following Coenagrioninae. The nymphs of the 9 known species are so very much alike that a short generic description will be given for them all, followed by a table giving the characteristics more or less peculiar to the species.

The nymph is short and thick and usually with dark colored legs and short oblong gill plates. The head is somewhat wider than long, flat above with very prominent eyes. The antennae are six or seven jointed, the third joint being the longest. The labium is short with the hinge reaching barely to the base of the middle legs; the median lobe is without mental setae but has a row of small setae on the lateral margins just posterior to the articulation of the lateral lobes: lateral setae 1–4; lateral lobe short with a short stout moveable hook and a small end hook which may or may not be separated from the inner margin by a notch (see column 5 of the table). Abdomen stout, some-

The Known Nymphs

| Species | Length* | Lat. set. | Notch** | Gills | | Described by |
				Greatest breadth	pigment	
agrioides	12 +6	2–4	absent	near m.	mottled	Smn. '26, p. 13
apicalis	14 +6	3–4	present	middle	3 x bands	Ndm. '03, p. 242
emma	17 +5	1	present	before m.	x bands	Kndy. '15, p. 271
fumipennis	10 +4	2–3	absent	middle	1 x band	Ndm. '04, p. 714
moesta	14 +5–6	1	present	before m.	uniform	Ndm. & Ckll. '03, p.136
sedula	12 +4	2	absent	middle	uniform	Smn. '26, p. 13
tibialis	12 +4.5	4	absent	beyond m.	apical	Ndm. '03, p. 244
translata	13 +5	1	present	beyond m.	3 confluent x bands	Brtn. '28, p. 34
violacea	17(?) +4.5	2–3	present	beyond m.	V-shaped apical	Ndm. '03, p. 242
vivida	12 +3	4	absent			Kndy. '15, p. 288

* Body +gills.
** In end of lateral lobe separating off the end hook.

what tapering, with its segments decreasing in length to the ninth, the tenth again a little longer. Gills oblong about half as wide as long. The shape and pigmentation of the gills varies with the species as indicated in the table.

The gills are easily broken off the nymphs of this genus both in the laboratory and in life. If their loss occurs early in nymphal life, they are regenerated, and it is no uncommon thing to find a specimen with one, two or three of the gill plates of smaller size than normal. The loss of gills seems not to seriously affect the respiration of the nymphs.

KEY TO THE SPECIES
Adults
1. Males

1 The total area of dark color on abdominal segments 3–6, *or* the thoracic dorsum, or both, *less* than the pale area of the same parts..2.

The total area of dark color on the abdominal segments 3–6, *and* the thoracic dorsum, *greater* than the pale area of the same parts ....12.

2 Black middorsal thoracic stripe a mere hair line. Antehumeral pale stripe very broad, 4–6 times as wide as the middorsal dark stripe..3.

Black middorsal thoracic stripe wide. Antehumeral pale stripe narrow, one-half to one and one-half times as wide as the middorsal stripe...6.

3 Humeral black stripe reduced to a hair line and of uniform thickness throughout its entire length........................4.

Humeral black stripe not of uniform thickness throughout, the ends being greatly thickened, while the median third or more is reduced to a hair line or is absent....................5.

4 Head with some black markings around the vertex and bases of the antennae at least.........................**tonto,** p. 299

Head with no black markings at all, pale colors being cream and violet......................................**solita,** p. 299

5 Abdominal terga 3–5 with less than the basal half black. Posterior lobe of the prothorax pale. No black spot on abdominal segment one..**emma,** p. 294

Abdominal terga 3–5 almost entirely black. Posterior lobe of the prothroax black. A black spot on the dorsum of abdominal segment one...............................**apicalis,** p. 292

6 Humeral stripe forked....................................7.

Humeral stripe not forked................................10.

7   Superior appendages bilobed or trilobed at apex, inner margin
    rounded and convex before the tip 8
    Superior appendages almost entire at the tip, the inner margins
    with an anteapical projection . . . . .9.

8   Inferior appendages bifid . . . .**hinei**, p. 295
    Inferior appendages not bifid . . . .**agrioides**, p. 291

9   Pale colors on thorax and abdominal segments 3–6 violet.
    Antenodals of the front wing 4 . . . .**violacea**, p. 300
    Pale colors of the thorax and abdominal segments 3–6 blue.
    Antenodals of the fore wing 3 . . . .**immunda**, p. 296

10 Dark humeral stripe wider than the pale antehumeral, straight
    and of equal width throughout . . . .**bipunctulata**, p. 293
    Dark humeral stripe narrower than the pale antehumeral, at least
    in the middle third of its length . . . . .11.

11 Dark humeral stripe a mere hair line throughout its entire length
    . . . .**tonto**, p. 299
    Dark humeral stripe not of uniform thickness throughout, the
    ends being greatly thickened, while the median third or more
    is reduced or wanting . . . .**vivida**, p. 301

12 Wings a uniform smoky brown . . . .**fumipennis**, p. 295
    Wings clear or with only the extreme tips smoky . . . . .13.

13 Stigma surmounting more than one cell in both wings. Superior
    appendages not bifid . . . . .14.
    Stigma surmounting one cell or less in both wings . . . . .16.

14 Abdomen 27–33 mm. long. Pale antehumeral stripe from one-third
    (young) to one-twelfth (older males) as wide as the black mid-
    dorsal, or absent entirely in very old individuals. Abdominal
    segment 8 black on dorsum with a pale transverse basal ring
    . . . .**translata**, p. 300
    Abdomen 35–37 mm. long. Pale antehumeral stripe one-half as
    wide as the dark middorsal one. Terga of abdominal segment 8
    usually entirely black, or, pale olive with a longitudinal black
    stripe on either side in young specimens . . . . .15.

15 Metepimeron pale or black. Abdomen with a pale longitudinal
    dorsal line on segments 3–7. Inferior appendages without a
    tubercle . . . .**moesta**, p. 297
    Metepimeron always pale. Abdomen with the dorsum entirely
    black on segments 3–7. Inferior appendages with a tubercle at
    the end . . . .**intruda**, p. 296

16   Tergum of 8 black..17.

      Terga of 8 to 10 blue...................................18.

17   Superior appendages bifid at the tip. Segment 9 mostly blue on dorsum................................**tibialis**, p. 299

      Superior appendages not bifid at tip. Segment 9 mostly black on dorsum................................**translata**, p. 300

18   Pale antehumeral stripe narrow, one-third to one-half as wide as the black middorsal. Humeral stripe wider than antehumeral pale one, and not split.....................**sedula**, p. 298

      Pale antehumeral stripe as wide or wider than the dark middorsal. Humeral stripe not as wide as the antehumeral and split in its upper third.....................**alberta**, p. 292

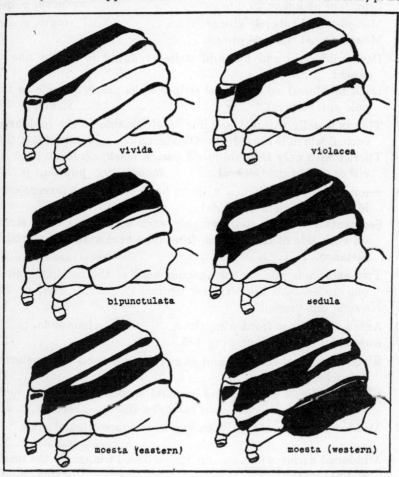

vivida   violacea

bipunctulata   sedula

moesta (eastern)   moesta (western)

2. Females

1 Dorsum of abdominal segments 3–6 mostly pale................2.
   Dorsum of abdominal segments 3–6 mostly black (4–6 in **bipunctulata,**)...15.

2 Post basal stripes present on abdominal segments 3–6 and confluent with the apical black.............................3.
   Post basal stripes present on abdominal segments 3- or 4–6, but
   not usually confluent with the apical black................8.

3 Dark humeral stripe forked.............................4.
   Dark humeral stripe not forked..........................5.

4 Length of abdomen 26 mm....................**hinei**, p. 295
   Length of abdomen 20 mm..................**violacea**, p. 300

5 Mesepisternal tubercle absent..................**tonto**, p. 299
   Mesepisternal tubercle present...........................6.

6 Dark middorsal and humeral stripes reduced to a thin line or
   absent..7.
   Dark middorsal and humeral stripes wide, nearly as wide as the
   pale antehumeral.........................**vivida**, p. 301

7 Thorax usually with a black line on either side of the middorsal
   carina, which is also black. Oklahoma........**intruda**, p. 296
   Thorax with only the middorsal carina black, no black lines on
   either side of it. General.......**moesta** (inc. **putrida,**) p. 297

8 Segments 8–9 of abdomen without black on dorsum (except on 9
   in some specimens of *vivida*)...........................9.
   Segments 8–9 of the abdomen pale, each with a long black stripe
   on each side of the dorsum, from base backward to a variable
   distance..13.

9 Two enormous pits on the anterior ends of the mesepisternum,
   one under each mesostigmal lamina............**rita**, p. 298
   No such pits present...................................10.

10 Antenodal cells in front wing three...........**immunda**, p. 296
   Antenodal cells in front wing 4–5......................11.

11 Black middorsal thoracic and humeral stripes and mesepisternal
   tubercles present....................................12.
   Black middorsal thoracic and humeral stripes reduced to a mere
   line or absent, mesepisternal tubercles absent....**sedula**, p. 298

12 Middorsal carina abruptly ending in the mesostigmal plate....
   ....**emma**, p. 294
   Middorsal carina widening out into a broad triangle in the mesostigmal plate................................**vivida**, p. 301

13 Mesostigmal lamina prolonged at the mesal end in a slender process..14.

Mesostigmal lamina rounded with no slender prolongation......

....**agrioides,** p. 291

14 Length of abdomen 20 mm. Mesostigmal lamina with a projection near the dorsal carina........................**violacea,** p. 300

Length of abdomen 22 mm. Mesostigmal lamina without a projection near the dorsal carina. California, Colorado and Utah

....**alberta,** p. 292

15 Wings smoky...........................**fumipennis,** p. 295

Wings clear.................................16.

16 Black middorsal thoracic stripe a mere hair line..**apicalis,** p. 292

Black middorsal stripe at least one third as wide as the pale antehumeral.....................................17.

17 Abdominal segments 2–3 mostly pale.......**bipunctulata,** p. 293

Abdominal segments 2–3 mostly dark.....................18.

18 Mesepisternal tubercle well developed. Dorsum of abdominal segments 8–9 pale with black markings.........**translata,** p. 300

Mesepisternal tubercles absent. Dorsum of segments 8–9 black

....**tibialis,** p. 299

275. Argia agrioides Calvert

Calv. '95, p. 476: Mtk. Cat. p. 45: Wmsn. '14, p. 444: Smn. '27, p. 12.

Var: nahuana Calv.

Length 28 (♂)–35(♀) mm. Expanse 37–45 mm.   **Calif., Ariz. and Tex.**

A southwestern Argia, that frequents desert streams.

Male.—Head predominantly pale with black lattice-like streaks on the vertex. Dorsum of the middle and posterior lobes of the prothorax narrowly black, with a median geminate pale stripe of blue; anterior lobe and sides broadly pale, except for a fine sinuate lateral line of black. Meso- and metathorax predominantly pale with the black middorsal stripe little or usually no wider than the pale antehumeral stripe. The humeral dark stripe is irregular, narrow and

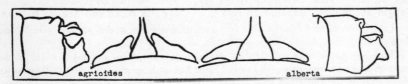
agrioides   alberta

forked, the posterior fourth appears as a basal spot, followed for another quarter of the length of the humeral suture by a fine brown line, the third quarter of the stripe is broad and subrectangular with a tail-like process trailing off posteriorly across the mesepimeron, giving the humeral a forked appearance, the fourth quarter of the suture is covered by a slightly broader black line than the 2nd quarter. A fine brown line on the third lateral suture. Abdomen mainly blue with reduced spots on 2; small apical rings on 3–6; most of 7; and slight lateral markings on 8–10, black.

Female—Similar to the male except the black markings of the head and thorax are more reduced. Segments 3–6 of the abdomen have in addition to the apical black rings of the male, long semilateral postbasal dark stripes on either side of the pale dorsum, on 6 these may fuse with the apical black rings, but usually they do not. Dorsum of 7 mainly dark. Dark semilateral stripes on 8–9. Segment 10 pale.

276. Argia alberta Kennedy

Kndy. '18, p. 257.
Length 27 mm. Expanse 38 mm.   Calif., Colo. and Utah

This species simulates *Argia sedula* in color and appendages, but the penis show this to be more nearly related to the northern *violacea* group, while *sedula* is nearer *translata* and a large series of Mexican species.

Male.—Head predominantly pale with black edging the postclypeus; a wide black bar through the paired ocelli; and a broad black stripe behind each postocular area. Prothorax black dorsally with a bluish spot on either side. Thorax predominantly pale. Dark middorsal stripe occupying one-third of the area between the humeral sutures. Humeral stripe about half as wide as the middorsal, its upper third forked. A black stripe, 1 mm. wide, on the third lateral suture. Abdomen with segments 1–3 dull blue. Segment 1 with a baso-dorsal black spot. Segment 2 with a narrow apical band and lateral stripe black. Segment 3 with the apical third and a lateral stripe black. Segments 4–7 with the apical third and the dorsum black, except a narrow basal band of blue, the sides bluish or brownish. Segments 8–10 pure pale blue the lower edges more or less blotched with black.

Female.—Color as in the male, but with the blue of the head and thorax paler. Humeral stripe about half as wide as in the male, its branches linear. Abdomen pale with a narrow apical band on segments 2–6, an apical dorsal spot, a lateral stripe, and an oblique spot on the lower apical angle of the sides black. Segment 7 with the dorsal half or more black. Segments 8–9 with the dorsolateral stripes of black. Segment 10 pale. In some females segment 6 is colored like 7.

277. Argia apicalis (Say)

Say '39, p. 40: Mtk. Cat. p. 45: Wlsn. '12, p. 197: Garm. '17, p. 503.
Length 36–38 mm. Expanse 50 mm.   Me., to N. C. and Ark. to N. Dak.

Like *violacea* and *tibialis* this is a common species about shaded ponds and rivers.

Male.—Colors blue and black. Head pale except for extended black areas surrounding the antennae, the ocelli, and the pale postocular area. Prothorax black except for the sides and a pair of large lateral spots on the median lobe. Thorax with the middorsal black stripe reduced to a mere hair line. The dorsal half of the mesinfraepisternum and the anterior fifth of the mesemiperon covered by a broad black band, remainder of the humeral stripe represented by a fine brown line on the humeral suture. Third lateral suture with a fine brown line.

Dorsum of abdominal segments 1–7 metallic black except for narrow interrupted basal rings of yellow on segments 3–7. and apical rings on 1 and 7; dorsum of 8–10 blue. Sides of 1–2 pale, of 3–6 pale with the apical fourth black, of 7–10 black.

Female.—Head entirely pale with a few isolated black streaks or spots. Thorax as in the male. Abdomen with the mid-carina blue, dorsum black, and sides mainly pale, on segments 2–7. Dorsum of 8–9 blackish with a dorsal yellow longitudinal stripe and dark brown and yellow on the sides; 10 dark above, paler on the sides.

Garman ('17, p. 505) says it is

A common species along all large-sized streams in Illinois. The nymphs live in the mud at the bottom, but when mature approach the banks and hide among dead submerged weeds or rubbish. The eggs are deposited below the water on driftwood, and large numbers of females may sometimes be seen congregated about the old log at the water's edge depositing eggs.

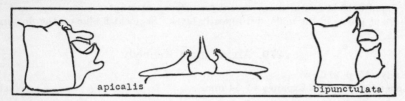

The following notes concerning this species are from a field record made by the senior author at Galesburg, Ill., in 1895.

Pale straw yellow males and females appeared first about the middle of May. These fluttered along in a weak and halting manner through the grass as if their flying apparatus were not quite equal to the task of carrying them. Older and sturdier bright blue males and lilac females gradually replaced these pale ones.

The species flies slowly at best and spends most of its time resting on grass stems and on twigs and pebbles near the water. It preys upon a large midge (a Chironomid) which is common in the same situations. It is oftener preyed upon, for many wings of this species may be seen in the calla-shaped ground webs of spiders, common on the slopes.

The nymphs cling to submerged vegetation, usually with the caudal gills slightly elevated and slowly swaying back and forth. When on dead small leaved aquatics, there is striking likeness of the broad gills to small brown leaves; and their motion hardly impairs their concealment, for it is like that of leaves swayed by currents in the water.

The nymphs are readily fed on entomostraca. They crawl slowly and swim indifferently by sculling with their broad gills. Transformation takes place early in the forenoon, a few inches from the edge of the water.

278. Argia bipunctulata (Hagen)

Hag. '61, p. 90: Mtk. Cat. p. 45: Garm. '27, p. 88.

Syn: bipustulata Kirby

Length 28 mm. Expanse 32 mm. N. Y. to Fla.

Male.—Color pale gray or brown and black. Face pale with a black spot at the base of the labrum and another and larger one at the base of the postclypeus. Pale transverse frontal band wide, reaching to the basis of the antennae and interdigitating with the black of the vertex on either side of the median ocellus. Top of head black except for spots on either side of the lateral ocelli, a pale post-ocellar stripe, and obscure pale postocular spots. Dorsum of the prothorax black except for a stripe on the anterior lobe, a pair of large lateral spots on the median lobe, and the sides of the posterior lobe which are pale. Sides of the median lobe pale. Thorax (fig. 289) predominantly black with wide middorsal and humeral dark stripes, which are twice as wide as the pale antehumeral stripe. A black line on the caudal end of the second lateral suture and another covering the third lateral suture. Abdomen predominantly blue, black as follows: a basal spot on the dorsum of 1; two small preapical spots and a fine preapical ring on 2; apical third or less of segments 3–6; apical five-sixths of 7; none of 8–9, sides inferiorly of 10.

Female.—Head and thorax as in the male. Abdomen with the dorsum of 4–7 and 9–10 brown or black except for narrow interrupted basal rings on 4–7. Sides of 1–5 as in the male, 6–10 mostly black. Segment 8 blue on the dorsum.

279. Argia emma Kennedy

Kndy. '15, p. 271.
Length 35–37 mm. Expanse 46–54 mm.   **Wash.**

Male.—Labrum, clypeus, frons, vertex, postocular area and occiput, rich violet. Genae lighter almost pinkish. Antennae black. A black line connecting each antennae with the median ocellus. A black T-spot extending forward from the median ocellus. The ocellar area black with large pale spots. Postocular area narrowly edged with black posteriorly. Prothorax pale the median lobe with two heavy median and two fine lateral longitudinal stripes of black, the

stripes joined by a fine brown transverse line across the anterior and posterior border of the middle lobe. Thorax predominantly pale. The dark middorsal stripe very narrow, not a fourth as wide as the pale antehumeral stripe. Humeral suture black as follows: a rectangular black spot below its anterior end from which a broad line extends dorsal to its middle point, where it tapers to a third of its previous width, extending thus narrowed to the dorsal fourth where it abruptly widens for the remainder of the extent of the suture. A black spot on the caudal end of the third lateral suture followed by a black line, also a short black line on the second lateral suture. Abdomen. Segment 1 pale violet with the sides and sternum brown overlaid with pruinose. Segments 2–7 violet, black as follows: 2, with a large lateral spot and narrow apical ring; 3–6 with a narrow line along the ventral edge of the plurite connected with an apical ring occupying from one-third to over one-half the length of the segment; about five-sixths of 7. Segments 8–10 blue on the dorsum with the sides black.

Female.—Head and thorax similar to the male. Abdomen pale black as follows; a pair of reduced dorso-lateral spots on 2; apical third of the dorsum of 3–6, and reduced postbasal streaks, not united with the apical black on 3–5, narrowly so on 6; segment 7 with a pair of dorso-lateral postbasal streaks but no apical black. Segments 8–10 entirely blue.

280. Argia fumipennis (Burmeister)
The Smoky-winged Argia

Burm. '39, p. 819: Mtk. Cat. p. 47: Garm. '17, p. 506.
Syn: obscura Ramb.

Length 33 mm. Expanse 41 mm.   **Ga., Ky. to Fla.**

This dark brown Argia is very common in the southeast where it can be easily collected from all types of environments.

Male.—Color obscure brown and black. Head dark brown and buff, with a black bar through the ocellar area, and the hind margins of the postocular area black. Dorsum of the prothorax and the sides of the median lobe narrowly black. Black middorsal thoracic stripe not quite as wide as the paler antehumeral, which latter is about as wide as the irregular humeral dark stripe. Abdominal segments 1–7 dark on the dorsum, sides lighter. Dorsum of 8–10 bluish-green, sides black. Wings uniformly dark smoky brown like those of *Agrion maculatum* or a little lighter.

Female.—Similar to the male. Dorsum of abdominal segments 8–10 dark sides paler. Segment 10 pale.

281. Argia hinei Kennedy

Kndy. '18, p. 258.
Length 31 mm. Expanse 42 mm.   **Calif. and Ariz.**

Male.—Labium and the rear of the head pale; labrum, face and the top of the head violet. A black bar through the ocelli; postocular areas edged posteriorly with black. Prothorax violet with a median dorsal stripe and a lateral stripe on each side of it, black. Thorax violet with the mid-carina edged with pale. The middorsal black stripe slightly wider than the pale antehumeral stripe. Black humeral stripe one-third as wide as the mesepimeron, forked in its posterior third. Third lateral suture narrowly black. Abdomen with segments 1–7 violet, segments 8–10 blue, with the following black markings: a dorso-basal

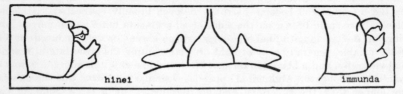

hinei   immunda

spot on 1; narrow apical rings on segments 2–7; segment 2 with a lateral stripe not reaching the apical edge; segments 3–5 with a spot covering the apical fourth of the sides, the pairs on segments 4–6 confluent on the middle line; a small antero-lateral spot on 6; segment 7 with the dorsal half black except a narrow basal band, and having a small latero-apical spot in the ventro-apical angle of the segment; segments 8–9 with more or less black on the lower sides.

Female.—Colored brown with the black markings on the head and thorax as in the male. The abdomen with lateral stripes on segments 2–9, those on segments 7–8 more or less confluent with their mates across the middle line. Segments 2–8 with latero-apical oblique spot on the lower apical angle of the side. Segments 2–7 with a narrow apical ring.

282. Argia immunda (Hagen)

Hag. '61, p. 93: Mtk. Cat. p. 47: Wmsn. '14, p. 415.
Length 30(♂)–36(♀) mm. Expanse 40–52 mm.   Tex.

Male.—Color, blue or violet and black. Face and rear of head pale, a black bar through the ocellar region. Prothorax black on the dorsum, sides pale. Pale antehumeral stripe from three-fourths to one and a half times as wide as the black middorsal. Humeral stripe forked in its upper third, never wider than the pale antehumeral. Abdomen blue, the following black: segment 2 each side with a dorso-basal spot, a large rounded spot near the apex, and an oblique inferior streak, the latter two or all three sometimes united; 3–6 each side with a postbasal streak and the apical third, the postbasal streaks from one side may unite with their fellows from the other across the meson, but never with the apical black; 7 entirely except a pale basal ring; an inferior stripe the length of the segment on 8–9.

Female.—Similar to the male. Differs as follows: Humeral stripe hardly more than a line throughout. Segment 7 like 6, but with the postbasal streak and apical black usually united; 8–9 entirely pale, unspotted.

283. Argia intruda Williamson

Wmsn. '12, p. 200.
Length 38–42 mm. Expanse 54–60 mm.   Okla.

This species of Argia is closely related to *moesta*, whose large size and general characteristics it shares.

Male.—Head dull pale brown, rear of head black above, pale brown below. Thorax pale brown, black as follows: a middorsal thoracic stripe, one either side occupying one-half of the front; a spot on the front against the humeral suture where it meets the mesinfraepisternum, and another above the caudal end of the second lateral suture; a faint line on the third lateral suture widened into a small spot on the rear end; in some specimens the two large black spots on the mesepimeron become narrowly or even broadly connected. Abdomen black above, pale brown on the sides of all segments but 7; pale narrow blue rings on 3–7; a longitudinal middorsal stripe absent or very reduced on 6–7; 9–10 variable, generally gray or light brown excepting the lower lateral margins and ventrally, and a black lateral spot on the middle of 9, this spot on 9 may be wanting or elongate. Abdominal appendages similar to *moesta*, but the inferiors are longer than the superiors, and are terminated by a large rounded pale tubercle.

Female.—Similar to the male. Darkest thoracic pattern: a black line on either side of the middorsal thoracic carina, separated from the black middorsal carina by a pale area equal in width to the black lines themselves, these black and pale areas occupy about one-half the surface of the mesepisternum on each side. This black area is developed in a pale area which is present on the mesepisternum as well as on the mesepimeron and the metepimeron, as in *moesta*. Abdomen darker than *moesta*, with a narrow pale dorsal longitudinal stripe, narrowest on 7. The lateral black is carried posteriorly onto 9, usually to its apex; 10 is pale colored. Sides of abdomen below the black, pale colored. The mesostigmal plates of *intruda* differ from *moesta* as follows: in *moesta* the posterior (or superior) lobe of the plate is symmetrical with the border of the plate on either side similarly curved, while the anterior (or inferior) border of the plate is distinctly concave, the external angle of the plate being correspondingly acute. In *intruda* the posterior border of the mesostigmal plate external to the lobe is straighter or less curved than internal to the lobe, resulting in an asymmetrical lobe, and the anterior border is straight or slightly convex, resulting in a less acute external angle.

284. Argia moesta (Hagen)

Hag. '61, p. 94: Mtk. Cat. p. 48: Wmsn. '12, p. 196: Smn. '27, p. 12: Garm. '27, p. 89.

Var: putrida Hag., *binotatum* Walsh, *fantum* Hag.

Length 43–45 mm. Expanse 50–56 mm.   **Okla., Tex., Ariz. and Calif.**

This is one of the largest of North American species, the typical form is confined to the southwestern United States and Mexico.

Male.—Head predominantly black or dark brown, face blue. Prothorax brown with a median black area. Middorsal thoracic stripe and carina dark brown, occupying about three-fourths of the front on each side, and being thus twice as wide as the pale antehumeral stripe. Humeral stripe a black line broadly

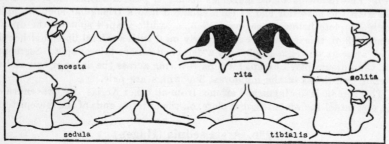

united below with another parallel band which reaches to the base of the fore wings. Metepimeron and adjoining parts of the metepisternum dark brown or black. These black areas of the thorax may become so large that the entire thorax is black save a very narrow pale antehumeral stripe, and an abbreviated streak on the metepisternum near its middle, just posterior to the interpleural suture. Abdomen with segment 2 blackish, with a middorsal yellow spot; 3–7 reddish brown with a narrow transverse basal yellow ring and a fine longitudinal, middorsal yellow line; 8–9 tawny, with a black stripe or a spot on each side near the base, the stripe extending sometimes nearly to the apex, the inferior margins blackish.

Female.—Differs from the male as follows: rear of head tawny with a vary-ing amount of black. Thoracic dorsum pale, the middorsal carina and a fine line on the humeral sutures black. Abdomen pale reddish brown, segments 3–7 each side with a longitudinal blackish stripe, paler below this; 8 as in male; 9 pale green or brown with or without black markings.

Both male and female have the stigma surmounting more than one cell in 98 per cent of cases. Also this species tends to become very pruinose very early in life, sometimes so much so as to entirely obscure the color pattern.

In the light colored eastern form (*A. putrida* Hagen), the face is yellowish. The antehumeral pale stripe is yellowish. The lower half of the sides of the thorax is pale, with only a narrow black stripe on the third lateral suture.

285. Argia rita Kennedy

Kndy. '19, p. 17.
Length 35 mm. Expanse 44 mm.   Ariz.

Male unknown.

Female.—Color of labium pale; labrum bluish; face and head otherwise violaceous, except the ventral surfaces which are pale buff. Each postocular area bounded anteriorly and posteriorly by a narrow bar of black. Prothorax violaceous, darker above, sides with a sinuous black line, the dorsum with a heavy black Y-mark, the fork opening caudal. Thorax with the middorsal carina pale, but edged by a very narrow, middorsal black stripe. Humeral stripe narrow in the lower half, narrowing to a hair line above, but widening into an oval spot at the alar ridge. Third lateral suture with a hair line of black. Ab-domen violaceous on segments 1–2, brown on segments 3–7, blue on segments 8–10. The following black markings occur: a pair of stripes on 2, mere hair lines with the posterior end of each enlarged into a triangular spot; an apical ring incomplete below on segments 2–6; a saddle-shaped spot on the apex of segments 3–6; this is connected anteriorly on 6 with a lateral line on either side which appears on segments 3–5 as a detached antero-lateral spot. Segment 7 with the dorsum black except for a narrow ring across the anterior end and the anterior two-thirds of the middorsal line which are pale.

This female is distinguished at once from all other Argias by two enormous pits, one under each mesostigmal plate, on the anterior ends of the mesepisterna.

286. Argia sedula (Hagen)

Hag. '61, p. 94: Mtk. Cat. p. 50: Wlsn. '12, p. 198: Garm. '17, p. 510: Smn. '27, p. 12.
Length 30(♂)–40(♀) mm. Expanse 40–45 mm.   C. and S. States to Ariz.

Male.—Face blue. Postclypeus blue with reduced black markings. Frons blue with a Y-shaped black mark anterior from the median ocellus. Ocellar area black with blue spots in the neighborhood of the lateral ocelli. Pale postocular spots large and contiguous with the margins of the compound eyes. Rear margin of the postocular area black. Dorsum of the prothorax black with a large lateral pale spot on either side of the median lobe, and smaller ones on the sides of the posterior lobe, sides pale. Thorax with the black middorsal and humeral stripes of about equal width, both twice as wide as the pale antehumeral stripe. A heavy black line on the third lateral suture (p. 289). Abdomen: segment 1 pale with a broad angulate basal spot and two small round lateral spots of black. Segment 2 black on the dorsum with small irregular basal pale greenish spot on either side of the meson. Segments 3–6 black on the dorsum with interrupted basal rings and two postbasal dorsal spots pale. Segment 7 almost entirely black. Dorsum of 8–10 blue, sides marked with black.

Female.—Like the male. Head brown above with a few black stripes in the ocellar region. Thorax with the black middorsal stripe wanting or feebly represented on either side of the carina. Dark humeral stripe represented by a hair line only. A black line on the metapleural suture. Abdomen segments 1–7 dull brown, sides tawny, basal rings ill defined. 8–10 tawny.

287. Argia solita Kennedy

Kndy. '18, p. 256.
Length 31 mm. Expanse 48 mm. **Ariz.**

Male.—Head creamy beneath, violet above, no black present at all. Prothorax violet with a small black spot on either side. Thorax violet. Black middorsal stripe narrow about one-sixth as wide as the pale antehumeral stripe. A mere hair line on the humeral and the third lateral sutures. Abdomen violet, black as follows: small lateral spot on the apex of 1; narrow apical ring on 2; lateral, irregular, apical spot, one-fourth the length of the segment, and a narrow apical ring on 3–6; segment 7 with an interrupted irregular stripe along the side, below the apical end of which is a small detached spot. Segments 8–10 blue.

Female.—Unknown.

288. Argia tibialis Rambur

Ramb. '42, p. 241; Mtk. Cat. p. 50: Whed. '14, p. 92: Garm. '17, p. 511.
Length 34–37 mm. Expanse 42–50 mm. **C., M. and S. States**

Found in June, July and August along the edge of streams or pools, flitting along the banks or resting among the bordering vegetation.

Male.—Mouth parts buff. Face blue or brownish. Vertex and occiput black with pale spots in the neighborhood of the ocelli. Prothorax black a lateral spot on each side of the middle lobe, brown. Black middorsal thoracic stripe about half as wide as the paler antehumeral, black humeral about as wide as the latter. Sides of the thorax tawny with a black line on the third lateral suture. Dorsum of abdominal segments 1–8 black, with narrow yellow basal rings on 2–7, sides of 2–7 narrowly pale. Dorsum of 9–10 yellow or blue, sides inferiorly black.

Female.—Light in color, much more so than the male. Humeral stripe narrower. Abdomen with segment 2 dark with a median pale spot, segments 3–6 with a fine pale line on the middorsum, sides broadly pale; 7–9 entirely black; 10 mostly pale, darker below.

289. Argia tonto Calvert

Calv. '02, p. 89: Mtk. Cat. p. 51.
Length 37–40 mm. Expanse 54–60 mm. **Ariz.**

Male.—Color violet and black. Black middorsal and humeral stripes reduced to little more than lines. Abdomen with segment 2 pale, each side with

a superior longitudinal black stripe not reaching the apex of the segment; 3–6
violet each side with a black spot on the apical fourth to third, united on the
meson with its fellow on the opposite side in segments 4 or 5–6, and with a black
transverse ring at the articulation between 3 and 4, and 4 and 5; 7 with a transverse basal ring and dorsal basal fourth, violet, apical dorsal three-fourths and
the greater part of the sides black and confluent; 8–9 with an inferior black
stripe on either side for the apical two-thirds of 8 and the entire length of 9.

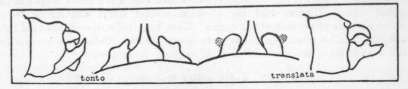

Female.—With the pale antehumeral stripe at mid-height one and one-
fourth times as wide as the black middorsal stripe; black humeral stripe not
forked, a mere line on its upper half, lower half one-fifth to a half as wide as the
pale antehumeral. The black postbasal stripe on either side of abdominal segments 3–6 is united with the apical black on 5 and 6 only; 8–9 blue. a narrow
black mark on either side of the dorsum in the basal fifth.

290. Argia translata Hagen

Hag. ’65, p. 410: Mtk. Cat. p. 51: Wlsn. ’12, p. 198: Garm. ’27, p. 90.
Length 40 mm. Expanse 46 mm.   N. Y., Va., to Wis., Ark. and Tex.

A large dark Argia found most commonly in the central and southern states.
Male.—Face dark brown, with black basal markings on the labrum and the
postclypeus. Top of head predominantly black. Brown postocular spots rather
small for Argia. Black middorsal thoracic stripe wide. Pale antehumeral stripe
irregular from one-third (young) to one-twelfth (old males) as wide as the black
middorsal, or absent entirely in very old individuals. Humeral stripe in young
males divided for almost its entire length, except at its lower end; in age these
two fuse to become even five times as wide as the pale antehumeral. A heavy
black line on the third lateral suture. Both the head and thorax are covered
with unusually long white fine hairs. Wings with the stigma surmounting more
than one cell in about 45½ of cases only. Abdomen with segments 2–8 almost
entirely black on dorsum, sides and basal rings paler. Segment 1 with a pale
spot on either side. Segment 9 pale on the dorsum with sides and apical markings
of black. Segment 10 predominantly dark.
Female.—Differs from the male as follows: Pale antehumeral stripe from
one-fifth to three-fifths as wide as the black middorsal. Humeral stripe as in
young males. Segments 2–7 with a pale longitudinal stripe on the middle line;
8–9 pale greenish on the sides with wide black stripes.

291. Argia violacea Hagen

Hag. ’61, p. 90: Mtk. Cat. p. 51: Garm. ’17, p. 515: Garm. ’27, p. 91.
Var: pallens Calv.
Length 32 mm. Expanse 42 mm.   Ont., Me. to Va., west to Mich. and Ariz.

While this, the most beautiful of the Argias, may occur generally throughout the whole of its range, it is found commonly only in the eastern states and southern Canada, where it becomes the dominant species of its genus. It frequents all types of aquatic situations but seems to prefer the dense reed grown banks of rivers and streams.

Male.—Mouth parts and head below gray. Frons, clypeus and genae purple or deep violet. Vertex mainly black. Large postocular spots and postocellar stripe gray or violet. Prothorax with the anterior lobe pale on the dorsum; middle lobe black with a large spot on either side and the sides inferiorly, violet; posterior lobe violet except two small lateral lines of black. Thorax (p. 289) with the middorsal black stripe not quite as wide as the pale antehumeral stripe. Humeral black stripe irregular and forked in its posterior third. Third lateral suture with a black line covering it. Sides of the thorax violet shading into gray along the dark stripes. Abdomen purple, black as follows: a basal, dorsal and lateral spots on 1; sides of 2 except apical fifth; sterna, pleura, narrow apical rings, and a lateral apical spot on segments 3-6, the latter occupying about one-fifth to one-fourth of the segment, on segments 5-6 at least they unite with their

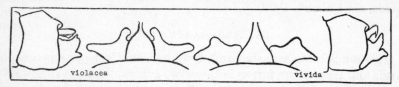

violacea   vivida

fellow from the opposite side across the dorsum, and are broadly joined with the black apical ring. Segment 7 entirely black, except for a narrow basal pale ring. Segments 8-10 purple on the dorsum black on the sides

Female.—The color similar to the male, the purple, however, in many specimens being replaced by brown. Head and thorax similar to the male. Abdomen with more black than the male, segments 2-9 with dorso-lateral stripes which are broad enough on segments 6-7 to fuse on the meson; lateral surface of 9 and all of 10 buff.

Pallens a subspecies of *violacea* is found in Arizona and Mexico, it differs from *violacea* type by having the humeral stripe of the thorax reduced to a mere line and the pale color of seg. 7 predominating.

292. Argia vivida Hagen

Hag. '65, p. 406: Mtk. Cat. p. 52: Kndy. '15, pp. 288, 298: '20, p. 84: Smn. '27, p. 13.

Var: munda Calv., *var. plana* Calv.

Length 34-38 mm. Expanse 46-52 mm.   B. C. and Mont. to Tex. and Calif.

A mountain species of Argia found commonly around springs and the boggy streamlets flowing from them.

Male.—Head pale beneath, mouth parts buff. Face blue. Ocellar region black with pale spots in the region of the ocelli. Postocular region blue except for a narrow black line on the posterior margins of the head. Prothorax pale blue with a pair of heavy median longitudinal black stripes on the dorsum, and a black sinuate line on either side. Thorax (p. 289) with the blue antehumeral stripe from two-fifths to nine-tenths as wide as the black middorsal. The black humeral stripe of unequal width throughout, the middle third sometimes wanting, seldom forked. A black line on the third lateral suture. Abdomen with segment 1 mostly blue. Segment 2 blue with a longitudinal black stripe on each side, the posterior end of which is triangularly dilated, and does not reach the apex, or this stripe represented only by a black anteapical spot. Segments 3-7 blue, each with a postbasal streak, and the apical third to fifth black, the postbasal streak usually not united with the apical black except on 7 and occasionally on 6 also; on 7 the black occupies the entire dorsum except a pale basal ring; the postbasal streaks are often absent on 3, and less frequently on 4 or 5; 8-9 blue unmarked.

Female.—Differs from the male as follows: Pale brown often replacing the blue of the male. Segment 9 as in the male, or, more frequently, with a short, black, basal stripe on each side of the dorsum.

For descriptions and notes regarding southwestern subspecies of *vivida*, see Calvert, 1902.

64. ARGIALLAGMA Selys

This genus belongs to the same division of the Coenagrioninae as does Argia and Hyponeura for, as in these two genera, the front row of setae on the tibia are all very long, being twice as long as the spaces separating them. It differs from these genera however, by the smaller number of these setae (5-7 on the 3rd tibia), in the reduced number of the postnodal cross veins with the result that M_2 arises nearest the 5th in the fore wing and the 4th in the hind, and in the presence of a ventral spine on the apical margin of abdominal segment 8 in the female.

There is but one known species:

293. Argiallagma minutum Selys

Selys '57, p. 464: Mtk. Cat. p. 52.
Syn: aduncum Hag.

Length 26 mm. Expanse 28-33 mm.   Fla.

A rare species of damselfly found in southern bogs and swamps.

Male.—Colors metallic black and pale yellowish. Head entirely pale beneath Labrum pale with the basal half black. Postclypeus black; anteclypeus pale. The pale transverse frontal stripe covering the vertical portion of the frons and the horizontal portion to the basis of the antennae. Antennae black, except the 2nd joint which has a broad median ring of pale. Vertex black. Pale postocular spots linear and broadly connected with the pale postocellar stripe on the caudomesal margin of the head, though separated from the pale color of the rear of the head. Dorsum of the prothorax metallic black, sides broadly pale. The hind margin of the posterior lobe high and convex throughout. Black middorsal thoracic stripe very wide touching the humeral suture at its caudal end, remainder of the humeral suture with a fine brown line separated from the mid-

dorsal stripe by a pale area. Sides of the thorax pale with a short dark spot on
the upper end of the second and third lateral sutures. Legs mostly pale. Stigma
with the proximal end tending to be more oblique than the distal end so that the
costal side is shorter than the posterior. 9–10 postnodal cross veins in the fore

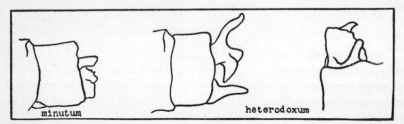

wing, 8 in the hind. Dorsum of abdominal segments 1–8 brassy black with pale
interrupted basal rings on 3–8; 9–10 usually entirely blue, 9 sometimes with a
dorsal black spot.

Female.—Similar to the male in all respects except the hind margin of the
prothorax is deeply trilobed, the dorsum of abdominal segment 9 is entirely
brassy black, and there is a well developed ventral spine on 8.

Nymph—unknown.

65. HESPERAGRION Calvert

These are small, brilliantly colored Sonoran damselflies that are
found only on our sothern border. The abdomen is moderately slender,
slightly widened at both ends. The wings have a rather long quadrangle
and a short stigma that is wider on its posterior than on its anterior
side. The stripings of the thorax and the pattern of the abdomen show
a remarkable variation of very brilliant colors; the changes are apparently due to age.

The nymph of this genus was reared by Mr. Frank C. Willard near
Tombstone, Arizona, and described by the senior author (Ndm. '04,
p. 717). "The situation was a deep reservoir of cold water, formed by
damming a stream that flowed through a narrow canyon. The imagoes
of the species 'spent most of their time among the joint-grass that grew
in the edge of the water.' "

294. Hesperagrion heterodoxum Selys

Selys '68, p. 69: Mtk. Cat. p. 53.

Syn: flavescens Selys

Length 28 mm. Expanse 36 mm.   **Ariz.**

This pretty species is remarkable for its extraordinary range of color. Changes
that seem to be due to age range from a pale yellow thorax without stripes,
through red with a middle bronze stripe, to blue with an antehumeral black
stripe each side of the front; from plain yellow on the top of the head, through
blue with red postocular spots, to wholly black; from pale abdomen with middle

segments only black above, through bright red at both ends, to black at ends and green in the middle. Face is pale except for a black postclypeus. The legs are yellow becoming striped with black in front with age. The wings are hyaline, with a stigma that is wider on the hind than on the front margin. Appendages pale.

66. AMPHIAGRION Selys

These are small stout-bodied black and red damselflies that frequent reedy, spring-fed swales. The abdomen is rather short and thick. The wings are hyaline. The stigma is notably longer in the front than on the hind margin, especially in the male, and the costal area of the wing tips beyond the stigma is richly charged with cross veins.

The sexes are colored alike except that the red of the male becomes brighter. The color changes with age are considerable. Size varies greatly also and a number of variations have been described. The species is wide ranging within our limits; frequenting meadow rivulets. Adults are found only in the vicinity of their native streamlets where they flit about among the stems in or overhanging the water.

The nymphs (Ndm. '03, p. 248) have a thick set body and remarkably prominent hind angles on the head.

In our fauna there is a single variable species.

295. Amphiagrion saucium Burmeister

Burm. '39, p. 819: Mtk. Cat. p. 66: Whed. '14, p. 92: Garm. '17, p. 562 and '27, p. 48.

Syn: abbreviatum Selys, *discolor* Burm., *amphion* Selys

Length 27 mm. Expanse 36 mm.   **Wash. and Calif. to Mass. and S. C.**

This is a stocky little red and black species with trapezoidal stigma with clear wings. The face is yellowish in front, becoming red with age, and black above. Thorax bronzy black without distinct stripings, but with paler carinae. Legs pale brownish. Abdomen yellowish to reddish brown, becoming bright red over the basal half. The apex suffused with blackish except for a median narrow red line and a red area inferiorly. Appendages reddish.

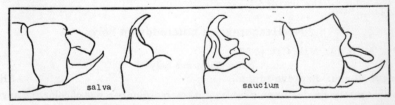

Whedon ('14, p. 92) discovered this species in "small numbers and in teneral condition along a very small stream leading from the 'slough' to the Minnesota River at Mankato on June 11, '13. A few days after, thousands of the fully colored individuals were copulating and ovi-positing in the shallow water among the sedges and the Sagittarias. A week later their numbers began to reduce and by July 7 but an occa-sional specimen could be found. During the whole period their distri-bution was limited to an area of 200 yards along this little rivulet, so narrow that one could easily leap across it anywhere, and but a few inches deep. Such a localization is not what would be expected of a species distributed from the Atlantic to the west."

67. TELEBASIS Selys

These are dainty little red damselflies of the southwest. The legs are weak and slender. The abdomen is moderately slender. The wings are hyaline with rather long quadrangle and rather short stigma that sur-mounts hardly one entire cell.

296. Telebasis salva Hagen

The Flapper

Hag. '61, p. 85: Mtk. Cat. p. 63: Ndm. '23, p. 130: Smn. '27, p. 16.
Syn: boucardi Selys

Length 27 mm. Expanse 30 mm. **Calif.**

This is a dainty little damselfly with brown striped thorax and red abdomen. The face is yellowish or reddish up to the ocelli. Top of head bronzy black. Front of thorax with a broad bronzy black middle stripe divided by the yellow carina, bifurcated above and notched on the outer margin at three fourths its length. Sides of thorax pale with a short oblique stripe behind the humeral suture and a spot on the suture. Legs yellowish with short black spines. Stigma yellowish. Abdomen red, paler beneath; a little suffused with brownish toward the tip. Appendages red with blackish tips.

It flies very low over the water—so low that one cannot get a net under it and avoid the water. It haunts the low vegetation, especially the spike-rush patches. The male accompanies the female while she deposits her eggs. They fly together in a straight line, tandem, and settle together on floating alga-mats or sticks. While the female is plying her ovipositor beneath the surface the male is held aloft solely by the clasp of his caudal appendages about her prothorax.

The nymph (Ndm. '09, p. 176) in life is very easily recognized, among the other very similar damselfly nymphs with which it is associ-ated, by reason of an odd little mannerism of its own: about once a second it flaps the lateral gills at the end of the body against the middle one. This act suggests the aimless manner in which a cat-bird flirts its tail; but the movement of the gills is lateral.

Transformation is apparently at its height about the latter end of August. It occurs always within a few inches of the surface of the water. The color changes that this species undergoes after transformation are very striking. It emerges from the nymph skin pale yellow and becomes more yellow before it turns red. The bronzy green-black stripes upon the thorax and across the top of the head are at first pale brown and then deep brown and acquire their metallic luster only at full maturity.

68. NEHALENNIA Selys

These are very delicate little bronzy green damselflies the entire dorsum of head and body is more or less completely rich bronzy green. The face is pale, cross lined with black. The legs are short, pale, with black stripings and black spines. Wings are hyaline with pale stigma covering a single cell and with narrow quadrangle. The abdomen is very slender widening a little toward both ends.

The nymphs (Ndm. '03, p. 249) are slender, climbing forms that inhabit dense beds of submerged vegetation. They are greenish in color with faint brownish rings on legs and with spots on the gill margins.

Our species of this Holarctic genus are distinguishable as follows:

KEY TO THE SPECIES*
Adults
1. Males

1   Superior appendages longer than the inferiors. Dorsum of abdominal segments 8–9 dark metallic blue, each with a narrow transverse pale line at base and apex, sides pale blue; 10 pale blue with a little black at the base middorsally............
....**pallidula,** p. 307
Superior appendages equal to or shorter than the inferiors......2.

2   Abdominal segment 8 blue, with a transverse dorsal basal black or metallic green line or spot, 9–10 entirely pale blue. Superior appendages nearly as long but not as high as the inferiors seen in profile view..............................**gracilis,** p. 307
Abdominal segment 8 with a broad dark dorsal band reaching nearly to the apical margin; 9–10 blue with dark markings..3.

* Prepared by C. F. Byers.

3   Dorsum of abdominal segment 8 dark metallic green with no pale dorsal spots; 9–10 blue, 9 with a metallic green stripe on each side of the dorsum reaching from the base to one-half to two-thirds the way to the proximal end, 10 with a transverse basal black line....................................**integricollis**, p. 308

Dorsum of abdominal segment 8 dark metallic green with a pale middorsal spot on the posterior fourth or less, and sides inferiorly pale blue; 9 pale blue with a triangular dark metallic green spot on each side of the dorsum in its basal half or more; 10 pale blue with a metallic green spot on each side of the dorsum at the base. Superior appendages smaller than the inferiors.......................................**irene**, p. 308

2. Females

1   Hind margin of the prothorax entire and convex. Abdominal segment 8–9 dark metallic blue-green, no pale dorsal spots on 8, a pale blue dorsal spot on 9, sides inferiorly and 10 pale blue with slight traces of black at extreme base....**integricollis**, p. 308

Hind margin of the prothorax emarginate...................2.

2   Hind margin of the prothorax bilobed. Segment 8 pale with a transverse stripe and lateral band of dark, or the dorsum of 8 almost entirely black; 9 blue with a triangular dark lateral band; 10 entirely blue.............................**gracilis**, p. 307

Hind margin of prothorax trilobed. 8–9 dark metallic green, 9 with a pale dorsal spot. Rarely 8–9 colored like male......
....**irene**, p. 307

Unknown................................**pallidula**, p. 308

297. Nehalennia pallidula Calvert

Calv. '13, p. 373.

Length 24 mm. Expanse 26 mm.   Fla.

Another delicate bronzy green species. Face pale, cross striped with black on the postclypeus, and a narrow line on the base of the labrum. Front of thorax bronze green. Sides yellow below the middle line. Sides of abdominal segments 1–6 pale bluish; of 7–8 yellowish; dorsum of 8 green with no dorsal spots; of 9–10 blue; 9 with a green stripe each side, 10 with a transverse basal black line. Appendages blackish.

298. Nehalennia gracilis Morse

Morse '95, p. 274: Mtk. Cat. p 64: Walk. '13, p. 161: Garm '27 p. 51.

Length 25 mm. Expanse 32 mm.   Mass., N. Y., N. J.

Another slender bronzy green species. Face is paler with blackish postclypeus and with a dark triangle projecting forward from the base of the labrum. Basal segments of the antennae ringed with black. Top of head black. Thorax and abdomen much as in *irene* except as noted in key.

This species is found at the edges of upland bogs where cotton grass and sphagnum grow.

299. Nehalennia integricollis Calvert

Calv. '13, pp. 312; p. 373: Garm. '27, p. 50.

Length 22 mm. Expanse 26 mm.   **N. J.**

This is one of the smallest of the damselflies. Face pale with black post-clypeus and a trilobed black line across the base of the labrum. Top of head black. Front of thorax black with metallic reflections becoming green towards the fore wing roots. Sides, below the middle, line yellow. Legs yellow; the femora lined and the tibiae dotted with black. Abdomen dark bronze green above becoming bluish toward the apex; yellow beneath. 8 above, wholly black; 10 blue; 9 blue with a pair of large basal black spots. Appendages black in the male, yellowish in the female.

300. Nehalennia irene Hagen

Hag. '61, p. 74: Mtk. Cat. p. 65: Butler '14, p. 346: Whed. '14, p. 92: Garm. '17, p. 559 and '27, p. 51.

Syn: carlotta Butler

Length 27 mm. Expanse 30 mm.   **Me. and N. D. to Fla.**

This is a delicate bronzy green species with blue tipped abdomen. Face pale, cross striped with black on the postclypeus and base of labrum. Basal segment of antennae ringed with black and white. Top of head metallic green. Front

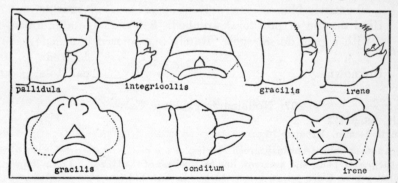

of thorax wholly metallic green except for narrow black lines on the carinae, and the sutures. Sides yellow below the mid line. Legs yellow with black marginal lines on the femora and tibiae, and with black spines. Abdomen bronzy green above, yellowish beneath; the yellow extending, encircling the base of segments 1–7. Black of dorsum restricted apically on 8–10; little on 8, two half length spots on 9, two basal spots on 10. Appendages black in male, brown in female.

Whedon ('14, p. 92) says: "It is usually found in the tall grasses about marshy places and kettle holes, never venturing into the higher

air but keeping close to the water along the shore line or fluttering un-
seen between the stems of the sedges."

69. CHROMAGRION Needham

These are damselflies of moderate size and rather unique coloration.
The bright yellow of the rear of the thorax beneath will at once distinguish them from all the others. The legs are rather long but their
spines are short.

The nymphs (Ndm. '03, p. 247) are climbers amid the submerged
vegetation of sheltered pools. The gills are long and rather narrow
and rather aburptly tapered at their tips.

There is but one species.

301. Chromagrion conditum Hagen

Hag. '76, p. 1305: Mtk. Cat. p. 67: Garm. '17, p. 565 and '27, p. 46.
Length 35 mm. Expanse 48 mm.   **Me. and N. J. to Ind. and Que.**

These are damselflies of blue and yellow coloration. The face is pale, cross
striped with black on postclypeus and base of labrum. Top of head black. Front
of thorax is well covered by a broad black stripe that is widest in the middle and
notched each side above. The sides are pale with only traces of stripes in the
depths of the sutures; yellow below the third lateral suture (or higher in the
female); becoming a robin's egg blue above. Legs blackish externally on the
femora and internally on the tibiae, becoming pruinose white basally, as in the
whole under surface of the thorax. Wings hyaline with rather long quadrangular
stigma surmounting a single cell. Abdomen blackish above with the blue of the
yellow of the sides, on its basal half, extending upward almost to the middorsal
line at the front of the segments. 6 and 7 wholly black; 8 and 9 in the male with
a dorsal pair of round spots on a blue ground, and an intervening, interrupted
middorsal blue line. Appendages black.

The imagoes appear to keep rather close to the shelter of their native
pool, spending but little time on the wing. Transformation takes place
for the most part in the morning or early forenoon, and the place
selected is but a few inches above the water. The species is of wide
distribution, but is every where quite local.

70. TELEALLAGMA KENNEDY

(Kndy. '20, p. 87 for *Telagrion daeckii*)

These are very long and slender and pale-hued damselflies in which
the wings are stalked, generally as far out as the anal crossing. Within
our range is found a single species.

The nymph (Ndm. '04, p. 715) is likewise elongate, but otherwise
similar to Enallagma.

302. Teleallagma daeckii Calvert

Calv. '03, p. 306: Mtk. Cat. p. 64: Wmsn. '15, p. 616: Garm. '27, p. 50.
Length 43 mm. Expanse 46 mm.   **Atl. Coast, N. J. to Fla.**

This is a long, thin, pale bluish species with obscure black markings and an extremely long abdomen. Face blue with a few black dots. Top of head blackish with a pair of 1 large, triangular, pale blue postocular spots. Front of thorax with carina black and narrowly bordered with black, and with a widely interrupted stripe on the humeral suture. Sides pale with a short black narrow line at the upper end of middle suture. Legs pale with a black stripe on all femora above and one on outside and front of tibiae. There is a blackish middorsal stripe on abdominal segments 1–6, widening before the apex on each segment, covering three-fourths of 7; apex of 7 and 8 to 10 pale blue. Appendages black-tipped.

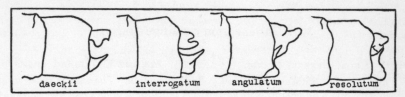

daeckii   interrogatum   angulatum   resolutum

71. Coenagrion

These are blue-and-back-ringed damselflies of moderate size, in which the wings are stalked almost to the anal crossing, and the rather short stigma surmounts less than a single cell.

The nymphs of none of our American species have as yet been made known.

KEY TO THE SPECIES

Adults

1   Pale stripes of front of thorax interrupted by a cross line of black
. . . .**interrogatum,** p. 310
    Pale stripes entire. 2
2   Dorsal black spot of second abdominal segment isolated. . . . . . .
. . . .**angulatum,** p. 311
    Dorsal black spot of second abdominal segment connected with
    the black at apex of segment. . . . .**resolutum,** p. 311

303. Coenagrion interrogatum Selys

Selys '76, p. 254: Walk. '15, p. 174.
Length 30 mm. Expanse 38 mm.   **Sask.**

This is a pretty blue and black species of average stature. Face greenish, postclypeus and heavy line at base of labrum black. Top of head black with bluish pyriform postocular spots. A narrow blue occipital line between them.

Thorax bronzy blue with two antehumeral stripes of blue interrupted at three quarters their height. Sides of thorax blue with traces of a black line on the upper part of the middle suture and a continuous broader irregular line on the third lateral suture. Legs blackish beyond the middle of the femora; tibiae greenish externally. Abdomen bronze black above on middle segments, most extensively black on 6 with two transverse crescents (♂) or a club shaped spot (♀) on 2; 8 and 9 blue with submedian dots (♂) or basal quadrangular spots (♀) of black. 10 black in male and blue in female.

This species inhabits reedy borders of trout streams

304. Coenagrion angulatum Walker

Walk. '12, p. 256: Whed. '14, p. 93: Whts. '17, p. 98.
Length 30 mm. Expanse 36 mm.   Man., Sask.

This is an azure blue species marked with black. Face pale green cross-lined with black on the postclypeus and base of labrum. Head black above with large pyriform postocular spots and no connecting line on the occiput. Front of thorax bronze black with blue antehumeral bands that are parallel sided and slightly convergent toward their isolated ends. Sides bluish. Legs pale yellow, femora and tibiae lined with black. Abdomen bluish above, yellowish beneath, marked with bronze black as follows: an isolated transverse crescent on the second segment; a broad band covering most of 3–7; and the dorsum of 10; and in the female all of 9 and basal three-fourths of 8, as well. Appendages blackish.

The nymph is at present unknown but its true habitat appears to be "a stagnant slough rather than a considerable body of clear water" (Whitehouse '17, p. 98).

305. Coenagrion resolutum Hagen

Hag. '76, p. 1263: Mtk. Cat. p. 66: Walk. '12, p. 255.
Length 30 mm. Expanse 37 mm.   Gr. Slave L., Hudson Bay, Wis.

Another bronzy black and blue species. Face pale greenish yellow except postclypeus which is bronze black. Postocular spots blue; a greenish line between them along the occiput. Front of thorax bronze black with two pale greenish antehumeral lines that are isolated at both ends and a little constricted towards the upper end. Sides bluish or yellowish green. Abdomen pale blue above, greenish below, marked with bronze black as follows: a club shaped spot at apex and a pair of longitudinal lines before it on 2; broad apical spots on 3–5, more extensive on 6–7; all of 10 but the hind margins. Appendages blackish. 8 and 9 are blue in the female and the black spot on 10 is smaller and basal in the female.

This is a widely distributed species.

72. ENALLAGMA Charpentier
The Bluets, etc.
By C. Francis Byers

This is the second largest genus of North American Odonata, numbering 38 species, and being surpassed only by the Anisopterous genus

Gomphus with its 45 species. In the suborder of the Zygoptera it is dominant, both in the number of described species and the number of individuals. In all faunal lists of Odonata, the term "common" appears frequently after the names of the species.

While Enallagmas frequent all types of aquatic habitat, being recorded even from brackish water and desert alkaline pools, they prefer still, shallow, fresh water, where there is an abundance of submerged and floating vegetation.

The adults spend most of their time over the surface of the water, or in the grasses along the shores of the lakes and streams, but occasionally they are found in the woods and fields. They fly from plant to plant, or from one mass of floating algae to another, they are particularly fond of resting on bulrushes and cat-tails, or on floating lily pads. They fly very low, some species so low that it is well nigh impossible to get a collecting net under them without dipping the water. In foraging they fly through the vegetation, seldom over it, and do not often depart very far from the borders of the water. They flit easily about among the grass stems and settle often in a rigidly horizontal position on the stems and leaves. Their food consists mainly of small Diptera, mosquitoes, midges, etc., that swarm in such places. They are eaten by frogs, which lie in ambush amid the floating algae, and catch them when they come to mate or oviposit; by swallows and other birds, that can fly close enough to the water to get them. They are snared in spiders webs, and are captured and eaten by robber-flies, dragonflies and other damselflies.

The eggs are deposited in punctures in the tissues of green plants just beneath the surface of the water. Floating leaves are preferred, but the stems of standing aquatics are often found thickly punctured and filled with eggs in all stages of development. Oviposition generally is performed *in copulo*, the male flying along with the female. They do not, as a rule, descend below the surface; however, several species have been observed to do so, in which case the female is unaccompanied by the male.

The adults divide sharply into two groups on color, the larger group, being bright blue and black, the other, black with yellow or orange markings. The head is predominantly black above, with the mouth parts, the anteclypeus, the genae, the postgenae and the occiput, pale. The postclypeus (nasus) is usually black, but in some if species is pale with reduced black markings. There is a pale transverse frontal band, just above the clypeus, on the frons, of varying width, sometimes extending as far as the median ocellus. The vertex is usually entirely black, with occasional pale spots around the ocelli. Antennae are entirely black, or black with the two basal joints pale. Pale postocular spots are always present, in some species small and entirely surrounded by the black of the head, in others large and united with each other by way of the pale occipital stripe on the rear of the head, or united with the pale of the rear of the head, that is, the postgenal and occipital region, in still other species they are very thin and linear. The prothorax is predominantly black, with superimposed pale areas and spots. Certain species have a pair of dorsal pits on the prothorax in the females. The thorax is always predominantly pale, never metallic green, with a black middorsal and humeral stripe of varying width and extent, and usually reduced basal black markings on the second and third lateral sutures. M_2 arises between the fourth and sixth, usually the fourth and fifth, postnodal cross vein in the fore wings, and between the third and fifth in the hind wings. The legs always have the front row of setae on the tibia less than twice as long as the spaces between their bases. The coloration of the abdomen varies greatly and is used for the determination of species. The females all have a ventral spine on the apical margin of abdominal segment eight. The appendages of the malevary greatly also, and are the final criteria for specific determination.

The nymphs live in tangled submerged vegetation, and are among the most numerous of the predatory hordes in such places, living on other insect larva, small crustaceans, etc. They are eaten by larger aquatic insects and vertebrates, especially the shallow-water fish.

Of the thirty-eight described species of North American adults, the nymphs of only eighteen are known, and only fourteen have been adequately described. Their identification is difficult and it is quite impossible to write a satisfactory key for their separation in the light of our present incomplete knowledge of them. In general, the nymph of Enallagma is slender, nearly smooth, with the head a third wider than the succeeding parts of the body. Antennae long slender, six or seven jointed, the segments generally increasing in length to the third, decreasing thereafter to the tip. Labium slender with a prominant median lobe, which has a row of 3–9 setae on the lateral margins in addition to the mental setae, numbering from 2–4 on a side. Lateral setae 4–6. Legs usually smooth with a preapical brown ring on the femora. The abdomen cylindric, each segment with lateral keels, well or poorly developed, and carrying in some species clumps or rows of heavy setae. The gills vary greatly as to size and pigmentation, but do not possess the long tapering points of Ischnura and Anomalagrion.

Enallagma is essentially a holarctic genus, with its center of distribution in the United States. However, a number of species have been described from Africa and from the islands of the Pacific. The present account embodies all the New World species with the exception of *E. krugii* Kolbe, *E. truncatum* Gundlach, from Porto Rico and Cuba, and probably *E. simile* Selys from Venezuela.

The Known Nymphs

Species	Length*	Setae		Ext†	Comb‡	Gills Pigmentation	Described by
		Lat.	Ment.				
antennatum	14+7.5	4–5	3	7–8	½	Basal ⅔ & apex	Ndm. '03, p. 257
boreale	15+7	6	4	5–6	½+	Tracheae only	Walk. '16, p. 192
carunculatum	14+6	6	3	8–9	⅓	Tracheae only	Ndm. '03, p. 255
civile	15+6	5–6	3–4	7–8	½—	Tracheae only	Ndm. & Ckll. '03, p. 137
cyathigerum	14+5	5–6	4	4–5	½+	Tracheae only	Lucas '00, p. 297 Walk. '16, p. 193
ebrium	13+5.5	6	2–4	6	½+	Tracheae only	Walk. '14, p. 351 Lyon '15, p. 57
exsulans	13+6	4–5	3	6–7	⅔	Basal ½ of tracheae	Ndm. '03, p. 255
geminatum	12+4.7	5	3	3–4	½—	Tracheae only	Ndm. '03, p. 254
hageni	15+5	5	3	3–4	½+	Tracheae only	Ndm. '03, p. 253
pallidum	14+7	4	2	6	½	Tracheae, base & apex	Byers '27, p. 00
praevarum	13+5	5	3	3	½	Tracheae only	Smn. '27, p. 14
signatum	17+5.5	5	3	3–4	?	3 dark bands	Ndm. '03, p. 258
traviatum	11(?)+6	4	6–7	2–3	0	Basal ½	Garm. '17, p. 556
vesperum	16+5.5	5	3–4	4	0	Uniform (?)	Walk. '13, p. 162 (as pollutum)

† Body +gills. * Spines on outer margin of mentum of labium.
‡ Spinous margin on base of dorsal edge of middle gill in terms of length of entire gill.

The keys for the separation of the adults follow. A key dealing with so many species is bound to be cumbersome, so final identification should only be made after a comparison with a written description and drawings of the male superior abdominal appendages. The identification of the females is notoriously difficult, and is in many cases only certain when the specimen has been taken mated with a known male, it is for this reason that collectors of Enallagma should be very careful not to separate such pairs in the killing and mounting processes.

The species of Enallagma may be broken up into four large groups, based in the main on the genitalia of the male. These groups may be roughly defined as follows:

Group A: Superior appendages distinctly shorter than the 10th abdominal segment; simple in form, not *distinctly* bifid, and without a tubercle. Color blue and black. Abdominal segment 2 with an apical black spot and ring, the remainder blue.

Group B: Superior appendages bifid; the inferior arm as long or longer than the superior.

Group C: Superior appendages bifid, the inferior arm never as long as the superior.

Group D: Superior appendages as long as, or longer than, the 10th abdominal segment. Not bifid. Color black with yellow or orange markings. Abdominal segment 2 with the black of the dorsum reaching from the base to the apex.

The species may be arranged under these groups as follows:

A.	*B.*	*C.*	*D.*
cyathigerum	ebrium	anna	cultellatum
		prevarum	
clausum	exsulans		
divagans	weewa	culicinorum	laurenti
			vesperum
hageni	antennatum	eiseni	pollutum
recurvatum	pallidum		
		basidens	signatum
geminatum			sulcatum
piscinarium	doubledayi	semicirculare	
	carunculatum		concisum
boreale		coecum	pictum
	civile	cardenium	dubium
durum			
minusculum		aspersum	
		travatum	
laterale			

KEY TO THE SPECIES

Adults

1. Males

1 Superior abdominal appendages not bifid, the distal margin at most only slightly indented giving the appendage a bilobed appearence (*pollutum, durum, divagans* and *minusculum*).......2.
 Superior appendages bifid, consisting of two distinct parts narrowly joined near the base. There may or may not be a clear yellowish tubercle between the arms in the notch of the fork..21

2 Superior abdominal appendages small, greatest length less than that of the 10th segment. Dorsum of abdominal segment 2 blue with a black dorsal spot or spots of varying size, but never covering the entire dorsum from base to apex of the segment (except *divagans*). Color blue and black.........................3.

Superior abdominal appendages large, greatest length as long or
longer than 10th segment (except *sulcatum*). Dorsum of abdominal segment 2 with the black of the dorsum extending from
the base to the apex of the segment. Color predominantly black
with orange or yellow markings, occasionally blue........13.

3   Abdominal segments 8–9 unmarked with black..............4.
Abdominal segment 8 marked with black, 9 blue entirely.....11.

4   Abdominal segment 2 with dorsum entirely black.**divagans**, p. 322
Abdominal segment 2 blue with a black spot...............5.

5   Inferior appendages longer than the superiors..............6.
Inferior appendages as long as the superiors or shorter........9.

6   M_2 arising between the 3rd -4th postnodal cross veins in the hind
wings.....................................**hageni**, p. 322
M_2 arising between the 4th–5th postnodals in the hind wing....7.

7   Superior appendages blunt, berry-like..........**boreale**, p. 323
Superior appendages with tips more or less acute............8.

8   Superior appendages with tip recurved. Humeral dark stripe
broken and very narrow...................**clausum**, p. 324
Superior appendages with tip directed posteriorly. Humeral stripe
wider and not broken...................**cyathigerum**, p. 324

9   Abdominal segments 3–5 at least one-third blue.............10.
Abdominal segments 3–5 mostly black.......**piscinarium**, p. 325

10 With 4–5 antenodal cells between M4 and Cu1...**durum**, p. 325
With 3 such antenodal cells...............**minusculum** p. 325

11 Abdominal segment 9 marked with black on the sides..........
....**geminatum**, p. 326
Abdominal segment 9 all blue...........................12.

12 Superior abdominal appendages with the tips recurved........
....**recurvatum**, p. 326
Superior abdominal appendages with the end truncate, distal margin slightly convex, inferiors longer than superiors............
....**laterale**, p. 327

13 Abdominal segment 2 with the dorsum entirely black........14.
Abdominal segment 2 with the black of the dorsum assuming a
U-shape, the arms of the U reaching from near the base to the
apex so as to isolate a pale median spot from the pale of the
sides................................**cultellatum**, p. 327

14 Dorsum of abdominal segment 9 pale blue or orange.........15.
Dorsum of abdominal segment 9 black. Pale postocular spots linear, not confluent with the pale color of the rear of the head. Pale antehumeral stripe narrower than the black humeral stripe 19

15 Pale postocular spots directly confluent with the pale color of the rear of the head. Middle prothoracic lobe predominantly pale on dorsum...............................**laurenti**, p. 327
Pale postocular spots not directly confluent with the pale color of the rear of the head, although they may be indirectly confluent therewith, by way of, the pale postocellar stripe. Middle prothoracic lobe predominantly black on dorsum..........16.

16 Pale antehumeral stripe narrower than the black humeral stripe ....17.
Pale antehumeral stripe as wide as, or wider than the dark humeral stripe..18.

17 Ninth abdominal segment orange..............·...**pollutum**, p. 328
Ninth abdominal segment blue...............**sulcatum**, p. 329

18 Ninth abdominal segment yellow..............**signatum**, p. 329
Ninth abdominal segment blue..............**vesperum**, p. 330

19 The two basal joints of the antennae black. No pale spots about the ocelli...................................**dubium**, p. 330
The two basal joints of the antennae pale. Two light spots between the lateral and median ocelli...... ....20.

20 Second lateral thoracic (metapleural) black stripe abruptly narrowed at three-fourths to two-thirds its length to a narrow line ....**pictum**, p. 331
Second lateral thoracic black stripe uniformly widening from anterior to posterior end....................**concisum**, p. 332

21 Superior abdominal appendages with the inferior arm as long or longer than the superior................................22.
Superior abdominal appendages with the superior arm always the longer, the inferior arm short and in some species assuming the form of a basal spine or flap............................29.

22 Without a clear tubercle between the arms of the superior abdominal appendages.....................................23.
With a clear tubercle between the arms of the superior abdominal appendages.......................................26.

23 Dorsum of abdominal segment 2 blue with a black spot........
....**ebrium,** p. 332
Dorsum of abdominal segment 2 wholly black..............24.

24 Superior appendages with the arms approximate, the inferior
longer than the superior.............................25.
Superior appendages with the arms widely divergent, the superior
as long as the inferior...............................27.

25 A line drawn through the long axis of the upper arm of the superior
appendages parallel to a similar line drawn through the lower
....**exsulans,** p. 332
A line drawn through the long axis of the upper arm of the superior
appendages meets a similar line drawn through the lower at an
acute angle.............................**weewa,** p. 333

26 Abdominal segment 8–10 almost entirely pale blue...........
....**pallidum,** p. 334
Abdominal segments 8 and 10 black on the dorsum...........
....**antennatum,** p. 334

27 Dorsum of abdominal segments 4–5 more than half black......
....**carunculatum,** p. 335
Dorsum of abdominal segments 4–5 less than half black......28.

28 Superior appendages with the tubercle projecting noticeably beyond the dorso-caudal angles when viewed from the side......
....**doubledayi,** p. 335
Superior abdominal appendages not as above. Arms longer and
more divergent.............................**civile,** p. 336

29 With a clear tubercle usually present on the inner face of the
superior appendages, usually visible in profile view between the
arms of the appendage, but not always..................30.
Without such a tubercle...............................32.

30 Superior appendages in dorsal view, with a long basal tooth just
beyond the point where the lower branch of the appendages is
attached to the upper. Lower branch broad, angulate and flap-
like.............................**culicinorum,** p. 336
Superior appendages in dorsal view without this tooth. Lower
branch not flap-like, more or less pointed.................31.

31 Superior appendages with the apex of the upper arm directed back,
lower arm with the apex directed posteriorly..**praevarum,** p. 337
Superior appendages with the apex of the upper arm directed
ventrally, the lower arm directed in the same direction......
....**anna,** p. 338

32   Abdominal segment 2 with the black of the dorsum extending from
     base to apex..33.
     Abdominal segment 2 with the black of the dorsum in isolated
     spots, streaks or bands...............................34.

33   M₂ arising nearest the 5th postnodal cross vein in the fore wings,
     4th in the hind. Eight to ten postnodals. Superior appendages
     with the lower arm appearing as a basal triangle, with the apex
     directed ventrally.............................**eiseni,** p. 338
     M₂ arising nearest the 4th postnodal cross vein in the fore wings,
     3rd in the hind. 5–6 post nodals............**basidens,** p. 339

34   Caudal half at least of segment 7 pale.........**aspersum,** p. 339
     Abdominal segment 7 with the dorsum mostly black.........35.

35   Segment 10 entirely blue.................**semicirculare,** p. 340
     Segment 10 with black markings...........................36.

36   Segment 10 entirely black on dorsum, sides of 8 with black streaks.
     ....**traviatum,** p. 340
     Segment 10 with some pale markings on the dorsum.........37.

37   Segment 10 with a narrow median stripe of black, remainder blue
     ....**eiseni,** p. 338
     Segment 10 with the sides and a narrow basal stripe black, leaving
     a pale apical area on the dorsum........................38.

38   Postocular spots wide, .45–.49 mm. from cephalic to caudal edge
     ....**coecum,** p. 341
     Postocular spots narrow, .28–.38 mm. from the cephalic to the
     caudal border.........................**cardenium,** p. 341

2. Females

1   Middle prothoracic lobes with a pair of dorsal pits............2.
     Middle prothoracic lobes without a pair of dorsal pits.......21.

2   Abdominal segment 10 usually without black markings on the
     dorsum..3.
     Segment 10 with black markings on the dorsum.............9.

3   Dorsum of segment 9 mostly black........................4.
     Dorsum of segment 9 entirely blue or with black lines or spots only
     ....5.

4   Antenodal cells, 4–5...................**durum,** p. 335
     Antenodal cells 2–3....................**antennatum,** p. 334

5   Dorsum of segment 9 all blue.............**traviatum,** p. 340
     Dorsum of segment 9 with black lines or spots.............6.

6   Dorsum of segment 9 with a pair of dorsal black spots on the basal
    half. . . . . .7.
    Dorsum of 9 without spots, these replaced by 2 dorso-lateral lines
    either joined or separated at the meson. . . . . .8.

7   Ten to eleven postnodal cross veins. Distribution: Eastern U. S.
    west to Texas. . . . .**exsulans**, p. 332, and **weewa**, p. 333
    Five to six postnodal cross veins. Distribution: Western U. S.
    east to Texas. . . . .**basidens**, p. 339

8   Segment 8 black with pale blue lateral spots. . . .**divagans**, p. 322
    Segment 8 blue with a dorsal stripe of black, fully four-fifths as
    wide as the segment in dorsal view. . . . .**pallidum**, p. 334

9   Segment 8 black on dorsum with a large blue subapical spot on
    each side. . . . . .10.
    Abdominal segment 8 not so marked. . . . . .11.

10 Abdominal segment 7 black. . . . .**geminatum**, p. 326
    Abdominal segment 7 blue, never with more than a line of black
    . . . .**aspersum**, p. 339

11 Abdominal segment 8 entirely blue. . . . . .12.
    Abdominal segment 8 with some black. . . . . .13.

12 Dorsum of abdominal segment 2 entirely black. . . . .
    . . . .**cardenium**, p. 341
    Dorsum of abdominal segment 2 blue with black spot. . . . .
    . . . . .**cyathigerum**, p. 324; **clausum** p. 324, and **boreale** p. 323

13 Black of abdominal segment 1 reaching from the base to the apex
    . . . .**civile**, p. 336
    Black of abdominal segment 1 not reaching the apex of the seg-
    ment. . . . . .14.

14 Western species. . . . . .15.
    Eastern species. . . . . .18.

15 Hind margin of the prothorax convex throughout. . . . . .16.
    Hind margin of the prothorax concave medially, slightly concave
    or truncate on either side. . .**praevarum**, p. 337, and **anna** p. 338

16 Segment 9 black on dorsum, 8 entirely blue, or with black band on
    dorsum narrower anteriorly than posteriorly. . . . . .17.
    Segment 9 black on dorsum with an apical blue spot, 8 blue, apical
    fourth and sides inferiorly black and confluent. .**coecum**, p. 341

17 Mesostigmal plates with a diagonal ridge from the caudo-mesal to
    the cephalo-lateral angles. . . . .**carunculatum**, p. 335
    Without such a ridge on the mesostigmal plates. . . . .
    . . . .**cyathigerum**, p. 324, and **boreale** p. 323

18   M_2 rising beyond the fourth postnodal cross vein in the hind
wings..**19.**

       M_2 rising between the 3rd and 4th postnodal cross veins in the
hind wings.......................................**ebrium, p. 332**

19   Mesostigmal plates with a diagonal ridge...**carunculatum, p. 335**

       Mesostigmal plate without such a ridge....................**20.**

20   Black color of the dorsum of abdominal segments 4–7 always
reaching the cephalic margin..............**doubledayi, p. 335**

       Black of the dorsum of 4–7 never reaching the cephalic margin
...................**cyathigerum, p. 324, and boreale, p. 323**

21   Abdominal segment 1 with the black of the dorsum extending from
the base to the apex....................................**22.**

       Black on the dorsum of segment 1 interrupted by an apical ring of
blue.................**hageni, p. 322, and recurvatum p. 326**

22   Prothoracic dorsal pits very shallow and situated near the hind
lobe which is trilobate...................**cultellatum, p. 327**

       Prothoracic pits deeper, hind lobe entire..................**23.**

23   Black humeral stripe not touching the lower end of the mesostigmal plates. Pale antehumeral stripe wider than the black
humeral...**24.**

       Black humeral stripe touching the lower end of the mesostigmal
plates..**25.**

24   Pale postocular spots broadly connected with the pale of the rear
of the head...............................**laurenti, p. 327**

       Pale postocular spots not directly connected with the pale of the
rear of the head........................**vesperum, p. 330**

25   Dorsum of segment 10 pale colored........................**26.**

       Dorsum of segment 10 black..............................**28.**

26   Prothoracic pits large, situated near the anterior border of the
middle lobe, a pale area posterior and external to each........
....**signatum, p. 329**

       Prothoracic pits smaller, situated at, or near, the mid-length of the
middle lobe, pale color adjacent to each more extensive anterior
to it, rather than posterior to it........................**27.**

27   Anterior end of the antehumeral pale stripe bordered with a broad
stripe of black on the mesostigmal plate, which black widely
separates the antehumeral stripe from the pale vertical stripe on
the plate...............................**sulcatum, p. 329**

       Antero-mesal end of the pale antehumeral stripe narrowly sepa-
rated by black from the extensive pale area of the mesostigmal
plate.......................................**pollutum, p. 328**

28 Prothoracic dorsal pits situated anterior to the middle of the me-
    dian lobe. The middorsal and humeral black stripes broadly
    joined by a black bar across the mesostigmal plate..........
    ....**pictum**, p. 331
    Prothoracic dorsal pits situated at about mid-length of the median
    lobe. Middorsal and humeral black stripes narrowly joined by a
    black stripe on the suture of the mesostigmal plate..........
    ....**concisum**, p. 332

N. B.   The females of the following species have not been included in
        this key, either because they are, as yet, not known, or have
        been inadequately described: **culicinorum, dubium, eiseni,
        laterale, minusculum, piscinarium** and **semicirculare**.

306. Enallagma divagans Selys

Selys '76, p. 52: Mtk. Cat. p. 58: Garm. '17, p. 536 and '27, p. 79.
Length 29–33 mm. Expanse 40 mm.   Mass. to Fla. to Ind., Mich. and Ill.
    Color dark blue and black.
    Male.—Face blue. Labrum with a black median spot, postclypeus black,
antennae black. Anterior part of frons blue, remainder of frons and vertex black.
Postocular spots subcuneiform and not connected. Prothorax black with spots
of varying sizes, one on the anterior lobe, sometimes very large, two lateral ones
on the middle lobe, two lateral ones and a median one on the hind lobe, all pale.
Thorax with the middorsal and humeral dark stripe wide, antehumeral pale
stripe narrower than either. A short black basal line on the second and third
lateral sutures. Abdomen blue-bronze, black as follows: a basal spot on 1;
entire dorsum of 2–7 and 10. 8–9 entirely blue except for an occasional minute
isolated black spot on the sides. Superior appendages black, shorter than 10, and
not bifid, but comma-shaped with a short rounded upper part followed by an
incurved slender process. In some specimens the differentiation between the
"head" and "tail" of the comma is so marked as to give the appendage a bifid
appearance.
    The female is similar to the male except the abdomen. The 8th abdominal
segment is black on the dorsum with pale blue lateral spots on the caudal margin.
Segment 9 blue with two short dorso-lateral black stripes that fuse at the base
of the meson. 10 blue.

307. Enallagma hageni Walsh

Walsh '63, p. 234: Mtk. Cat. p. 60: Whed. '14, p. 93: Garm. '17, p. 547 and '27,
    p. 75.
Length 30 mm. Expanse 38 mm.   Me. and Pa. to N. Dak.
    This species is probably our most common northeastern Zygopteron, being
rivaled in its range only by *Ischnura verticalis* for number of individuals. During
the summer it is usually present about ponds in such quantities as to be taken
by the netful rather than as individuals. Masses of floating vegetation are dotted

with its bright blue and black. Male. Face blue. Postclypeus black. Pale transverse frontal band reaching the basis of the antennae. Vertex, antennae and the remainder of the frons black. Pale postocular spots wide, cuneiform, and entirely surrounded by the black of the head. Pale postocellar stripe vestigial. Anterior and posterior lobes of the prothorax mostly pale. Middle lobe black on dorsum, with two lateral spots and sides pale. Thorax with the usual wide middorsal and humeral black stripes, and the pale antehumeral stripe. Remainder of the thorax pale. M_2 arising between the 4th and 5th postnodal cross veins in the fore wings, the 3rd and 4th in the hind. Abdomen blue, black as follows: a basal spot on 1; an apical ring and spot on 2; spots on the apical third to fourth of 3–5; half of 6; nearly all of 7; the dorsum of 10. 8–9 entirely blue. Superior appendages shorter than 10, simple, not bifid. The inferior appendages longer than the superiors.

The female is colored a yellow-green and black. Head and thorax like the male. Abdomen with segments 1–10 black except the lateral surfaces and an apical ring on the first; lateral surfaces of 2–10, and interrupted basal rings on 3–6 inclusive, which are pale blue or greenish.

308. Enallagama boreale Selys

Selys '75, p. 242: Mtk. Cat. p. 55: Garm. '17, p. 525 and '27, p. 65: Walk. '24. p. 173.

Syn: calverti Morse

Length 33–35 mm. Expanse 42–46 mm.   Northern U. S. and Canada to Pa.

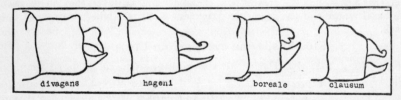

divagans   hageni   boreale   clausum

A common damselfly of the blue-black group. Male with the head buff below. Postclypeus black, except for the lateral margins. Pale transverse frontal band. Vertex, antennae and the remainder of the frons black. Postocular spots large and isolated, entirely surrounded by black. Prothorax mostly black, with the anterior lobe, two large lateral spots and the sides of the middle lobe, and the posterior margin of the hind lobe pale. Thorax with a wide middorsal black stripe (sometimes divided by a fine blue line), a wide antehumeral blue stripe, and a narrow black humeral stripe. A black basal spot on the third lateral suture extending usually only one-third to one-half the distance to the bases of the posterior legs, but occasionally being prolonged into a fine line that reaches the entire distance. M_2 arising between the 5th and 6th postnodal cross veins in the front wing, and between the 4th and 5th in the hind. Abdomen blue with the following black: a basal spot on 1; an apical spot and narrow ring on 2; an apical spot connected with an apical band on 3–4; apical third of 5; two-thirds of 6; five sixths of 7; and all of the dorsum of 10. Superior appendages black, short, one-third as long as 10, blunt, and with no tubercle.

Female similar to the male. Abdomen with the first segment as in male, 2nd with the spot connected with the apical ring and a line on the meson to the base of the sclerite, 3–6 with narrow dorsal black lines widened near the apices, 7 with a similar but broader dorsal line, caudal half of 8 and all of 9–10 black.

309. Enallagma clausum Morse

Morse '95, p. 209: Mtk. Cat. p. 56: Kndy. '15, p. 299 (Annals E. S. A.): Kndy. '17, p. 619.

Length 31–33 mm.   Expanse 42 mm.   **Kan., Nev. and Wash.**

A western intermountain species, an inhabitant of the desert and seemingly enjoys its life in the alkaline ponds of this barren region. Color, blue and black. Male. Head pale beneath. Postclypeus with a wide black basal spot. Pale postocular spots wide, triangular, and entirely surrounded by the black of the head. Prothorax black with the anterior lobe transversely lineate with pale, middle lobe with or without pale lateral spots, posterior lobe margined with pale. Thorax with the mid-carina black or lineate with pale; middorsal black stripe rather narrow; dark humeral stripe very narrow, widest at and more or less broken at the suture; pale antehumeral stripe wide, at least two-thirds as wide as the middorsal dark stripe. Abdomen blue, black as follows: a basal spot on 1; an apical spot and ring on 2; apical two-fifths to two-thirds of 3–5; with a longitudinal stripe narrowed submarginally; apical two-thirds of 6; almost all of 7; and all the dorsum of 10. 8–9 entirely blue. Superior appendages not bifid, shorter than 10, pointed and recurved at the tip, somewhat like *E. recurvatum.*

Female, similar to the male, except the apical black spots on the abdominal segments 3–7 occupy the greater part of the dorsum, however, they do not reach the basal margins of the segments. Segment 8 entirely blue. Dorsum of 9–10 black.

310. Enallagma cyathigerum Charpentier

Charp. '40, p. 163: Mtk. Cat. p. 57: Garm. '17, p. 534 and '27, p. 70: Smn. '27, p. 14.: Lucas, W. J., *The Entomologist*, 34:69, pl. 2, S. 5, 1900.

Syn: annexum Hag., *robustum* Selys.

Length 31–32 mm.   Expanse 44 mm.   **North America**

This species enjoys the widest distribution of any of the New World Enallagma, being found the world over, except in the tropics. Color blue and black. Male. Head buff beneath. Postclypeus black with wide blue lateral margins, and blue transverse area above on the frons. Vertex, antennae and the remainder of the frons black. Postocular spots large, pear shaped and separate. Prothorax black with the most of the anterior lobe, 2 spots on the median lobe, the caudal margin of the posterior lobe, and the sides blue. A narrow humeral black stripe, a wide antehumeral blue, and middorsal black, stripe. A black spot at the base of the third lateral suture. Remainder of the thorax blue. M_2 arising between the 4th and 5th postnodal cross vein in the fore wings, the 3rd and 4th in the hind. Abdomen blue with the following black: a basal spot on 1; a subapical dorsal spot and apical ring on 2; apical spots and rings on 3–5; caudal half of 6, four-fifths of 7, and all of the dorsum of 10. Superior appendages black, short, bent downward with apices acute, not blunt as in *boreale.*

Female like the male, blue generally replaced by yellow. Abdomen with broad longitudinal stripes on the 2nd segment, those on 3–7 narrower and expanded near the caudal margin, that on 8 reduced near the front margin.

311. Enallagma piscinarium Williamson

Wmsn. '00, p. 273: Mtk. Cat. p. 61.

Length 28 mm. Expanse 34 mm.   **N. Y., N. J., Pa. Ind.**

One of the rarer blue and black Enallagmas found around fish ponds. The following description of the male is taken from Mr. E. B. Williamson's original one: "Head blue, beneath pale. Vertex, antennae (except the first joint), and the postclypeus, black. Postocular spots rounded, cuneiform, narrowly connected. Prothorax black, posterior lobe narrowly margined with blue. Thorax blue, a middorsal and a humeral stripe and a spot on the second and third lateral sutures just under the wing bases, black. Abdomen blue, black as follows: a basal spot and a narrow apical ring on 1; an apical spot connected with an apical spot connected with an apical ring on 2; very narrowly interrupted basal rings on 3–6 (these rings are wider anteriorly becoming narrower successively); all of 7 and 10. Sides of 1 and 2 blue, posteriorly the black of the dorsum extending more unto the sides." Superior appendages very similar to *E. geminatum*. Male.

312. Enallagma durum Hagen

Hag. '61, p. 87: Mtk. Cat. p. 58: Wmsn. '22, p. 142: Root '23, p. 202: Garm. '27, p. 83.

Length 32–38 mm. Expanse 48–52 mm.   **Mass., R. I., to Fla. and La.**

One of our largest bluets, frequently recorded from brackish water ponds. Colors, blue and black. Head typical of the blue-black Enallagmas, postocular spots usually united. Prothorax and thorax not differing from those of this group already described, except that the middorsal carina is yellow or blue

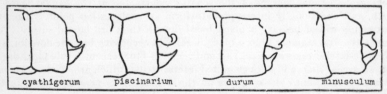

cyathigerum   piscinarium   durum   minusculum

separating the middorsal black stripe into two parts. Wings with 4–5 antenodal cells. Abdomen blue with the following black: a basal spot on 1, wider than long; a rounded apical spot with an apical "tail" on 2; apical part of 3–6, pointed anteriorly; all of 7, except a transverse basal ring; the dorsum of 10. 8–9 blue. Superior appendages one-fourth to one-third as long as 10, excavated within, but not bifid, inferior apical angle with a small tubercle. Inferior appendages a little longer than the superior.

Female. Color, yellowish-red and black. Similar to the male in the head and thorax. Dorsum of 1–9 with a broad black band widened before the apices, and interrupted transverse basal yellow rings on 3–7. Dorsum of 10 mostly pale.

313. Enallagma minusculum Morse

Morse '95, p. 207: Mtk. Cat. p. 60: Howe '17, p. 16: Garm. '27, p. 77.

Length 26 mm. Expanse 34 mm.   **Mass. and N. H.**

A rare species very muchly circumscribed in its range. Described by Dr. Morse as follows: "Cuneiform postocular spots small, more or less rounded.

Posterior lobe of pronotum black, unspotted, margined with yellow; anterior lobe with pale transverse band. Thorax with the following black: a wide mid-dorsal stripe, widest in front; a wide humeral (wider than pale antehumeral) stripe, widest below, expanded on and just behind its crossing of the humeral suture. Abdomen black as follows: dorsum of 1, divided by an apical spot of blue or purple; posterior half of 2, third of 3, two-fifths of 4, half of 5, three-fourths of 6, four-fifths of 7, and all of 10; 8–9 blue. Superior appendages half as long as 10, in profile view broader than long." The superiors are not bifid, however, the posterior margin is shallowly excavate, giving the appearance of two parts *broadly connected*.

The female is still unknown after some thirty-eight years of collecting.

314. Enallagma geminatum Kellicott

Klct. '95, p. 239: Mtk. Cat. p. 59: Garm. '17, p. 544 and '27, p. 73.
Length 26–27 mm. Expanse 35 mm.　　　　**N. Y. to Wis., Ill. to Fla. and La.**

This species is regionally common or rare, collected mostly at ponds where it flies very close to the water. Colors, light blue and black. Male. Face light blue, the labrum with a black basal spot. Postclypeus black. The frontal transverse pale band reaching just to the basis of the antennae. Vertex, antennae and the remainder of the frons, black. Pale postocular spots oval, their margins frequently serrated, and not connected. The usual pale postocellar stripe is wanting. Dorsum of the prothorax with the anterior and the posterior lobes mostly blue; the middle lobe entirely black on the dorsum, sides pale. Thorax with the middorsal black stripe wide. Pale antehumeral stripe irregular, not reaching the caudal margin of the sclerite, contracted at the caudal third or fourth, and occasionally interrupted to form an exclamation point. Humeral black stripe widest below. A black basal line on the third lateral suture. Abdomen: the first segment blue, a black basal spot occupying half the dorsum, and the caudo-lateral margins black; second segment blue, except a subapical dorsal spot, an apical ring, and a longitudinal lateral stripe, which are black; segments 3–7 with longitudinal black stripes on the dorsum from near the bases to the apices. 8–9 with the dorsum blue, but with a lateral marginal stripe from the the bases to the apices dark brown or black. Superior appendages shorter than 10, and not bifid.

The female is similar to the male, except abdominal segments 9–10 are entirely brown on the dorsum; 8 brown with two large blue spots occupying most of the segment and separated by a dark mesal line.

315. Enallagma recurvatum Davis

Davis '13, p. 15: Garm. '27, p. 78.
Length 30 mm. Expanse 34 mm.　　　　**N. Y. and N. J.**

A species very closely related to *E. hageni*, and as yet only recorded from the vicinity of New York City. Male. Color pale blue and black. Head black, beneath pale, the following blue; band on front between eyes and postocular spots. Prothorax black above, pale beneath; thorax with a middorsal, a humeral stripe, and a basal spot on the third lateral suture, black. Abdomen blue, black as follows: a basal spot on the dorsum of 1; apical ring and spot on 2; apical ring on 3; apical half of 4; apical two-thirds of 5; apical three-fourths of 6; almost all of 7; a narrow linear spot on each side of 8; dorsum of 10. Colored in general very much like *hageni*. Superior appendages like *hageni*, but with the tips recurved, and the superiors and inferiors of almost equal length.

The female cannot yet be distinguished from that of *E. hageni*.

316. Enallagma laterale Morse

Morse '95, p. 274: Howe '17, p. 18: Mtk. Cat. p. 60: Garm. '27, p. 77.
Length 26 mm. Expanse 34 mm. **Mass.**

A very rare bluet. In absence of specimens in our collection, the following description of the male has been taken from the original one by Morse: "Postocular spots of moderate size. Middorsal thoracic and humeral dark stripes of median width. Abdomen blue with the dorsum black as follows: apical half of 2, fourth of 3, third of 4, half of 5, three-fourths of 6, all of 7 except an interrupted basal ring, a stripe each side on 8, all of 10. Dorsum of 10 emarginate. Superior appendages short, one-fourth to one-third as long as side of 10, in side view nearly as broad as long, directed caudad or slightly deflexed, sides parallel, apex bluntly emarginate. . . . . Inferior appendages nearly twice as long as the superiors."

The female is unknown.

317. Enallagma cultellatum Hagen

Hag. '76, p. 524: Mtk. Cat. p. 57: Kndy. '20, p. 86.
Length 31 mm. Expanse 36 mm. **Tropic**

While no definite record is available of the capture of this species within the political bounds of the United States, it is found in the life zones that include Florida and the U. S.-Mexican boundary; so it is included here for completeness. In color it varies from yellow through orange to blue, and black. Face yellow, rear of head black. Postclypeus entirely yellow. Postocular spots separated. Prothorax marked as in *E. basidens*. Abdomen with dorsum of 2 with a horse shoe-shaped black mark, 8–9 blue, remainder black.

The female has the postclypeus mainly black, abdominal segment 2 with a wide dorsal band, 8 blue with a dorsal black band, 9 black, 10 black at base only.

Dr. C. H. Kennedy places this species in a genus by itself, which he calls *Neoerythromma*.

318. Enallagma laurenti Calvert

Calv. '19, p. 379: Byers '27, p. 388.
Length 36 mm. Expanse 44 mm. **Fla.**

A long thin lemon yellow and black damselfly found about ponds in non-tropical Florida. Male. Face yellow with vestigial black streaks at the base of the labrum and postclypeus. The transverse frontal pale stripe reaches to or a little beyond the median ocellus. Base and the first two segments of the antennae pale yellow. Vertex black with a pair of yellow spots between the lateral and the median ocelli. Pale postocular spots linear joined together by the pale postocellar stripe, on the occipital margin of the head, also broadly joined with the pale color of the rear of the head, i.e., the occipital and postgeneal region. Prothorax predominantly orange or yellow. The middle lobe with a transverse black stripe along its hind margin, where it joins the hind lobe, from which extends forward, on each side, a longitudinal black stripe. Thorax yellow except for the middorsal black stripe (.35–.42 mm. wide), and a very narrow black humeral stripe varying in width from a mere line to .10 mm. Antehumeral pale stripe wide (.49–.56 mm.). A short black basal streak also present on the upper ends of the second and third lateral sutures. Vein M_2 rises nearest the 5th postnodal cross vein in the fore wings, the 4th in the hind. Stigma bright yellow. Abdomen with the entire dorsum of 1–8 and 10 metallic black, except for narrow interrupted pale basal rings on 3–6.9 and sides of 10 blue. Superior appendages longer than 10, resembling those of *vesperum* and *pollutum*.

Female similar to the male in most respects. The color pattern of the postclypeus varies from almost entirely pale to black with a median yellow spot. Yellow areas of the head large, making the black appear as an interocular stripe. Prothorax sometimes predominantly black with large yellow spots. Black of the humeral stripe never touches the mesostigmal plate (lamina). Abdomen as in the male except segment 9 has a large triangular basal black spot on the dorsum, covering about three-fourths of the surface, but not reaching the apical margin. Segment 10 entirely blue.

319. Enallagma pollutum Hagen

Hag. '16, p. 83: Mtk. Cat. p. 61: Calv. '19, p. 378.
Length 32 mm. Expanse 36 mm. Fla.

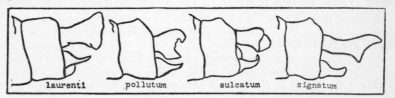

laurenti   pollutum   sulcatum   signatum

One of the yellow-black species occurring commonly in ponds and swamps where there is an abundance of standing vegetation. Male. Face yellow, a fine black line at the base of the labrum. Postclypeus usually entirely black, occasionally with one or two median yellow spots. Pale frontal transverse band narrow, not reaching the middle ocellus. Base and first segment of the antennae yellow. Vertex black except for a pair of yellow spots between the lateral and the median ocelli. Postocular spots linear and very narrowly connected with the pale postocellar stripe, but not connected with the pale color of the rear of the head. Anterior and posterior lobes of the prothorax yellow. Middle lobe predominantly black, with only the sides and two lateral spots yellow. Thorax with the pale antehumeral stripe narrower than the black humeral. Middorsal dark stripe .53–.63 mm., pale antehumeral .25–.28 mm., dark humeral .37–.42 mm. wide. Third lateral suture with a black stripe on the upper five-sixths or more of its length. Dorsum of abdominal segments 1–8 and 10 entirely metallic black. Segment 9 entirely orange. Superior appendages longer than 10 and though irregular, are not bifid.

The female is similar to the male. The lateral end of the mesostigmal plate is margined with the black of the humeral stripe. Width of black middorsal stripe .56–.63 mm., of pale antehumeral stripe .28–.42 mm., of the dark humeral stripe .28–.35 mm. Black on the dorsum of abdominal segment 9 of almost uniform width from base to apex.

320. **Enallagma sulcatum** Williamson

Wmsn. '22, p. 114.

Length 32–35 mm. Expanse 36–42 mm.   Fla.

Male. Color, orange, blue and black. Face orange. Postclypeus entirely shining black or with superimposed pale areas making it almost entirely orange in some specimens. Pale transverse frontal band not reaching the pale area an terior to the median ocellus. Antennae with the base and the first segment, at least, orange, remainder black. Vertex black except for a small pale spot anterior to each ocellus. Postocular spots linear and joined together by way of the pale postocellar stripe, or narrowly separated from it, never joined with the pale color of the rear of the head. Anterior and posterior lobes of the prothorax largely orange. Middle lobe black except for the sides and two lateral spots of orange. no median orange spot on the dorsum. Thorax with the pale antehumeral stripe narrower than the black humeral. Width of the black mid-dorsal stripe .87 mm., of the pale antehumeral stripe .26 mm., of the black humeral about .55 mm. Third lateral suture covered with a black stripe for about the upper five-sixths of its length. A short black spot on the caudal end of the second lateral suture. Abdomen with the dorsum of segments 1–8 and 10 entirely metallic black, except for narrow interrupted basal rings on segments 3–6. Segment 9 entirely *blue*. Superior appendages not quite as long as 10.

Mesostigmal plate largely black, in the female, with a pale stripe, the posterior and inferior black portion grooved. Width of the black mid-dorsal thoracic stripe .78 mm., of the pale antehumeral stripe .27 mm., of the dark humeral about .5 mm. Black stripe on the second lateral suture on slightly less than the upper five-sixths of its length, continued as a thread of black to the inferior end of the suture. Black on the dorsum of abdominal segments 1–9, that on 9 not reaching the apex. Segment 10 pale.

321. **Enallagma signatum** Hagen

Hag. '61, p. 84: Mtk. Cat. p. 61: Garm. '17, p. 553: Calv. '19, p. 337: Garm. '27, p. 62.

Syn: dentiferum Walsh

Length 33 mm. Expanse 38 mm.   U. S. east of Miss. R.

A large black and orange damselfly occurring quite commonly, at times, about floating vegetation. Male. Face pale. Postclypeus usually entirely black, sometimes with margins and median spots or streaks of orange. Pale transverse frontal band not reaching the median ocellus. Base and the first segment of the antennae pale. Vertex black except for a small pale spot anterior to each ocellus. Pale postocular spots linear and connected with each other, by way of the pale postocellar stripe, but never connected with the pale color of the rear of the head. Anterior and posterior lobes of the prothorax pale. Middle lobe black with the sides, a median spot and two lateral spots, pale. Thorax with the pale antehumeral stripe as wide as, or wider than, the black humeral. Width of the mid-dorsal black thoracic stripe .63–.7 mm., of the pale antehumeral stripe .35–.42 mm., of the black humeral stripe .24–.35 mm. Third lateral suture with a blackish-brown stripe, or line, for the uppermost fourth to three-fourths of its distance. Dorsum of abdominal segments 1–8 and 10 metallic black. Segment 9 entirely yellow.

Female. Color sometimes blue and black. Lateral end of the mesostigmal plate black, the humeral stripe touching the lower end. Prothoracic pits large. Widths of the black thoracic mid-dorsal stripe .63–.7 mm, of the pale antehumeral .35–.42 mm., of the dark humeral .28–.42 mm. Black of the dorsum of segment 9 usually narrowed posteriorly.

322. Enallagma vesperum Calvert

Calv. '19, p. 380: Garm. '27, p. 64.

Length 30–34 mm. Expanse 34–42 mm.   **U. S. east of Miss. R.**

A species that is found abundantly along the shores of the Great Lakes, but not at all restricted to them. Color, orange or yellow and black. Face yellow. Postclypeus entirely black or with two median spots and margins of yellow. Pale transverse frontal band sometimes attaining the pale spot immediately anterior to the median ocellus, and indundating the black of the superior surface more deeply than in *E. pollutum.* Postocular spots connected with each other, but not confluent with the pale of the rear of the head. First two segments of the antennae pale. Vertex black, except for two pale ocellar spots. Anterior and posterior lobes of the prothorax mostly yellow; middle lobe usually predominantly black on the dorsum, a spot on each side, a pair of median spots or lines, and the sides inferiorly yellow. Thorax with the pale antehumeral stripe wider than the dark humeral. Width of black mid-dorsal thoracic stripe .28–.67 mm., of the pale antehumeral stripe .35–.7 mm., of the dark humeral stripe, from a mere line to .28 mm. Third lateral suture with a black stripe on its uppermost fourth or fifth only. Abdomen with the dorsum of 1–8 and 10 entirely metallic black, reduced somewhat on 10. 9 entirely *blue.*

Female: Lateral margins of the mesostigmal plate not margined with the black of the humeral stripe, but having a black spot on itself. Postocular spots as in the male, not connected with the pale color of the rear of the head. Width of black thoracic mid-dorsal stripe .33–.63 mm., of the pale antehumeral stripe .42–.63 mm., of the black humeral, from a mere line to .14 mm. Dorsum of 9 black, not reaching the apical margin.

The *E. pollutum* of most writers on northern species of Enallagma is synonymous with *E. vesperum.* The true *pollutum* is entirely southern.

323. Enallagma dubium Root

Root '24, p. 317: Byers '27, p. 388.

Length 26 mm. Expanse 28 mm.   **Ga. and Fla.**

A small very dark Enallagma collected in cypress swamps. Color, metallic black and yellow-red. Male: Head pale beneath. Postclypeus black. Frons with the pale transverse anterior band reaching the basis of the antennae. Antennae entirely black. Remainder of frons and the vertex black (no pale markings about the ocelli). Pale postocular spots linear cuneiform, broadly separated by black from the pale color of the rear of the head, and narrowly separated from, or joined with, the pale occipital stripe. Dorsum of the prothorax mainly black, a transverse yellow bar on the anterior margin of the anterior lobe, small indistinct pale spots laterally on the posterior lobe, dorsum of the middle lobe without pale markings, but with the sides yellow inferiorly. Width of black thoracic middorsal stripe, .62 mm.; of pale antehumeral stripe .1–.2 mm.; of the black humeral stripe .49 mm. Third lateral suture with a black stripe for its entire length, narrowed below. Abdomen all black dorsally, except for a very narrow apical (1, 7, 9) or basal (3–7) rings. Sides and venter of abdomen orange or yellow. Superior appendages longer than 10, not bifid, resembling those of *laurenti* or *signatum*.

The female is unknown.

vesperum   dubium   pictum   concisum

324. Enallagma pictum Morse

Morse '95, p. 307: Mtk. Cat. p. 60: Calv. '19, p. 385: Garm. '27, p. 61.

Length 30 mm. Expanse 38 mm. **Mass. and N. J.**

A very dark species, not common. Color black with orange or yellow markings. Male. Postclypeus orange, a transverse basal black stripe, trilobed distally, the three lobes of varying prominence; or, black predominating, rather broadly margined with orange. Frons with pale transverse stripe of its anterior surface not attaining the median ocellus, a mere yellow line bordering the ocellus anteriorly. The first two segments of the antennae pale. Vertex black excepting two spots anterior to the lateral ocelli. Postocular spots linear, orange, connected with each other usually, but not confluent with the pale color of the rear of the head. Middle prothoracic lobe in dorsal view, metallic black, usually a small yellow spot on each side of the anterior half. Remainder of the prothorax predominantly yellow. Width of the black middorsal thoracic stripe .7–.77 mm., of pale antehumeral stripe .28–.35 mm., of black humeral .42–.49 mm. Third lateral suture with a black stripe on the upper three-fourths to two-thirds of its length, the stripe continuing as a line the remainder of the distance of the posterior legs. Abdomen black as follows: dorsum of 1–10; on 2 in the form of an orbicular apical spot narrowly connected to the base; on three terminating in a sharp point basally; 1 with a wide apical, and 2–7 with narrow interrupted basal rings.

Female similar to the male. Mesostigmal plate (lamina) mostly black, margined with the black of the mid-dorsal and the humeral stripes. Width of black middorsal thoracic stripe .84–.91, of antehumeral pale stripe .18–.21, of dark humeral stripe .48–.56 mm. Third lateral suture with the black stripe for its entire length. Black of the dorsum of segment 9 of uniform width.

325. Enallagma concisum Williamson

Wmsn. '22, p. 117.

Length 31 mm. Expanse 34 mm. Fla.

This species, but recently described, is generally found resting on the vegetation of ponds where the water is about waist deep. It is one of the species belonging to the orange-black group. Male. Postclypeus orange, a transverse black stripe at the base and on either side; at mid-length a small black or brown depression. The pale transverse frontal band is wide reaching the level of the median ocellus on either side, but the latter is bordered in front with a small pale area of varying size and an anterior projecting quadrangle of black, the latter often unsymmetrical. Pale postocular spots linear, cuneiform, widely separated by black from the pale color of the rear of the head, but joined with each other by way of the pale postocellar stripe on the caudo-mesal margin of the head. Vertex black with a pair of pale spots near the lateral ocelli. Prothorax shining greenish-black, front and hind lobes broadly edged with orange; sides of the middle lobe pale orange, dorsum of middle lobe with a round orange spot, of varying size, on either side, and with a median orange twin spot of varying size present or wanting. Thorax with black middorsal stripe about .67 mm. wide, pale antehumeral stripe about .33 mm. wide, and black humeral stripe about .43 mm. wide. Third lateral suture with a black stripe for its entire length, widening above from a narrow line at its lower end. Abdomen with the segments dark except 9 which is orange on the sides and apical membranous rings of orange. Superior appendages not bifid and longer than 10.

326. Enallagma ebrium Hagen

Hag. '61, p. 89: Mtk. Cat. p. 59: Garm. '17, p. 540: and '27, p. 71.

Length 29 mm. Expanse 38–40 mm. N. S. to Md. and Wash.

A common species that often leaves the lakes to fly in the woods and fields. Colors, blue and black. Male. Head below pale. Face blue. Postclypeus black. Pale transverse frontal band reaching the basis of the antennae. Vertex, antennae and the remainder of the frons black. Postocular spots large, oval and isolated. Prothorax black on the dorsum with the usual pale markings, i.e., a transverse pale stripe on the anterior lobe, two lateral spots on the middle lobe, and the posterior margin of the posterior lobe. Thorax with the middorsal dark stripe and the antehumeral pale stripe of about equal width, both being wider than the dark humeral stripe. Third lateral suture with a black basal spot. Abdomen blue, black as follows: a basal semi-ring on 1; apical spot and ring on 2; apical third of 3–5; apical half to two-thirds of 6, almost all of 7; all the dorsum of 10. 8–9 entirely blue. Superior appendages black, bifid, the notch formed being circular. Upper and lower arms of equal length and width. No tubercle.

Female: Color, blue or yellow, and black. Head and thorax similar to the male. Abdomen with broad dark dorsal stripes on 2–10, the stripes contracted to the meson on the basis of segments 3–7, and widened subapically on segments 2–7. First segment pale with black basal spot.

327. Enallagma exsulans Hagen

Hag. '61, p. 82: Mtk. Cat. p. 59: Garm. '17, p. 542: and '27, p. 80: Byers '27, p. 387.

Length 32–53 mm. Expanse 42–44 mm. Eeastern U. S. west to Tex.

A very attractive dark blue and black damselfly found commonly, especially near rivers and streams. Male. Face blue. Base of labrum brown or with a black spot. Postclypeus entirely black, or black with two lateral blue spots. Blue transverse frontal band reaching to the basis of the antennae. Vertex, antennae and the remainder of the frons, black. Pale postocular spots narrow and irregular, connected with, or very narrowly separated from, the pale occipital stripe. Dorsum of the prothorax black, blue as follows: a large median and two small lateral spots on the anterior lobe; a paired median and two large lateral spots, and the sides of the middle lobe; and median and lateral spots or lines on the posterior lobe. Black middorsal thoracic stripe wide, antehumeral pale stripe narrower than either the middorsal or the humeral dark ones. The humeral black stripe is often split longitudinally near its caudal end, leaving that part of the humeral suture pale. A short black stripe on the second and third lateral sutures at the upper end. Wings with a brownish tinge. Abdomen with dorsum of segments 1–8 and 10 entirely metallic black, except for basal rings on 3–6.9 entirely blue. Superior appendages shorter than 10, bifid, the upper arm shorter than the lower, no clear tubercle between them and both produced on the same plane, i.e., the long axis of the lower arm is parallel to the long axis of the upper arm, and not at angles to it.

Female colored pale green and black or brown. Abdomen with broad black dorsal stripes on segments 1–8, the one on 9 being reduced to a triangular spot at the base. Remainder of 9 and all of 10 blue.

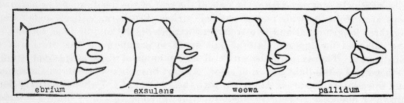

ebrium   exsulans   weewa   pallidum

328. Enallagma weewa Byers

Byers '27, p. 385.

Length 38 mm. Expanse 42–46 mm.   S. C., Ga. and Fla

Male. Color in dried specimens, light tan and metallic greenish-black, becoming violet-gray pruinose in old specimens. Mouth parts, genae, postgenae and occiput, pale. Mandibles pale with a black basal spot. Basal half of the labrum and of the postclypeus, black. Pale transverse frontal band narrow, hardly reaching the basis of the antennae. Vertex, antennae and the remainder of the frons, black. Pale postocular spots linear, narrowly joined, or separated from the pale postocellar stripe, not connected with the pale color of the rear of the head. Prothorax predominantly black, most of the anterior lobe, the sides, a pair of lateral spots, a dorsal twin spot of the median lobe, and the posterior margin of the hind lobe, pale. Thorax with the middorsal carina broadly brown, separating the usual wide middorsal dark stripe into two narrower stripes. The humeral dark stripe very irregular and split longitudinally in the middle of its length, so that almost the whole of the humeral suture is pale. The pale antehumeral stripe narrow. A black basal streak on the second and third lateral sutures, that on the latter usually prolonged as a narrow line to the base of the posterior legs. Abdomen pale, segments 1–8 inclusive with the dorsum entirely metallic black, except for narrow basal rings on 3–6. Segment 9 entirely pale except for a transverse apical line of black. Segment 10 entirely black on the dorsum. Superior appendages black, bifid, shorter than 10. No tubercle present. The upper arm short, subtriangular; the lower, oval and semirotated under the upper, so that a line drawn through its long axis would meet a similar line drawn through the upper arm at an acute angle. Otherwise similar to *E. exsulans*.

Female is similar to the female of *E. exsulans*.

329. Enallagma pallidum Root

Root '23, p. 202: Byers '27, p. 389.

Length 32–36 mm. Expanse 38–44 mm.   **Md. and Fla.**

A large, delicate, pale gray-blue, and black species, resembling *Teleallagma daeckii* in coloration and appearance, and *Enallagma antennatum* in nymph and some adult structural features.

Male. Face pale. A black mid-basal dot on the labrum. Postclypeus pale with a dark basal line and two lateral dark stripes or spots. Frons entirely pale, except for a dark spot anterior to the median ocellus. Antennae mostly pale or with tips light brown. Vertex black, the following pale: a small pair of spots anterior to the lateral ocelli, a large lateral spot at the side of each lateral ocellus, and a posterior spot between the ocelli. Postocular pale spots very large, angulate, narrowly separated from the pale of the rear of the head, joined or narrowly separated from the wide postocellar pale stripe. Prothorax entirely pale except for three longitudinal and two transverse stripes on the middle lobe, formed by the enlarged median and lateral pale spots so common on the prothorax of Enallagma. Thorax with the humeral and middorsal dark stripes very much reduced and often light brown in color. A short basal black streak on the second and third lateral sutures. Abdomen with the dorsum of 1–7 almost entirely dark brown or black. *8–10 entirely blue*. Superior appendages widely bifid, the upper arm broad, the lower narrow, in profile view. Similar to *E. antennatum*.

Female similar to the male. Humeral stripe ill defined, a brown line the entire length of the third lateral suture. The anterior two-thirds of abdominal segment 8 has a wide dorsal black stripe. There is a narrow transverse basal brown stripe on 9.

330. Enallagma antennatum Say

Say '39, p. 39: Mtk. Cat. p. 54: Garm. '17, p. 521.

Syn: fischeri Klct.

Length 34 mm. Expanse 42 mm.   **N. Y. and Pa. to Iowa**

This was the first known North American species. Color blue or greenish-yellow and black. Found, not commonly, on standing aquatic vegetation and seldom goes far from waters edge. Head black above, buff below. Postclypeus black, with the pale transverse frontal band above it orange. Pale postocular spots narrowly cuneiform and usually connected with each other by way of the pale postocellar stripe, seldom narrowly separated from it. Prothorax mainly black, with a transverse stripe across the posterior lobe and the sides pale. Thorax with wide middorsal and humeral black stripes and consequently very narrow pale antehumeral stripe. Sides of the thorax pale with a short basal black line on the second and third lateral sutures. Abdomen with the dorsum of 1–8 and 10 practically entirely black, sides and all of 9 pale, except for a pair of black dorsal spots on 9. Superior appendages black, widely bifid, the two arms of about equal length, with no tubercle.

The female has the dorsum of 1–9 broadly black and 10 pale.

331. Enallagma carunculatum Morse

Morse '95, p. 208: Mtk. Cat. p. 56: Garm. '17, p. 528 and 27, p. 67: Ndm. '23, p. 131: Smn. '27, p. 14.

Length 33 mm. Expanse 42 mm.   B. C., Calif., Nev. to N. Y. and Conn.

A very common damselfly about large bodies of water, remaining late into the autumn after most other Enallagma have disappeared. Color, dark blue or buff and black. Male with the head below blue and buff; above entirely black, except the narrow lateral margins of the postclypeus, the transverse frontal band, and the two isolated postocular spots, which are blue. Prothorax black, with a transverse median stripe on the anterior lobe, the posterior margins of the hind lobe and a pair of small crescent shaped spots and the sides of the middle lobe, blue. Thorax with the mid-carina black or lined with pale, middorsal dark stripe broad; humeral dark stripe of moderate width, variable; antehumeral pale stripe varying in width from nearly twice as wide to only two-thirds as wide as the

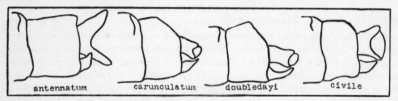

antennatum   carunculatum   doubledayi   civile

humeral. Third lateral suture with black basal spot. Abdomen blue, black as follows: 1 with a basal spot and a short lateral apical line; an apical spot broadly connected with an apical ring on 2; apical third to half of 3–4; one-half to three-fifths of 5–6; almost all of 7; none of 8–9; all the dorsum of 10. Superior appendages black, shallowly bifid, with a clear yellowish tubercle between the arms, shorter than 10.

Female similar to male except the abdomen has the dorsum of 1–10 with broad black stripes widened subapically and narrowed to a median line near the base of the segments, where the pale of the sides meets across the dorsum.

There is apparently a great variation in the color pattern of this species, some individuals possessing a great deal more black than others, the pale spots of the prothorax tending to disappear and the postocular spots to be reduced.

332. Enallagma doubledayi Selys

Selys '50, p. 209: Mtk. Cat. p. 58: Garm. '17, p. 538 and '27, p. 71: Root '24, p. 319.

Length 31 mm. Expanse 40 mm.   Mass. to Ohio, Ill. and Fla.

One of the commonest damselflies of the south, occurring in large numbers throughout the summer at all permanent and semipermanent ponds and swamps.

Not common in the northern states. Color, light blue and black. Male. Face yellowish and blue to the basis of the antennae, with only the postclypeus and a line at the base of the labrum, black. Vertex, antennae and the remainder of the frons black. Postocular spots irregular, oval and not connected. Prothorax black with the usual transverse pale stripe on the anterior lobe, the two lateral spots on the middle lobe, and pale line on the posterior margin of the hind lobe. Middorsal black stripe of the thorax wide, pale antehumeral stripe about as wide as the black humeral. A short line of black at the posterior end of the second lateral suture, connected with the humeral by a dark band across the wing base. A black basal spot on the third lateral suture. Vein M_2 arises between the 5th and 6th postnodal cross veins in the fore wing, the 4th and 5th in the hind. Abdomen blue with the following black: a basal spot on 1; an apical spot and ring occupying the dorsal half of 2; a third to a fourth of 3–5; two-thirds of 6; nearly all of 7; and all the dorsum of 10. 8–9 entirely blue. Superior appendages similar to those of *carunculatum* and *civile* but differ in having a smaller pale tubercle at the end and in being much wider proximal to the tubercle.

Female, similar to male. Abdomen with segments 1–10 with broad dorsal black stripes and interrupted basal rings.

333 Enallagma civile Hagen

Hag. '61, p. 88: Mtk. Cat. p. 56: Garm. '17, p. 531 and '27, p. 68.

Syn: canadense Prov.

Length 29–32 mm.   Expanse 38–44 mm.   **North America**

A common species about ponds from June to September and generally dis tributed. Color blue and black. Male. Mouth parts buff. Head pale. Post clypeus with a dark basal spot. Pale transverse frontal band wide, reaching to, and sometimes including the basis of the antennae. Vertex, remainder of an tennae and remainder of the frons, black. Pale postocular spots large and oval and usually separated from the pale postocellar stripe, and the pale of the rear of the head. Prothorax black, the anterior lobe with a pale transverse line, and the middle lobe with a pale spot on the lateral margins, and the sides pale, and the posterior lobe with the hind margin, pale. Thorax with the middorsal black stripe broad, the pale antehumeral stripe broad, and the dark humeral stripe narrow, widest anteriorly. A black basal spot on the third lateral suture. Ab domen blue, the following black: basal spot on 1; apical spot and ring on 2: apical fourth to third of 3–5; half of 6; nearly all of 7; and all the dorsum of 10. 8–9 entirely blue. Superior appendages black, shorter than 10, widely bifid, the two arms of nearly equal length with a large tubercle between them.

Female similar to the male. Abdomen: the dorsum of all segments have a black longitudinal stripe from their basis to the apices, and a short narrow apical black ring. Pale color of the sides of the segments extending onto the dorsum at the basis of 2–6, but never connecting across the middorsal line as they do in *carunculatum*.

334. Enallagma culicinorum Byers

Byers '27, p. 249.

Length 30 mm.   Expanse 44 mm.   **Utah**

A recently described species, known as yet from one male taken in the vegetation in still water along Logan River. Color, yellow and black (probably blue and black in older specimens). Male. Face pale. Postclypeus black with pale margins. Pale transverse frontal band wide, reaching the basis of the antennae. Vertex, antennae and remainder of frons entirely black. Pale postocular spots, large, cuneiform and isolated. The pale postocellar stripe wide and well developed, but separated from the postocular spots. Anterior and posterior lobes of the prothorax predominantly yellow, merely edged with black. Middle lobe mainly black, with the sides and two very large lateral spots, pale. Middorsal carina pale. Middorsal black stripe wide. Pale antehumeral stripe much wider than the dark humeral, which latter is extremely irregular. Small black basal spot on the third lateral suture, none on the second lateral suture. Abdomen pale, black as follows: a small basal spot on 1; an apical spot and ring on 2; apical fourth of 3–4; apical two-thirds of 5–6; four-fifths of 7; all the dorsum of 10. 8–9 entirely pale.

Superior abdominal appendages about as long as 10, bifid, the lower basal branch short and flap like, the upper branch slender and turned up slightly at the tip. In an interio-dorsal view there is a distinct heavy spine at the base of the superiors and a small tubercle just before it. *Culicinorum* is related to the *anna-praevarum* group, but in profile view the appendages superficially resemble those of *coecum* and *traviatum*.

The female is unknown.

335. Enallagma praevarum Hagen

Hag. '61, p. 88: Mtk. Cat. p. 61: Ndm. '23, p. 131: Smn. '27, p. 15.

Length 31 mm. Expanse 40 mm.   **Kan. and La. west to Calif.**

Male. Colors yellow or blue, and black. Head below pale. Postclypeus black. Pale transverse frontal band narrow, not reaching to the basis of the antennae. Vertex, antennae and remainder of the frons, black. Postocular spots large and triangular, narrowly joined to the pale postocellar stripe, or separated from it, sometimes also joined with the pale color of the rear of the head. Pro-

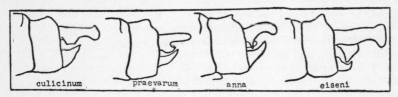

culicinum   praevarum   anna   eiseni

thorax black with a median spot on the anterior lobe, the sides and a pair of large lateral spots on the median lobe, and the posterior margin of the hind lobe, pale. Thorax with the middorsal carina pale; a wide middorsal black stripe and pale antehumeral stripe, both of which are wider than the irregular dark humeral stripe. A short black basal spot on the third lateral suture. Abdomen pale, black as follows: a basal spot on 1; an apical spot and ring on 2; apical half to third of 3; three-fourths of 4; nearly all of 5–7, except rather wide basal bands on 5–6, and a very narrow one on 7; all the dorsum of 10. 8–9 entirely pale. Superior appendages bifid, shorter than 10, usually with a small internal tubercle.

The female is similar to the male. Abdomen with the dorsum of 2–10 black as in *E. anna*, black of 1 not reaching the apex of the segment.

336. Enallagma anna Williamson

Wmsn. '00, p. 455: Mtk. Cat. p. 54: Kndy. '17, p. 616.
Length 32 mm. Expanse 45 mm.   Wyo., Ariz., Utah

This very pretty blue and black western damselfly is one of the few species in which the females submerge in ovipositing, unaccompanied by the male, although the male is present with her as usual until submergence takes place. The head of the male is blue above, yellowish below, vertex and frons black above. The first joint of the antennae is blue, the remainder black. Postocular spots connected with the postocellar pale stripe. Prothorax black, blue as follows: a transverse stripe covering the anterior half of the first lobe, a spot on either side and the sides of the middle lobe, and the posterior border of the hind lobe, which is entire and flattened above. Thorax with the following black: a middorsal stripe, a humeral stripe, wider below, and a line on the basal third or fourth of the third lateral suture. Abdomen blue with the following black: a basal spot on 1; an apical spot and narrow ring on 2; apical half or third of 3; apical half to three-fourths of 4; apical three-fifths or two-thirds of 5, apical two-thirds or three-fourths of 6; nearly all of 7; none of 8-9; all of 10. Superior appendages in profile view, about as long as 10, bifid, inferior arm shorter than the superior, a small pale tubercle usually present between them.

The female is similar to the male except the posterior border of the prothorax has a low median elevation with a lower one on either side. Abdomen with the dorsum of 2-10 black, 10 very narrowly, sides and basal rings of abdomen yellowish or greenish. The wings of the female, as in all Enallagma, are slightly longer than those of the male.

337. Enallagma eiseni Calvert

Calv. '95, p. 486: Mtk. Cat. p. 59.
Length 32 mm. Expanse 40 mm.   B. Calif.

Colors, blue and metallic black. The black as follows: a small median dot at the base of the labrum; the postclypeus; the antennae, except the first and the front of the second joint; the vertex; a narrow transverse band behind the blue postocular spots, these spots being cuneiform and connected with each other. Dorsum of prothorax black except the anterior and posterior borders, and a median twin spot, and lateral spots, and the sides of the middle lobe, which are pale. Thorax with the middorsal stripe black, but with the middorsal carina blue. Black humeral stripe, and a short black stripe at the base of the third lateral suture sometimes prolonged into a fine line, the only other black on the thorax. Abdomen blue, black as follows: a dorsal spot on the base of 1; on 2 varying from a rather narrow middorsal band reaching from the base to the apex, narrowed at the middle of the segment, with an angular dialiation before the apex, to a round apical spot connected by an apical tail with the apex of the segment; 3 with lanceolate middorsal spot, pointed posteriorly, on the basal half, and a broader spot or band on the apical fourth; 4-6 similar to 3; 7 almost entirely; 8-10 blue, 8 with a minute middorsal, basal point, 10 with a narrow median stripe, black. Superior appendages longer than 10, bifid, the upper arm long, the lower arm appearing as an inferior basal triangle with the point directed ventrally.

The female is unknown.

338. Enallagma basidens Calvert

Calv. '02, p. 114: Mtk. Cat. p. 55.

Length 24 mm. Expanse 28 mm. Southwest into Tex.

This blue and black damselfly has its home primarily in the state of Texas, but is probably to be found all along the Mexican-United States border. Mouth parts, genae, first joint of the antennae, and the frontal transverse band above the postclypeus, pale blue or buff. Remainder of frons and vertex black. Pale postocular spots narrow, serrated and connected with each other by way of the pale postocellar stripe, separated by black from the pale color of the rear of the head. Prothorax black, with the following blue: anterior half of anterior lobe, a median round spot, two lateral crescent shaped spots, and the sides of the median lobe, and a narrow line on the posterior margin of the hind lobe. Middorsal carina of the thorax blue, thus splitting the black middorsal stripe. Pale antehumeral stripe narrow. Black humeral stripe split longitudinally by a fine blue line, the upper part of the humeral being connected with the middorsal stripe by a black bar along the upper margin of the thorax. Sides of thorax blue. Vein M_2 arises nearest the 4th postnodal cross vein in the fore wings, the 3rd in the hind. Abdomen blue with the following black: dorsum of 1–3 for their entire length, the black being wider at the base and before the apex on 2, on 3 having a hastate form which widens greatly in the apical sixth; a hastate spot on 4–6, occupying the apical half to three-fourths on 4, half to three-fifths on 5, and 6; almost all the dorsum of 7; dorsum of 10. Superior appendages about three-fourths as long as 10, black, bifid, upper arm heavy and broad, the lower appearing as a basal spine-like projection from the upper. No tubercle.

The female is similar to the male, the blue of the male, however, is replaced by yellow or pale green in the female. In the abdomen segments 4–6 are like 3 of the male, 7 is like the male, 8 with a middorsal black band for its entire length, 9 with a pair of dorsal black spots on the basal half, remainder of 9 and all of 10 blue. Hind margin of the prothorax entire, convex and somewhat flattened dorsally (as it is also in the male).

339. Enallagma aspersum Hagen

Hag. '61, p. 97: Mtk. Cat. p. 55: Garm. '17, p. 524 and '27, p. 84.

Length 27–34 mm. Expanse 36–44 mm. N. E., N. Y. and N. C. to Mo. and Wis.

This blue and black damselfly is not a common species, but is found about small ponds, often temporary ones. The mouth parts of the male are buff. Post-

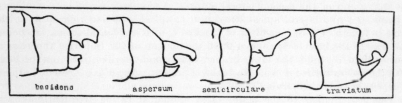

clypeus black with the usual pale transverse frontal band above. Remainder of frons, the vertex and antennae black. Pale postocular spots connected with the pale of the rear of the head but separated from each other. Prothorax mainly black except for the pale anterior lobe. Thorax with broad black middorsal and humeral stripes. Abdomen blue, the following black: a basal spot on one; an apical spot and ring on 2; at least the apical half of 3; 4–6 except an interrupted transverse basal ring on each; basal half to quarter of 7; all of the dorsum of 10. Superior appendages black, bifid, the upper arm much longer than the lower, without a tubercle.

The female is like the male except that abdominal segments 7–8 have a black dorsal stripe reduced to a line on the basal three-fourths and suddenly widened at the apex. 9–10 with the dorsum entirely black.

340. Enallagma semicirculare Selys

Selys '76, p. 517: Mtk. Cat. p. 61.

Length 32 mm. Expanse 40 mm.   **Tropic**

This species is not as yet recorded from within the political boundaries of the United States, but it may be found along the United States-Mexican border or perhaps in tropical Florida. Color, blue and black. Abdomen blue, black as follows: a basal spot on the dorsum of 1; a transverse isolated anteapical streak or semicircular spot, connected, or not connected, by a "tail" with the apex of segment 2; apical fifth or sixth of 3–4; usually the whole of 5–6 metallic green, except a narrow transverse basal ring; 7 almost entirely. *8–10 entirely blue.*

The female is unknown.

341. Enallagma traviatum Selys

Selys '76, p. 521: Mtk. Cat. p. 62: Garm. '17, p. 557 and '27, p. 81.

Length 31 mm. Expanse 38 mm.   **Mass. to Fla.**

Color, pale blue and black. Male. Face pale. Postclypeus with the basal half black. Pale transverse frontal band narrow not reaching the basis of the antennae. Vertex, the antennae and the remainder of the frons, black. Pale postocular spots small, circular or triangular and entirely surrounded by the black of the head. Postocellar pale stripe is vestigial or more often entirely lacking. Dorsum of the prothorax black, with a spot on the anterior lobe, two reduced lateral spots and the sides of the middle lobe, and a spot or a line on the posterior lobe, pale. Thorax with a wide middorsal black stripe. Pale antehumeral stripe somewhat wider than the dark humeral, and cut off short at the caudal end, not reaching the wing basis. Third lateral suture with a black spot on the end followed for the remainder of the suture with a fine black line. A black spot on the upper end of the second lateral suture. Abdomen blue, black as follows: a basal spot and lateral apical streaks on 1; apical spot and ring on 2; apical third to fourth of 3–5; four-fifths of 6; all of 7; a lateral apical streak extending half way to the base of 8; none of 9; all the dorsum of 10. Superior appendages shorter than 10, bifid, the lower branch square and flap-like, the upper slender with the apices turned down. No tubercle present. Appendages resemble those of *aspersum* and *culicinorum.*

Female. Similar to the male. The middorsal carina frequently brown. Abdomen with a basal dark spot on 1; 4–7 with narrow longitudinal dorsal stripes of black, widened suddenly near the caudal margins and narrowed to the meson on the cephalic margins; 8 blue with a narrow dorsal stripe on the basal half or more; 9–10 blue.

342. Enallagma coecum Hagen

Hag. '61, p. 84: Mtk. Cat. p. 56: Calv. '19, p. 350.

Var: novae-hispaniae Calv.

Length 34 mm. Expanse 44 mm. Tropic Calif.

It is doubtful whether or not this species has been collected in the United States; certainly its nearest relative *cardenium* has, and probably this one has also. Color is "rosy-blue" and black. Male. Head black with wide blue postocular spots, measuring .45–.49 mm. from cephalic to caudal edge. Prothorax black, with the anterior lobe transversely pale, middle lobe with or without pale lateral spots, posterior lobe with a pale spot on the caudal margin. Sides with the black of the middle lobe sinuately, and not deeply emarginated by the pale color inferiorly. Thorax rosy-blue marked with the usual black stripes. Abdomen with the black on segment 2 in the form of a U, the open end directed forward. Segment 3 with the sides and the apex black. 8–9 with inferior longitudinal black stripes on each side. The dorsum of 9 and usually 8 entirely blue. Superior appendages bifid, the cleft tending to fill out in some specimens, upper arm longer, lower arm short and flap-like, a small single tooth on the inner margin of the upper arm at about two-thirds its length.

Female similar to the male except the abdomen which is mainly brassy black; segments 3–7 with yellow basal rings, the sides and the 8th segment almost entirely blue.

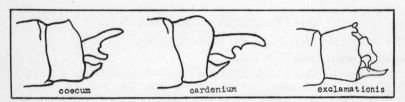

coecum   cardenium   exclamationis

343. Enallagma cardenium Selys

Selys '76, p. 530: Mtk. Cat. p. 56: Wmsn. '22, p. 143: Calv. '19, p. 351.

Length 34 mm. Expanse 44 mm. Fla.

This is an Enallagma of tropical distribution and is recorded from United States only in the Florida region, where it frequents floating water hyacinths in running water, in sandy bottomed creeks. The color is dull violet gray and black, quite un-Enallagma-like, and this color is lost or obscured by post mortem changes in old museum specimens. Head pale, except for a black band between the eyes covering part of the frons and the vertex. Postocular spots narrow, irregular, and usually separated, measuring from .28–.38 mm. from caudal to cephalic border. Prothorax mostly black, except for a transverse area on the anterior lobe and a fine line on the posterior lobe, and occasional spots on the middle lobe. The black of the sides of the middle lobe angularly and deeply emarginated by the pale color inferiorly. Thorax dull violet marked with the usual dark stripes, the middorsal stripe is metallic black, and the one on the third lateral suture extends to the base of the posterior legs. Abdomen with the pale markings dull violet, black as follows: a basal spot on 1; a lateral longitudinal stripe on each side of 2, connected with a subapical dorsal band to form a U-shaped mark, also an apical ring on 2; apical third or more of 3–7; sides of 8–9; and sides and part of the dorsum of 10. The color pattern of the abdomen is very hard to make out in dried specimens. Superior appendages long, bifid and with no tubercle.

The female is like the male, only the abdomen has broad metallic greenish-black stripes covering the entire dorsum of segments 2–7; 8 pale, 9 black with two large apical pale spots; 10 black.

73. Zoniagrion Kennedy

These are slender dragonflies similar to the blue members of the preceding genus, with vein M_2 arising near the sixth post nodal cross vein in the fore wing and the fifth in the hind wing. Wings stalked to a distance before the anal crossing about equal to the length of that cross vein. Female with a large ventral spine on 8; male with the apex of segment 10 cleft and slightly elevated.

The nymph (Kennedy '17, p. 493) is similar to that of Enallagma but the gills are acuminately pointed and the six pigmented cross bands are more or less confluent toward the base and interrupted toward the apex of the gill plate. Lateral setae 5; mentals 3–4 each side.

344. Zoniagrion exclamationis Selys

Selys '76, p. 125: Mtk. Cat. p. 65: Kndy. '17, p. 488.
Length 36 mm. Expanse 44 mm.   Calif.

Face greenish blue with blackish basal suture to the labrum. Top of head black with pure blue postocular spots and a wavy line of blue between them Front of thorax black with a pair of broad isolated stripes of blue interrupted in the male near the upper end (whence the specific name). Sides blue with blackish edgings above and below, with a line on the third lateral suture. Legs black. Wings hyaline, stigma black. Abdomen black with blue and brown markings. Segment 1 blue above; 2 black, with a large quadrangular blue basal spot; 3–6 mostly black; 7–10 blue above, covering 8 and portions of adjacent segments. Lateral inferior pale stripe extends the length of the abdomen. Appendages black.

74. Ischnura Charpentier

Fork-tails

By C. Francis Byers

The genus Ischnura is world wide in its distribution, and is represented in North America by 15 species.

The adults are the first damselflies to appear in the spring and they persist until late autumn. They are to be found, sometimes in countless numbers, in all aquatic situations where there is an abundance of vegetation. Sometimes in low marshy spots, in fields, where there is no open water at all, they occur commonly. Unlike the larger Enallagmas the adults seldom venture out over the open water, but seem well contented to spend their lives flitting about among the grasses, lakes, swamps and ponds. Copulation takes place in these situations, sometimes on the wing, but generally while at rest on the stems and leaves of the aquatic vegetation. The male does not, as a general thing, accompany the female while ovipositing. The eggs are laid singly in the stems and leaves of the surrounding plants. The nymphs occur in the shallow waters of the same types of habitat that the adults frequent.

The males of Ischnura may be characterized as follows: Mouth parts genae and postgenae, pale. Labrum bluish-green with a broad black basal band. Postclypeus black; anteclypeus pale. The top of the head predominantly black; the pale transverse frontal band on the vertical portion of the frons narrow; the postocellar stripe vestigial or generally, entirely wanting; and the postocular spots are extremely small, round, and never connected with any other pale area of the head. The pale antehumeral stripe of the thorax is variable, in most of the species it is entire, and whether wide or narrow, it is of equal width throughout its length; in others it is interrupted in its middle length by a fusion of the black middorsal and humeral stripes, resulting in an anterior and a posterior pale spot, or spot and abbreviated stripe, on either side of the mid-carina; in still other species the antehumeral pale stripe is entirely absent, the dorsum of the thorax being solid black. The coloration of abdominal segments 8–9 are of specific value, but are unfortunately somewhat unconstant. On the apical margin of the dorsum of abdominal segment 10 there is an elevated, bifid process, differing in size and shape in the various species, but never as long as segment 10, as it is in the genus *Anomalagrion*.

In both males and females vein M_2 arises between the 3rd and 4th postnodal cross vein in the forewing, and the 2nd and 3rd in the hind. Setae of the front row on the tibia are all short.

A ventral spine on the apical margin of abdominal segment 8 in the female is variable generic character.

Those species which always possessing this spine are *barberi, kellicotti, cervula* and *verticalis*. Those which never possess it are *perparva, posita* and *prognatha*. Those that may or may not have it are *credula, demorsa, denticollis, erratica, gemina*, and *ramburii*. Unknown with respect to it are *damula* and *utahensis*.

The *mature* females of certain species exhibit dichromatism. That is, in fully matured specimens there are two kinds of females, separated by their *color* and their *color pattern*. To one of these phases has been given the name Homœochromatic or black female; to the other, Heterochromatic or orange female. They may be characterized as follows:

Homœochromatic female (mature): Color blue or green, and black. Pale postocular spots small and not confluent with the pale color of the rear of the head. The predominant color of the thorax is pale bluish. The black humeral stripe is wider than the pale antehumeral. The dorsum of abdominal segment one is dark metallic blue or green, only the articular membrane between 1–2 is pale. The dorsum of segment 2 is dark metallic green or blue for its entire length, narrowed at its hind margin. Dorsum of segment 3 metallic green or blue contracted at the anterior end to a middorsal line, and at the hind end to a smaller degree. The sides of segments 1–3 are pale bluish.

Heterochromatic female: Color yellow or orange, and black. Pale postocular spots more or less confluent with the pale color of the rear of the head. The predominant color of the thorax is yellow or pale orange. The black humeral stripe narrower than the pale antehumeral stripe. Dorsum of abdominal segment 1 orange with pale black dots; 2, yellow or orange with black markings varying from a narrow crescent at two-thirds the segments length to spot on the first—and one on the third—third, connected by a fine dorsal line; 3, yellow or orange the hindmost fourth dark metallic green prolonged forward as a tapering black line almost to, or to, the fore end of the segment; sides of 1–3 yellow or orange.

Both of these forms have, when newly emerged, the 8th and 9th abdominal segments pale blue, each segment with a short basal black stripe on each side of the segments, connected across the dorsum by a black basal line, wider on 8 than on 9. There is no constant difference in the size of these two females.

It will be observed from the above descriptions that the Homœochromatic female has in general the same color and color pattern as the male, while the Heterochromatic female has the customary blue-green color of the male replaced by orange or yellow, and the color pattern radically altered.

The nymphs of only six of our fifteen described species of Ischnura are known. The nymph of this genus resembles that of Enallagma very closely but the gills have long tapering points, while those of Enallagma are more blunt, sometimes being quite rounded. The number of described nymphs are too few to make the writing of a key practical. The following table of characters has been drawn up instead:

The Known Nymphs

Species	Length *	Setae		Ext †	Comb ‡	Gills Pigmentation	Described by
		Lat.	Ment.				
barberi	15+5.5	5	4	5–7	⅓	Tracheae only	Byers '27, p. 000
cervula	12+6	5	4–5	4–5	⅓	Uniform	Kndy. '15, p. 309
denticollis	10+5.5	5	4	(0)?	⅓	Uniform	Kndy. '17, p. 505
perparva	11+5	5	3–5	5	½+	Uniform	Ndm. & Ckll. '03, p. 139
posita	11+5.5	5	4	4	⅓	4 x-bands & apex	Ndm. & Ckll. '03, p. 260§
verticalis	14+6.5	6	4–5	6–7	½	Variable	Ndm. '03, p. 260§

* Body +gills.

† Spines on outer margin of mentum of labium.

‡ Spinous margin on base of dorsal edge of middle gill in terms of length of entire gill.

§ Also by Garman '17, and Howe '21.

KEY TO THE SPECIES

Adults

1. Males

1 Anterior surface of the thorax. Solid black, no antehumeral stripes. Penis without a pair of erect spines on the penultimate segment. (CELANURA, Kennedy)...........................2.

Anterior surface of the thorax not solid black. Penis with a pair of erect spines on the penultimate segment................3.

2 Inferior appendages viewed in profile two branched, the inferior branch a rounded tubercle, the superior branch short, turned up, and covering the inferior branch of the superior appendage ....**gemina**, p. 349

Inferior appendages viewed in profile two branched, the inferior branch sharp and pointed, the superior branch short and not turned up, and not covering the inferior branch of the superior appendages.............................**denticollis**, p. 348

3 Apical fork on segment 10 elongated into a spine. The paired spines of the penis external. (ANOMALURA, Kennedy)..........

....**prognatha**, p. 349

Apical fork on segment 10 not elongated into a spine. Paired spines of the penis internal...................................4.

4 Antehumeral green strip present (a superior spot and a smaller inferior one, appearing as an exclamation mark in *posita*)...5.

Antehumeral green stripe indicated by a pair of widely separated angular spots...14.

5   Abdominal segment 9 wholly black on dorsum..............6.
    Abdominal segment 9 with blue on dorsum predominating.....7.

6   Abdominal segment 8 blue, antehumeral stripe complete.......
    ....**ramburii,** p. 350
    Abdominal segment 8 bronze-black, antehumeral stripe like an in-
    verted exclamation mark......................**posita,** p. 350

7   Abdominal segment usually 9 entirely blue, except for apical teeth
    ....8.
    Abdominal segment 9 with lateral, or broad transverse black
    stripes or spots..11.

8   Abdominal segment 10 with a dorsal bifid process...........9.
    Abdominal segment 10 with cylindrical, entire process.........
    ....**kellicotti,** p. 351

9   Abdominal segment 8 entirely blue except for apical teeth....10.
    Abdominal segment 8 usually with lateral black markings......
    ....**demorsa,** p. 352

10 Superior appendages decurved, one-half the length of 10, with an
    acute, curved apical process; inferiors nearly the length of 10
    with an outer acute process................**barberi,** p. 352
    Superior appendages, in profile view, appearing as a small rounded
    lobe, one-fourth the length of 10; inferiors one-half the length
    of 10, an outer acute process with tip deflected inwardly......
    ....**utahensis,** p. 353

11 Abdominal segment 8 with black markings.................12.
    Abdominal segment 8 entirely blue..............**credula,** p. 353

12 Process of inferior appendage not bifid at apex..............13.
    Process of inferior appendage bifid or trifid at apex...........
    ....**perparva,** p. 353

13 Inferior appendages much longer than the superior, cylindrical,
    notched at tip; superior appendages with slender, straight pro-
    longation.................................**erratica,** p. 354
    Inferior appendages hardly longer than the superiors, a rectangular
    superior basal lobe, not notched at apex; superior appendages
    with decurved prolongation.................**verticalis,** p. 355

14 Bifid process on 10 as high as 10 is wide, forked in apical half....
    ....**cervula,** p. 355
    Bifid process on 10 only about one-fourth as high as 10 is wide,
    forked in less than apical half.................**damula,** p. 356

2. Females

1   Prothorax with no teeth or tooth like processes.............2.

    Prothorax with at least a tooth like process on the hind lobe...12.

2   Size large, length of abdomen over 21 mm..................3.

    Size smaller, length of abdomen under 20 mm..............8.

3   Hind wings under 14 mm. in length.....................4.

    Hind wing over 19 mm. in length........................5.

4   Abdominal segment 9 black on dorsum........**ramburii**, p. 350

    Abdominal segment 9 with at least some blue on dorsum......

    ....**credula**, p. 353

5   With a spine on the apical margin of the sternum of abdominal

    segment 8...6.

    Without such a spine on 8.............................7.

6   M_2 rising nearest the 5th postnodal cross vein in the front wing.

    Species East of the Mississippi..............**kellicotti**, p. 351

    M_2 rising nearest the 4th postnodal cross vein in the fore wings,

    Species west of the Mississippi...............**barberi**, p. 352

7   M_2 arising nearest the 6th postnodal. Species west of the Missis-

    sippi.......................................**erratica**, p. 354

    M_2 rising nearest the 5th postnodal. Species east of the Mississippi.

    (Anomalura, Kennedy)...................**prognatha**, p. 349

8   Hind margin of the prothorax convex throughout, with a small

    median notch...........................**demorsa**, p. 352

    Hind margin of the prothorax high, sides straight and convergant,

    convex medially, no notch.............................9.

9   Pale antehumeral stripe entire...........................10.

    Pale antehumeral stripe usually interrupted to appear as an in-

    verted exclamation mark. Abdominal segment 8 without a

    ventral spine. Eastern species................**posita**, p. 350

10 Abdominal segment 8 without a spine on the apical margin of

    sternum..11.

    Abdominal segment 8 with a ventral spine on apical margin. Dis-

    tribution east ot Texas...................**verticalis**, p. 355

11 Species west of the Mississippi...............**perparva**, p. 353

    Species east of the Mississippi..................**posita**, p. 350

12 Middle prothoracic lobe with a small tooth on each side. (Celae-

    nura, Kennedy).......................................13.

    Middle prothoracic lobe without teeth. Hind prothoracic lobe

    with a median truncate tooth-like process, with a pencil of erect

    hairs on either side.........................**cervula**, p. 353

345. Ischnura denticollis Burmeister

Burm. '39, p. 819: Mtk. Cat. p. 68: Kndy. '17, p. 500: Smn. '27, p. 15.
Syn: exstriata Calv.

Length 28 mm. Expanse 30 mm.   **Calif., Ariz., Nev. and Utah**

This small feeble western damselfly has the face of the male, including the mouth parts, the genae, the postgenae, and the anteclypeus, pale. Labrum pale with a black basal line. Postclypeus black. Pale transverse frontal band wide, reaching to, and including the basal segments of the antennae. The vertex, remainder of the frons and antennae black. Pale postocular spots very small and entirely surrounded by black. Prothorax entirely metallic black except for a transverse stripe on the anterior lobe, and the sides of the middle lobe, which are pale blue. Thorax greenish blue, the dorsum entirely black: this color extends rearward along the sides to half way between the first and second lateral sutures. Third lateral suture narrowly black, this color widening above into a spot. Abdomen shining black, except as follows: sides of segments 1-3 and 8-10 blue. The apex of 2 blue. A trifoliate pure blue spot on the apex of the dorsum 8-9. Sides of segments 4-7 yellow. Segments 3-7 with narrow, pale basal rings, interrupted middorsally.

Female, usual adult coloration. Labrum greenish edged with black above. Anteclypeus, genae, vertical surface of the frons, and the base of the mandibles bluish-green. Postclypeus and vertex black. Postocular spots moderate, blue, and confluent with the pale color of the rear of the head. Prothorax bluish-green on the sides, the dorsum black, except the anterior lobe. Thorax blue with wide middorsal black stripe and antehumeral pale stripe. A very narrow humeral dark stripe and basal spots at the base of the second and third lateral sutures. The abdomen has the dorsum entirely black, or is colored as in the male.

"The female of this species from the teneral to the senile color passes through several remarkable color stages, and it is dichromatic and possibly trichromatic in color."—Kennedy.

The following account of its habits has been taken from Dr. Kennedy's ('17) account of this species.

This smallest of western dragonflies occurs throughout the warmer valleys of Calif., Nev., Ariz. and N.W. Mex. . . . . This species is found commonly on the high central plateau of Mexico . . . . at an elevation of over 6000 feet. In Calif. and Nev. it is found from sea-level up to 4400 feet. It is in these states distinctly a spring stream form, though in southern Calif. it is found about almost any permanent sluggish water.

The habits of this species are in general Ischnuran but indicate greater feebleness. Early in the morning it is found in the sedges and grasses bordering the water, but during the heat of the day it spends the greater part of its time over the surface of the water, usually seated on trash or aquatic vegetation.

. . . . several nymphs ready to transform were taken from the trash around the edge of a warm spring and the exuviae were common on the grass stalks fringing the water.

The females resorted to the little drain ditches to oviposit; there the males in great numbers awaited their coming. After a considerable time in copulation, seated on some grass stem the female, still accompanied by the male, would fly to the surface of the stream, preferably a quiet lateral pool, and commence ovipositing.

In ovipositing the male held the female by the head. The pair would alight on floating vegetation, in a horizontal position, and the female would bend her abdomen slightly and make one or two incisions, after which she would raise the end of her abdomen considerably above the horizontal and wait in this position several seconds, when the pair would fly to another straw and repeat the one or two thrusts followed by the wait with the tip of the female's abdomen in the air. This was kept up by a pair under observation, for 20 minutes. In no place did they make more than one or two thrusts. Further, I was not positive at the time that the ovipositor was actually thrust into the plant tissue, as the females observed put forth none of that painstaking effort usually shown by ovipositing dragonflies. Later, when these grass blades were examined in the laboratory, eggs were found in pairs. This species is undoubtedly the feeblest of all the western Odonata. . . . .

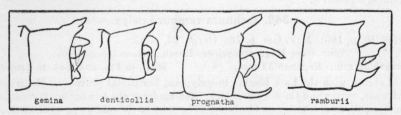

gemina   denticollis   prognatha   ramburii

346. Ischnura gemina Kennedy

Kndy. '17, p. 497.

Length 28 mm. Expanse 30 mm. **Calif.**

This species is similar in coloration and probably in habits to *I. denticollis*. The structural points separating the two species are given in the keys. Like that species the anterior surface of the thorax is solid black, there being no pale antehumeral stripe present. The differences are shown in our figures.

347. Ischnura prognatha Hagen

Hag. '61, p. 83: Mtk. Cat. p. 69: Kndy. '20, p. 88.

Length 36–38 mm. Expanse 45 mm. **Va., Tenn. and Fla.**

This is the largest and probably the most attractive of our fork-tails. It is not common. Labrum greenish-yellow with a black basal band. Mouth parts, genae, postgenae, anteclypeus and the vertical portion of the frons green or yellowish. Postocular spots small, round, blue and isolated. A narrow green postocellar stripe present on the causo-mesal margin of the head. Remainder of the head black. Prothorax with the anterior lobe and the sides of the middle lobe pale, remainder black. Thorax with wide middorsal and humeral black stripes. The pale antehumeral stripe present and complete though narrow. A black basal spot on the second and third lateral sutures, that on the latter followed by a pale black line. Stigma bicolored, the outer margin white, the inner black, the stigma of the fore wing much larger than that of the hind. Dorsum of abdominal segments 1–8 and 10 black except for an apical ring on 1 and interrupted basal rings of yellow on segments 4–7. Segment 9 blue. The dorsal apical process on segment 10, very long and tubular, notched only at the extreme tip. The superior appendages long and delicate, consisting of two processes, one, black in color, directed backward, the other, yellow, directed ventrally.

Female. Homochromatic only. Young specimens bright orange and black, older ones as in male. Head as in male. Thorax with the black mid-dorsal stripe about .5 mm. wide, a distinct spot on the meso-, inter-, and metapleural sutures at the base of each wing, and an indistinct short stripe on the interpleural suture bronze. First abdominal segment indistinctly darker apically; 2–3 with dorsal apical rings of bronze, and 3 with a subapical dorsal spot; 4 with a dorsal stripe occasionally apical six-sevenths of the segment apically abruptly dilated into an urn-shaped spot; from segment 4 the bronze dorsal stripe is continuous, with narrow basal interruptions at each segment, to one-third the length of 9; remainder of the abdomen yellow. No ventral spine on the apical margin of abdominal segment 8.

348. Ischnura ramburii Selys

Selys '50, p. 186: Mtk. Cat. p. 70: Garm. '27, p. 43.
     Syn: iners Hag., *senegalense* Ramb., *tuberculatum* Selys
Length 32 mm. Expanse 33 mm.   **R. I., to Fla. and Tex. to Tropics**

Labrum with the base black. Postclypeus, horizontal portion of the frons, antennae, vertex and the occiput, black. Remainder of the head pale. Postocular spots, small, round, green and isolated. The sides of the middle prothoracic lobe and the dorsum of the anterior lobe pale, remainder of the prothorax black. Black mid-dorsal and humeral thoracic stripes wide. The pale antehumeral stripe narrow and complete. A black spot at the base of the second lateral suture; a black line on the third lateral suture. Abdomen with the dorsum of abdominal segments 1–7 and 9–10 metallic black, with narrow, interrupted, yellow basal rings on 3–7. Segment 8 blue with a black basal ring.

The females of *ramburii* exhibit the dichromatism so common to many of the Ischnuran species. The Homochromatic (black) female is colored like the male. The Heterochromatic (orange) female has the blue or green of the male replaced by orange. The postocular spots large and confluent with the pale color of the rear of the head. Thorax orange with the customary black mid-dorsal stripe but no humeral stripe. Abdominal segment 1 and the base of 2 orange, remainder of the abdomen black on the dorsum.

349. Ischnura posita Hagen

Hag. '61, p. 77: Mtk. Cat. p. 69: Garm. '17, p. 570 and '27, p. 41.
Length 24–29 mm. Expanse 26–36 mm.   **Me. and N. Dak. to Fla. and Mo.**

A not uncommon damselfly found in the thick vegetation of swamps and marshes. Labrum greenish-yellow with the base black. Pale postocular spots small, circular and isolated. Mouth parts, genae, postgenae, anteclypeus and the vertical portion of the frons, pale. Postclypeus, antennae, horizontal portion of the frons, vertex and the occiput, black. Dorsum of the prothorax black with a pale spot on the anterior lobe and the sides pale. Thoracic dorsum black, the pale, antehumeral stripe interrupted in its middle length by a fusion of the black middorsal and humeral stripes, to form a pale exclamation point mark on either side. Sides greenish-yellow except for a black basal spot on the second lateral suture and a heavy black stripe covering the third lateral suture. Dorsum of abdominal segments 1–10 black, except for narrow interrupted basal rings of yellow on segments 3–7, and apical crescent-shaped half rings of blue on the dorsum of 8–9.

Female. Color pale blue and black, no heterochromatic phase known. Head similar to that of the male. Thorax lacking the black stripe on the metapleural suture, and occasionally having the pale antehumeral stripe complete, not interrupted to form an exclamation mark. Abdomen like the male. No ventral spine on the apical margin of abdominal segment 8.

350. Ischnura kellicotti Williamson

Wmsn. '98, p. 209: Mtk. Cat. p. 69: Garm. '17, p. 568.

Length 29 mm. Expanse 36–38 mm.   Me., R. I., N. Y., to Ind. and Mich.

Head blue below. The labrum blue with a black basal line. Anteclypeus blue; postclypeus black. Vertical portion of the frons blue. Remainder of the frons, the vertex and the antennae black. Pale postocular spots not connected with any other pale area of the head. Dorsum of the prothorax black with a transverse line on the anterior lobe, occasionally two lateral spots on the middle lobe, sides of the middle lobe, and the posterior margin of the hind lobe, pale. Thorax blue, black as follows: a wide middorsal stripe; a humeral stripe which

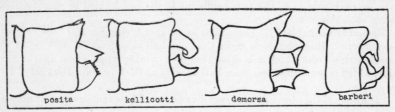

posita   kellicotti   demorsa   barberi

widens suddenly just posterior to the mesinfraepisternum which it covers; a very narrow interrupted line at the basal half of the second lateral suture; a narrow stripe on the third lateral suture, widening below to cover the metainfraepisternum; a line connecting these stripes posteriorly. Pale antehumeral stripe of equal width throughout. Abdomen with the dorsum bronze-black, blue as follows; a wide apical ring on 1; a large basal spot and a wide apical ring on 2. the extreme base and apex of the segment black; pale narrow interrupted basal rings on 3–7; apical ring on 7; all of 8 except a narrow basal ring; all of 9, the blue narrowed on either side near the middle; two small round basal spots on 10, and the tip of the elevated process on 10 which is scarcely bifid. Sides of 1–2 blue and black; of 3–7 and 10 brownish or yellowish; of 8–9 black bordered with blue.

Homochromatic female, similar to the male. Postocular spots larger prolonged to meet the pale color of the rear of the head. Middle lobe of the prothorax with an occasional additional geminate spot. Abdomen with the blue on 1–2 more extensive, 8–9 with the pale color more variable but usually more extensive also.

Heterochromatic female like the homochromatic female but the orange color replaces the blue-green of the latter.

351. Ischnura demorsa Hagen

Hag. '61, p. 81: Mtk. Cat. p. 68.

Length 24–27 mm. Expanse 26–34 mm.   Mont. and Colo. to Ariz. and N. Mex.

Male. Head predominantly black with the mouth parts, the anteclypeus, vertical portion of the frons, and two small postocular spots, pale. Dorsum of the thorax with well defined blue antehumeral stripe, remainder metallic black, sides pale. Abdomen brassy green, the sides and basal rings on segments 3–6, yellow. Segments 8–9 entirely blue, or with a short basal black stripe on the sides of each, or in still other specimens, on the sides of one and not the other. Segment 10 black on the dorsum with the usual narrow elevated bifid process. Inferior appendages bifid.

Females. *Heterochromatic* (orange). Postocular spots large, orange, and connected with the pale color of the rear of the head. Dark humeral stripe reduced to a mere line, consequently widening the pale orange antehumeral stripe, which becomes more than half as wide as the black middorsal stripe. Abdomen largely orange, becoming yellowish posteriorly, the following black on the dorsum: a basal spot on 1; a median line on 2; a median line on 3, except at base, expanded into a wide spot on apical fourth; a broad middorsal stripe on 4–7, more or less constricted at three-fourths the length of the segment; a stripe on each side of 8, the two confluent in the basal third or more; a basal spot on each side of 9.

Homochromatic (black): Postocular spots small, circular and blue or green, not connected. Black humeral more than one-half as wide as the dark middorsal thoracic stripe, from which it is separated by a complete pale green antehumeral stripe, which is sometimes less than half as wide as the humeral. Dorsum of 1–10 black.

Variations of the above color forms may occur. These females may or may not have a ventral spine on 8.

352. Ischnura barberi Currie

Currie '03, p. 302: Mtk. Cat. p. 68.

Length 32–35 mm. Expanse 35–42 mm.   Colo., N. Mex., Utah

Greenish-yellow, blue and black in color. Head of the male pale beneath, with the occipital region and a line at the base of the labrum black. Postclypeus entirely shining black or black with a fine pale marginal line. Pale transverse frontal band reaching the basis of the antennal fossae. Antennae, the remainder of the frons, and the vertex, except for two small ocellar spots, black. Pale postocular spots usually very small and widely separated from the pale postocellar stripe, occasionally large and narrowly connected with it. The anterior half of the anterior lobe, the sides of the middle lobe, and the posterior lobe of the prothorax, pale. Dorsum of the middle lobe entirely black, or with a small pale spot on each side. Thorax with a wide pale antehumeral stripe. Sides pale except for a basal black line on the third lateral suture reaching as far as the basis of the posterior legs, and a small black spot on the base of the second lateral suture. Abdominal segment 1 pale with a basal black spot on the dorsum; segments 2–7 with dorsum entirely black except pale narrow interrupted basal rings on segments 3–6, and preapical rings on segments 3–5. Segments 8–9 entirely blue except for a very fine transverse black line covering the preapical teeth. Segment 10 entirely black on the dorsum, with the forked elevation well developed.

Female. Heterochromatic. Differs from the male as follows: Pale areas of the head very much larger, the transverse frontal band of yellow nearly reaching the median ocellus, the pale postocular spots wide and broadly joined to the yellow of the rear of the head. The dark middorsal and humeral thoracic stripes very narrow. Abdominal segments 8–9 broadly brown on the dorsum. A well developed ventral spine on the apical margin of segment 8 of the abdomen. Hind margin of the prothorax convex throughout, no teeth nor tooth like processes.

353. Ischnura utahensis Muttkowski

Mtk. '10, p. 9.

Length 33 mm. Expanse 36 mm. Utah

Coloration the same as in *Ischnura barberi*. The differences between the two species are to be found in the superior and inferior abdominal appendages as described in the key. Possibly, a synonym of *I. barberi*.

The female is unknown.

354. Ischnura credula Hagen

Hag. '61, p. 80: Mtk. Cat. p. 70: Calv. '28, p. 11.

Syn: defixa Hag.

Length 29 mm. Expanse 32 mm. Fla. and Calif.

This damselfly is commonly considered as a subspecies of *Ischnura ramburii*. It differs little from it except in the coloration of the 9th abdominal segment of the male. In *ramburii* this segment is entirely black on the dorsum, while in *credula* it is blue with wide irregular basal and apical transverse bands of black.

355. Ischnura perparva Selys

Selys '76, p. 263: Mtk. Cat. p. 69: Kndy. '15, p. 310.

Syn: defixa

Length 24 mm. Expanse 27 mm. B. C., Mont. to Calif. and Tex.

Head greenish below, black above. The mouth parts, genae, postgenae, anteclypeus and the vertical portion of the frons, pale. The labrum green with a black basal stripe. The postclypeus, the horizontal portion of the frons, the antennae, the vertex and the occiput, black. Pale postocular spots small and isolated. Prothorax black with a transverse stripe on the anterior lobe, a pair of lateral spots and the sides of the middle lobe, pale. Thorax with a broad mid-dorsal and humeral black stripe; a broad pale antehumeral stripe; a short black basal spot on the second lateral suture; and a black line widened above on the third lateral suture. Abdomen with the abdominal segments 2–7 and 10 black, the sides pale, with a basal spot and an apical ring of black on the dorsum. Segments 8–9 pale blue, with a large rectangular black basal spot on either side. The dorsal bifid process on 10 well developed with arms enclosing an angle of more than 90°. Inferior appendages bifid or trifid.

The females of *perparva* do not possess the two color forms in the mature imago; however, the teneral colors are orange and black. The following black markings appear on the mature female. All the dorsal surface of the head black except the pale transverse frontal band. Entire dorsum of the prothorax black. Wide middorsal and humeral stripe of black on the thorax, as well as a basal spot of black on the second and third lateral sutures. All the abdominal segments black except narrow, pale apical cross lines on segments 1, 7, 8, 9. The pale colors are olive green. The entire body and legs are more or less pruinose, making a slate gray insect.

Kennedy ('17) reports that "*Ischnura perparva* occurs during the entire season and is frequently as abundant along the stagnant side pools of fresh streams as it ever is about alkaline ponds, where it occurs in equal abundance with *cervula*. In other words, it seems to be adapted to a wider variety of conditions than *cervula*.

In habits it resembles *cervula* but, when at rest in copulation, or ovipositing, the wings are usually held tightly closed. Being a heavier bodied insect the abdomen is seldom bent into the U-shapes common with ovipositing *cervula*. As in *cervula* the males rarely accompany the females while the latter are ovipositing."

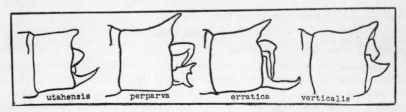

utahensis   perparva   erratica   verticalis

356. Ischnura erratica Calvert

Calv. '95, p. 491: Mtk. Cat. p. 69.

Length 30–32 mm. Expanse 36–44 mm.   **B. C. to Calif.**

The following description of the male is taken from Dr. Calvert's original one: Black, the following blue or green: mouth parts, head below, frons anteriorly, postocular spots, a complete antehumeral stripe each side, sides of the thorax (except a black line on the base of the second lateral and a complete line on the third lateral sutures), abdomen below, apical dorsal spot of 1, a wavy, transverse, apical band on 2, a dorsal band on the apical five-sixths of 7–9 (except a lateral black band on the sides of each, reaching from the base to the apex, those of 8 united by a narrow, transverse, basal black band, and of 9 by a transverse apical band in some specimens, but not united on either 8 or 9 in others. A narrow, transverse, interrupted, basal yellow ring on 3–7. Forked process on 10 about half as high as 10 itself. Superior appendages black, very short, one-fourth as long as 10, tubercular, with a slender, inner inferior prolongation reaching to the base of the inferior appendages. Inferior appendages two-thirds as long as 10, similar to those of *denticollis*, but with the apical processes a little more robust and curved upwards as well as inwards at the extreme tip.

The females of this species exhibit the usual homochromatic and heterochromatic phases so common to the species of this genus. The prothorax of the female has the hind margin distinctly bilobed. The ventral spine on the apical margin of abdominal segment 8 is either vestigial or entirely wanting.

357. Ischnura verticalis Say

Say '39, p. 37: Mtk. Cat. p. 70: Lyon '15, p. 59: Calv. '15, p. 62: Garm. '17, p. 572 and '27, p. 44.

Syn: discolor Burm.

Length 20–30 mm. Expanse 32–38 mm. Me., Ont. and N. Dak. to Ga. and Texas

Within its range, this is the most common Zygopteran in North America, occurring in large numbers everywhere that there is enough water for the nymphs to live. The adults appear early in May and continue to emerge until September or later. Male. Labrum pale green with a black basal stripe. Postocular spots bluish-green, round, and isolated. A narrow pale postocellar stripe present. Anteclypeus pale; postclypeus black. Vertical portion of the frons pale; horizontal portion black. Antennae, vertex and occiput black. Mouth parts, genae and postgenae pale bluish-green. Dorsum of middle prothoracic lobe and posterior lobe black, remainder of the prothorax pale. Black middorsal and humeral stripes wide. The pale antehumeral stripe entire and narrow. A black spot on the base of the second lateral suture and a black spot and indefinite brown line on the third lateral suture. Dorsum of abdominal segments 1–7 and 10 black with narrow, yellow interrupted basal rings on segments 3–7. Segments 8–9 blue, with large rectangular basal black spots on either side, those on 8 connected across the dorsum by a black basal line.

The females exhibit the homochromatic and heterochromatic phases, and as this is the most common damselfly showing this phenomenon, much work has been done on it. For a fuller account of this interesting matter see the introduction to this genus and the 1915 papers of Dr. Calvert and Miss Lyon cited above.

358. Ischnura cervula Selys

Selys '76, p. 262: Mtk. Cat. p. 68: Kndy. '17, p. 295: Ndm. '23, p. 131.

Length 29 mm. Expanse 34 mm.   **B. C. and Calif., Utah, Ariz., N. Mex.**

A far western all-summer species. Male. Color of the head mainly black with reduced pale markings as follows: Mouth parts, labrum except for a basal line, anteclypeus, vertical surface of the frons, and two very small postocular spots. The prothorax black except for a transverse pale stripe on the anterior lobe, and an interrupted bluish-green vertical stripe on each side which runs down into the coxa. Thorax with the sides blue. A black spot and line on the third lateral suture and a black basal spot on the second lateral suture. Dorsum of the thorax entirely black, the pale antehumeral stripe being represented by two widely separated blue spots on the upper and lower end of each mesinfrae-pisternum. Dorsum of abdominal segments 1–7 metallic black. Segments 8–9 blue, each with a rectangular black spot at the basal end of each, joined across the dorsum by a fine black basal line; preapical teeth also black. Segment 10 mainly black above, the bifid process being conspicuous. The inferior abdominal appendages are deeply bifid.

Female. The coloration in the female is very variable ranging between the light phase, Heterochromatic, where the extent of the black on the head and thorax has been reduced to a minimum, i.e., the postclypeus is entirely yellow, the postocular spots are large and joined, the dark middorsal and humeral thoracic stripes are mere lines and the legs are entirely pale; to the dark phase, homochromatic, where head and thorax are colored as in the male. The extent of pale coloration of the abdomen is less variable and resembles the male, except that the dorsum of segment 9, to a greater or less extent, inferiorly, is always black. On the hind margin of the prothorax there is a medium truncate tooth-like process with a pencil of erect hairs on either side. The females of *cervula* do not possess the ventral spine on the apical margin of segment 8.

Dr. Kennedy ('17) gives the following interesting account of this species as observed by him in Washington and Oregon.

While occurring from early spring till heavy frosts in autumn, *Ischnura cervula* reaches its greatest abundance during the months of May and June. About running water it is scarce, in such places choosing the more stagnant spring laterals and side ponds. As with the other species of this genus, it is seldom found over the water or on land far from the moist banks of a pond or stream.

It emerges in the day time usually between 9 and 11 o'clock in the morning, when it can sometimes be found emerging in swarms. At such times the nymphs can be seen swarming to the bank with a tadpole-like wriggling motion. They usually wait about 15 minutes after crawling from the water until they dry and the back splits. A half hour later they are on the wing. This species has, especially during imaginal life, the *Lestes* habit of hanging among aquatic vegetation and dodging among the reed stems to avoid capture.

Copulation takes place with the couple moving about among the vegetation or at rest on some leaf, and lasts for many minutes.

In oviposition, the female usually unaccompanied by the male, deposits her eggs in any vegetable matter under the surface of the water which is soft enough to be pierced by her ovipositor, usually the stems of aquatic plants, but some-times she will alight on the surface of a floating mass of filamentous algae and oviposit in the tangle of filaments. Usually the abdomen is bent U-shaped and the wings are loosely folded as in copulation, but occasionally she assumes the poses of *perparva*, with the wings tightly folded.

359. Ischnura damula Calvert

Calv. '02, p. 126: Mtk. Cat. p. 68.
Length 27–30 mm. Expanse 32–34 mm.   N. Mex. and Colo.

This species of Ischnura is similar to *cervula* in coloration. It differs mainly in the structure of the superior and inferior abdominal appendages and the dorsal process on segment 10, as follows: Superior appendages not quite half as long as segment 10, heavy, blunt and ending in a short, acute spine-like process, directed ventrally. Inferiors a little longer than the superiors, *not bifid*, turned up at the tip. The dorsal process on the 10th segment less elevated than in *cervula*, bifid in less than its apical half, and its branches enclosing an angle of 90°.

Female unknown.

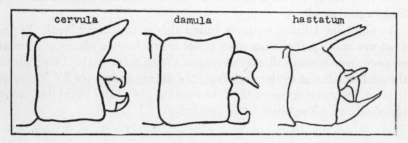

75. ANOMALAGRION Selys

These are among the smallest and daintiest of damselflies, with short, weak legs, slender bodies, and very much attenuated abdomen. The stigma in the wings of the male is remarkable for its ovoid shape and its separation from the costal margin; that of the hind wing is similar to the more normal stigma of the female.

The nymphs (Ndm. '03, p. 263) are very local. They are found in the shallow water among club rushes, to the vertical stems of which they habitually cling. The gills are regularly widened to about two-thirds of their length and then regularly narrowed to a long tapering point.

360. Anomalagrion hastatum Say

Say '39, p. 38: Mtk. Cat. p. 71: Davis '13, p. 18: Root '24, p. 319: Garm. '27, p. 39.

Syn: anomalum Ramb., *venerionotatum* Haldemann

Length 23 mm. Expanse 21 mm.   **Me. and N. D. southward**

This is one of the smallest and most delicate of our damselflies. Face is yellow cross lined with black on postclypeus and base of labrum. Head black above with violet reflections when mature and sometimes a pair of minute postocular pale spots. Front of thorax metallic blue black, including carina, with pale straight edged antehumeral stripes each side. Sides of thorax pale with short black lines in the sutures above. Legs yellow with black stripes on the top of the femora and short black spines. Wings hyaline with yellowish stigma. Abdomen orange and black in the male; wholly dark above in the female. Basal segments of the male abdomen with a blackish stripe that is narrowed and widened again on 3 and reduced to spots at ends on 4–6, and terminates in a broad band at three-fourths the length of 7. 8 and 9 wholly yellow, as are the sides of all the other segments. Venter of all, in the female, yellow. Appendages yellow in the male, black in the female.

Root ('24, p. 319) says it is in Lee County, Georgia. "The commonest and most widely distributed damselfly of the region. Found about all kinds of ponds, swamps, ditches, etc., throughout the summer.

Davis ('13, p. 18) says it is found in salt meadows as well as about fresh-water ponds.

In northern Illinois we have found this species very local. Permanent wet spots rather than open pools are its home: places of constant seepage from springs thickly overgrown with spike rush. Down among the rushes, almost under ones feet, the dainty creatures flit from stem to stem, the red stigmas of the fore wings of the males twinkling among the shadows. Exquisite little creatures.

BIBLIOGRAPHY

Books especially devoted to dragonflies are few. Tillyard's *Biology of the Dragonflies* is the one good general treatise. For Great Britain there is W. J. Lucas' *British Dragonflies*. Kirby's *Synopsis-Catalogue of the Neuroptera, Odonata or Dragonflies*, now out of date (1890), is the latest list for the world fauna. Of entirely different character is the book that was made out of the Lamborn Prize essays on possibilities of economic control, and published in 1890 under the title *Dragonflies vs. Mosquitoes*. Among the general books of natural history are a few that treat the dragonflies somewhat adequately: notably L. O. Howard's *Insect Book*, V. L. Kellogg's *American Insects* and the senior author's *Outdoor Studies*.

Muttkowski's Catalogue of 1910 is the source book for North America. We have duplicated the bibliographic references of that work only to the extent of citing the original description under each species.

All citations in the preceding pages, by author, year and page, are to the papers in the following list. When two or more papers by the same author have been published in a single year, the page references will enable the reader to find the one desired.

Abbott, C. E. 1926. Death Feigning in Anax Junius and Aeschna sp. Psyche 33: 8–10.

Bethel, E. 1915. Sympetrum Corruptum, a Dragonfly at a High Altitude. Ent. News 26: 119.

Bodine, Joseph H. 1918. Experimental Results in Ischnura and Enallagma. Proc. Acad. Nat. Sci. Phil. pp. 103–113.

Brimley, C. S. 1903. List of Dragonflies from North Carolina, especially from the vicinity of Raleigh. Ent. News 29: 150–157.

——— 1920. Notes on North Carolina Dragonflies. Ent. News 31: 138–139.

Bromley, S. W. 1924. New Ophiogomphus from Massachusetts. Ent. News 35: 343–344.

——— 1928. A dragonfly Ovipositing on a Paved Highway. Bull. Brooklyn Ent. Soc. 23: 69.

Broughton, Elsie. 1928. Some New Dragonfly Nymphs. Can. Ent. 60: 32-34.

Butler, Hortense. 1904. The Labium of the Odonata. Trans. Am. Ent. Soc. 30: 111–133. 3 pl.

——— 1914. Three new species of Odonata. Can. Ent. 46: 346–348.

Byers, C. Francis. 1925. Odonata collected in Cheboygan and Emmet Counties, Mich. Mich. Acad. Sci. 5: 389.

——— 1927. An Annotated List of the Odonata of Michigan. Occ. Papers Mus. of Zoo. U. of Mich. No. 183: 1–16.

——— 1927. The Nymph of Libellula incesta and a Key for the Separation of the Known Nymphs of the Genus Libellula. Ent. News 38: 113, 1927.

—— 1927. Notes on Some American Dragonfly Nymphs. Jour. N. Y. Ent. Soc. 35: 65–74. 1 pl.

—— 1927. Key to the North American Species of Enallagma, with a description of a new species. Trans. Am. Ent., Soc, 53: 249–260.

—— 1927. Enallagma and Telagrion from Western Florida, with a Description of a New Species. Annals E. S. A. 20: 385–392.

Calvert, Philip P. 1912. The North American Dragonflies of the Genus Aeschna. By E. M. Walker. Ent. News 23: 283–286.

—— 1913. The Species of Nehalennia including one from the eastern United States hitherto undescribed. Ent. News 24: 310–316.

—— 1915. The Dimorphism or Dichromatism of the Females of Ischnura Verticalis. Ent. News 26: 62–68.

—— 1917. On Hagenius Brevistylus. Proc. Acad. Natur. Sci. 69: 205.

—— 1919. Gundlach's Work on the Odonata of Cuba: A Critical Study. Trans. Am. Ent. Soc. 45: 335–396, 3 pl.

—— 1921. Gomphus Dilatatus, Vastus and a new species, Lineatifrons. Amer. Entom. Soc. 47, pp. 221–232, 2 pls.

—— 1923. Supplementary note on Gomphus dilatatus. Leucorhinia proxima at a high altitude in Colorado. Ent. News XXIV: 87–88.

——— 1924. The supposed Males of Ophiogomphus howei. Ent. News 35: 345–7.

—— 1926. Relations of a late autumnal dragonfly to temperature. Ecology 8: 185–190.

—— 1928. Report on Odonata . . . . . Collected by the Barbados Antigua Expedition. Univ. Iowa Stud. Nat. Hist. 12: 1–44, 5 pl.

Coombs, A. F. 1917. Notes on a collection of Odonata from Schoolcraft Co. Mich. Occ. Papers, Mus. of Zoo. U. of Mich. 41, 8 pp.

Cullen, Anna M. 1918. Rectal Tracheation of Argia Putrida Larva. Proc. Acad. Nat. Sci. Phil. 75, 81.

Currie, Bertha P. 1917. Gomphus parvidens, a new sp. from Maryland. Proc. N. S. Nat. Mus. 53: 223–226. 2 pl.

Davis, Wm. T. 1913. Dragonflies of New York City. Jour. N. Y. Ent. Soc. 21: 12–24.

—— 1914. The Dragonfly Anax Longipes on Long Island, N. Y. Bull. Brook. Ent. Soc. 9: 34–37.

—— 1922. A New Dragonfly from Florida. Bull. Brook. Ent. Soc. 16: 109–111.

—— 1927. A New Dragonfly from Virginia. Bull. Brook. Ent. Soc. 22: 155–156.

Garman, Philip. 1917. The Zygoptera, or Damselflies, of Illinois. Bull. Ill. St. Lab. Nat. His. 12: 410–587, 16 pls.

—— 1927. The Odonata or Dragonflies of Connecticut. Conn. Geol. and Nat. Hist. Survey Bull. 39.

Hine, J. S. 1925. Tachopteryx thoreyi, recorded from Ohio, with notes on its near relatives. Ohio Jour. Sc. 25: 190–192.

Holland, W. J. 1922. Calopteryx maculata, an interesting photograph. Proc. Ent. Soc. Wash. 24: 117–118.

Howe, R. H. 1916. A preliminary list of the Odonata of Concord, Mass. Rep. Psyche. 23: 12–15.

—— 1917–1923. Manual of the Odonata of New England. Memoir Thoreau Museum Nat. Hist. II: 1–138.

—— 1918. Distributional Notes on New England Odonata. Part II. Psyche. 25: 106–110.

—— 1919. Odonata of the Franconia Region, N. H. Can. Ent. 51, pp. 9–15.

—— 1921. Supplement to Manual of Odonata of New England. Mem. Thoreau Mus. Nat. Hist. 2: 1–14.

—— 1921. Distribution of New England Odonata. Proc. Boston Soc. Nat. Hist. 36: 105–133.

—— 1922. A new Dragonfly from New England (Gomphus alleni). Acc. Papers Boston Soc. Nat. Hist. 5: 19–20.

—— 1924. Williamsonia lintneri Hagen, its history and distribution. Psyche 30: 222–225.

—— 1925. Another instance of northward migration of Odonata in the spring. Psyche 32.

Kennedy, Clarence H. 1913. Notes on Odonata or Dragonflies of Bumping Lake, Washington. Proc. U. S. Nat. Mus. 46: 111–126. 57 fig.

—— 1915. Interesting Western Odonata. Ann. Ent. Soc. Am. 8: 297–303.

—— 1915a. Notes on the Life History and Ecology of the Dragonflies of Washington and Oregon. Proc. U. S. Nat. Mus. 49: 259–345.

—— 1917. The Dragonflies of Kansas. The Odonata of Kansas with Reference to Their Distribution. Bull. Kan. Univ. 18: 127–145. 7 pls.

—— 1917. Notes on the Life History and Ecology of the Dragonflies of Central California and Nevada. Proc. U. S. Nat. Mus. 52: 483–635.

—— 1917. A new species of Somatochlora. Can. Ent. 49: 229–236.

—— 1918. Varieties of the Dragonfly Agrion aequabile. Can. Ent. 50: 406–410.

—— 1918. New species of Odonata from the Southwestern United States. Can. Ent. 50: 256–261, 297–300. 1 pl.

—— 1919. The Naiad of the Odonate genus Coryphaeschna. Ent. News 30: 105–108.

—— 1919. A New Species of Argia. Can. Ent. 51: 17–18.

—— 1920. Forty-two hitherto unrecognized genera and subgenera of Zygoptera. Ohio Jour. Sci. 21: 83–88.

—— 1920. The Phylogeny of the Zygopterous Dragonflies as Based on the Evidence of the Penes. Ohio. J. Sci. 21: 19–29. 3 pl.

—— 1921. Some Interesting Dragonfly Naiads from Texas. Proc. U. S. Nat. Mus. 59: 595–598. 1 pl.

—— 1922. The Phylogeny and the Geographical Distribution of the Genus Libellula. Ent. News 33: 65–71 and 105–111.

—— 1922. The Homologies of the Tracheal Branches in the Respiratory System of Insects. Ohio J. Sci. 22: 84–88.

— —— 1922. The Ecological Relationships of the Dragonflies of the Bass Islands of Lake Erie. Ecology 3: 325–336.

—— 1922. The Morphology of the Penis in the Genus Libellula. Ent. News 33: 33 40. 2 pls.

— —— 1923. The Naiad of Pantala Hymenea. Can. Ent. 54: 36–38.

—— 1923. Phylogeny and Distribution of Genus Erythemis. N. Mich. Misc. Pub. No. 11: 19–21. 1 pl.

—— 1924. Notes and descriptions of Naiads belonging to the Dragonfly Genus Helocordulia. Proc. Nat. Mus. 64: 1–4. 1 pl.

Lamb, L. F. 1925. A tabular account of the differences between the earlier instars of Pantala flavescens. Tr. Amer. Ent. Soc. 1: 289–312.

Lucus, W. J. 1922. Color Preservation in Dragonflies. The Entomologist, p. 209.

Lyon, Mary B. 1915. The Ecology of Dragonfly Nymphs of Cascadilla Creek. Ent. News 26: 1–15.

—— 1915. Miscellaneous Notes on Odonata. Ent. News 26: 56–62.

Marshall, Wm. S. 1914. On the Anatomy of the Dragonfly Libellula Quadrimaculata, Linne. Trans. Wisc. Acad. Sci. Arts and Letters 17: 755–790. 4 pl.

McDunnough, J. 1922. Dragonflies of the Lake of the Bays Region and Additional Records of Dragonflies from the Ottawa Region. Can. Ent. 53: 6–8, 14.

—— 1923. Notes on Canadian Dragonflies for the season of 1922. Can. Ent. 54: 255–257.

—— 1924. Distributional Notes on Canadian Dragonflies. Can. Ent. 55: 72–73.

Montgomery, B. E. 1924. Records of Indiana Dragonflies I. Proc. Ind. Acad. Sci. 34: 383.

Munz, P. A. 1919. A Venational Study of the suborder Zygoptera (Odonata), with keys for the identification of Genera. Amer. Ent. Soc. Mem. No. 3, pp. 1–78, 20 pls.

Muttkowski, R. A. 1910. Miscellaneous Notes and Records of Dragonflies. Bull. Wisc. Nat. Hist. Soc. 8: 170–179.

—— 1910. Catalogue of the Odonata of North America. Bull. Pub. Mus. City of Milwaukee 1: 1–207.

—— 1910. The Applicability of Certain Generic Names of Odonata. Bull. Wisc. Nat. Hist. Soc. 8: 158–160.

—— 1910. Gomphus Cornutus Tough in Milwaukee County. Bull. of Wis. N. H. Soc. VIII, p. 110.

—— 1910–11. New Records of Wisconsin Dragonflies. Bull. Wis. Nat. Hist. Soc. 8: 53–59, 9: 28–41. Fig. 1–16.

—— 1911. A new Gomphus. Ent. News. 22: 221–223.

—— 1911. Studies in Tetragoneuria. Bull. Wis. Nat. Hist. Soc. 9: 91–134. 3 pl. Fig. 1–7.

—— 1911. A Synonymical Note. Bull. Wis. Nat. Hist. Soc. 9: 166–169.

—— 1913. New Species of Dragonflies. Bull. Wis. Nat. Hist. Soc. 10: 164–170. 1 pl. 1 fig.

—— and Whedon, A. D. 1915. On Gomphus Cornutus Tough. Bull. Wis. Nat. Hist. Soc. 13: 88–101

—— 1915. Studies in Tetragoneuria II. Bull. Wis. Nat. Hist. Soc. 13: 49–61.

Needham, J. G. 1911. Notes on a few Nymphs of Agrioninae of the Hagen Collection. Ent. News 22: 342–345. 1 pl.

—— 1911. Notes on Nymphs of Gomphinae of the Hagen Collection. Ent. News XXII: 392–396. 1 pl.

—— 1911. Descriptions of Dragonfly Nymphs of the Subfamily Calopterygenae. Ent. News 22: 145–154. 2 pls.

—— 1917. Notes on some recent studies of Dragonfly Wing Tracheation. Ent. News 28: 169–173.

—— 1918. Aquatic Insects. Ward and Whipple's Fresh Water Biology, pp. 867–946.

—— 1923. Observations of the Life of the Ponds at the Head of Laguna Canyon. Pomona Jour. Ent. & Zoo. 16: 123–134.

—— 1925. Some Aquatic Neuropteroid Insects of Lake George. Ent. News 36: 110–116.

—— 1927. Some Economic Insects in the Streams of Northern Utah. Utah Agri. Sta. Bull. 201.

Needham, J. G. and Broughton, Elsie. 1927. The Venation of the Libellulinae. Trans. Am. Ent. Soc. 53: 157–190.

Osburn, R. C. 1916. A Migratory Flight of Dragonflies. J. N. Y. Ent. Soc. 24: 90–92.

Pierson, E. L. 1923. A list of Odonata collected at Concord, Mass. Proc. Thoreau Mus. Nat. Hist. 1: 41.

Rich, Stephen G. 1918. The Gill Chamber of Dragonfly Nymphs. J. of Morph. 31: 317–349.

Riley, Curtis C. F. 1912. Observations on the Ecology of Dragonfly Nymphs: Reactions to light and contact. Ann. Ent. Soc. Amer. 5: 273–292.

Ris, F. 1909–1916. Collections Zoologiques de Selys—Longchamps: Libellulinae. Brussels, pp. 1–1245.

Root, Francis M. 1923. Notes on Zygop. from Maryland—Enallagma pallidum Ent. News 34: 200–204.

—— 1924. Notes on Dragonflies from Lee Co., Ga. Enallagma dubium. Ent. News 35: 317–323.

Schmieder, Rudolf G. 1922. Tracheation of Wings of Early Larval Instars of Anisoptera with special reference to development of Radius. Ent. News 33: 257–262, 299–303. 2 pl.

Seemann, Theresa Marian. 1927. Dragonflies, Mayflies and Stoneflies of S. California. Jour. Ent. & Zoo., Pomona College, 19: 1–68. 4 pls.

Shafer, G. D. 1924. The Growth of Dragonfly Nymphs at Moult and Between Moults. Stanford Univ. Pub. 3: 307–337.

Stout, Alice L. 1918. Variation in Labial Characters in the Nymphs of Gomphus spicatus. Ent. News 29: 68–70. p. 1.

Walker, E. M. 1912. N. A. Dragonflies of Genus Aeschna. Univ. of Toronto Studies, Biol. Series. 1 pl.

—— 1912. Odonata of Prairie Provinces of Canada. Can. Ent. 44: 253–268. 1 pl.

—— 1913. Mutual Adaptation of the Sexes in Argia Moesta Putrida. Can. Ent. 45: 277–279. 1 pl.

—— 1913. New Nymphs of Canadian Odonata. Can. Ent. 45–6: 161–170. 2 pl.

—— 1914. The Known Nymphs of the Canadian Species of Lestes. Can. Ent. 46: 189–200. 2 pl.

—— 1914. New and Little Known Nymphs of Canadian Odonata. Can. Ent. 46: 349–356, 369–377.

—— 1915. The Re-Discovery of Agrion Interrogatum, Selys. Can. Ent. 47: 174–176.

—— 1916. A few Days in Newfoundland. Can. Ent. 48: 257–261.

—— 1916. A Curious Trap for Dragonflies. Can. Ent. 48: 314–315.

———— 1916. The Nymphs of the North American Species of Leucorrhinia. Can. Ent. 48: 414–422.

———— 1916. The Nymphs of Enallagma cyathigerum and E. calverti. Can. Ent. 47: 192–196.

———— 1917. The Known Nymphs of the North American species of Sympetrum. Can. Ent. 49: 409–418. 2 pl.

———— 1917. Seasonal Irregularities in the Occurrence of Dragonflies. Can. Ent. 49: 171–178.

———— 1917. Some Dragonflies from Prince Edward Island. Can. Ent. 49: 117–119.

———— 1918. Notes on Agrion aequabile hudsonicum Hagen. Can. Ent. 50: 406–410.

———— 1918. On the American Representatives of Somatochlora Arctica with Descriptions of two new species. Can. Ent. 50: 365–376. 1 pl.

———— 1921. Nymph and Breeding Place of Aeschna sitchensis. Can. Ent. 53: 221–226.

———— 1923. Notes on the Odonata of Godbout, Que. Can. Ent. 55: 5–12.

———— 1924. Odonata of the Thunder Bay District, Ontario. Can. Ent. 56 170–176.

———— 1925. The N. A. Dragonflies of the Genus Somatochlora. U. of Toronto Studies, Biol. Series, 1–202.

———— 1927. Odonata of the Canadian Cordillera. Brit. Col. Special Pub. Victoria, B. C. pp. 3–15.

———— 1928. The Nymphs of the Stylurus Group of the Genus Gomphus with Notes on the Distribution of this Group in Canada. Can. Ent. 60, pp. 79–88.

Warren, Alfred. 1915. A Study of the Food Habits of Hawaiian Dragonflies. College of Hawaii Pub. Bul. 3: 1–36. 4 pl.

Weber, L. 1918. Odonata of Iowa. Proc. Iowa Acad. Sci. 24: 327–333.

Whedon, A. D. 1914. Preliminary Notes on the Odonata of Southern Minnesota. Rep. of State Ent. Minn. 13 and 14, 78–103. 4 pl. 3 fig.

———— 1919. The Comparative Morphology and Possible Adaptations of the Abdomen in the Odonata. Trans. Am. Ent. Soc. 44: 373–437.

Whitehouse, F. C. 1917. The Odonata of the Red Deer District, Alberta. Can. Ent. 49: 96–103.

———— 1918. Dragonflies of Alberta. Pub. Alta. Nat. Hist. Soc. 16 pp.

Williamson, E. B. 1910. A new species of Celithemis. Reprinted from Ohio Naturalist May '10, 153–160. 3 pl.

———— 1912. The Known Indiana Somatochloras. Ent. News 23: 152–155.

———— 1912. The Dragonfly Argia moesta and a New Species. Ent. News 23: 196–203.

———— 1912. Hetaerina titia and tricolor. Ent. News 23: 98–101.

———— 1913. The Medio-anal Link in Agrioninae. Ent. News 24: 258–261.

———— 1913. Some Colorado Dragonfly Records. Ent. News 24: 372.

——— 1914. September Dragonflies about Mesa Arizona. Ent. News 25: 225–226.

———— 1914. Sympetrum obtrusum and costiferum in Maine. Ent. News 25: 456.

———— 1914. Gomphus pallidus and Two New Related Species. Ent. News 25: 49–58. 2 pl.

—— 1914. Dragonflies collected in Texas and Oklahoma. Ent. News 25: 411–415, 444–455.

—— 1915. Notes on Neotropical Dragonflies. Proc. U. S. Nat. Mus. 48: 601–638. 7 pl.

—— 1916. Directions for Collecting and Preserving Specimens of Dragonflies for Museum Purposes. Univ. Mich. Zoo. Misc. Pub. 1: 5–15.

—— 1917. The Genus Neoneura. Amer. Ent. Soc. 43: 211–246. 11 pl.

—— 1917. An Annotated List of the Odonata of Indiana. Univ. Mich. Mus. Zoo. Miscel. Pub. 2: 5–13. 1 map.

——1919. Variation in Color Pattern of Dragonfly Gomphus Crassus Ent. News 30: 294–296.

—— 1920. Notes on Indiana Dragonflies. Ind. Acad. Sci., pp. 99–104.

—— 1921. Two Days with Indiana Odonata. Ent. News 32: 19–23.

—— 1922. Libellulas collected in Florida by Jesse H. Williamson, with Description of a new species. Ent. News 33: 13–19.

—— 1922. Notes on Celithemis with Descriptions of two new species. Occas. pap. Mus. Zoo. Univ. Mich. 108: 1–22. 2 pl.

—— 1922. Enallagmas Collected in Florida and South Carolina by Jesse H. Williamson with Descriptions of Two New Species. Ent. News 33: 114–118.

—— 1923. Odonatological Results of an Auto Trip Across Indiana, Kentucky and Tennessee. Ent. News 34: 6–9.

—— 1923. Notes on American species of Triacanthagyna and Gynacantha. Univ. of Mich. Misc. Pub. No. 9.

—— 1923. Notes on genus Erythemis—with a description of a new species. Univ. of Mich. Misc. Pub. No. 11.

—— 1923. A New Species of Williamsonia. Can. Ent. 55: 96–98.

Wilson, Chas. B. 1909. Dragonflies of the Mississippi Valley collected during the Pearl Mussel Investigation on the Mississippi R., July and Aug., 1907. Proc. U. S. Nat. Mus. 36: 653–671.

—— 1912. Dragonflies of the Cumberland Valley in Kentucky and Tennessee. Proc. U. S. Nat. Mus. 43: 189–200.

—— 1920. Dragonflies and Damselflies in relation to Pond-fish culture, with a list of those found near Fairport, Iowa. Bull. Bureau Fisheries 36: 182–264. 1 pl.

Woodruff, Lewis B. 1914a. Some Dragonflies of a Connecticut Brook. Jour. N. Y. Ent. Soc. 22: 155–159.

—— 1914. The Nymph of Ophiogomphus Johannus Needham. Jour. of N. Y. Ent. Soc. 22: 61–63.

CHECKING LIST

Column 1

1. Tan
1. hag
2. Tac
2. tho
3. Pro
3. obs
4. Gmd
4. sti
5. Aph
5. pro
6. Cyc
6. pro
7. Hag
7. bre
8. Oph
8. col
9. ano
10. pha
11. occ
12. asp
13. crl
14. rup
15. ari
16. sev
17. mon
18. mor
19. how
20. car
21. bis
22. mai
9. Erp
23. dia
24. lam
25. des
26. com
10. Gom
27. bre
28. par
29. all
30. abb
31. vir
32. hyb
33. fra
34. ext
35. cra
36. cnf
37. don
38. cns
39. ade

Column 2

40. scu
41. amn
42. vas
43. ven
44. dil
45. lin
46. int
47. oli
48. not
49. pla
50. spn
51. liv
52. mil
53. cav
54. bri
55. gra
56. wil
57. min
58. exi
59. spi
60. aus
61. des
62. bor
63. abd
64. qua
65. len
66. sbm
67. sba
68. pal
69. cor
70. whe
71. fur
72. vil
11. Dro
73. arm
74. spo
75. spi
12. Lan
76. alb
77. par
13. Oct
78. spe
14. Gsh
79. fur
15. Bas
80. jan
16. Boy
81. vin
82. gra

Column 3

17. Ana
83. lon
84. ama
85. jun
86. wal
87. arm
18. Opl
19. Crp
88. ing
89. vir
20. Nas
90. pen
21. Epi
91. her
22. Aes
92. cae
93. sit
29. Epi
94. cal
95. mul
96. mut
97. umb
98. wal
99. ari
100. pal
101. con
102. int
103. cle
104. ere
105. jun
106. sub
107. tub
108. can
109. ver
23. Gyn
110. tri
111. ner
112. bif
24. Crg
113. dia
114. say
115. err
116. dor
117. obl
118. fas
119. dis
120. mac
25. Mac
121. ill
122. all

Column 4

123. tae
124. wab
125. pac
126. ann
127. mag
128. geo
129. aus
26. Did
130. tra
131. flo
27. Pla
132. xan
28. Neu
133. obs
134. yam
135. vir
136. pri
137. reg
30. Tet
138. cyn
139. ste
140. spg
141. can
142. spn
31. Hel
143. uhl
144. sel
32. Som
145. geo
146. lin
147. ens
148. ten
149. pro
150. fil
151. alb
152. hud
153. cin
154. min
155. wal
156. for
157. elo
158. sem
159. wil
160. inc
161. sal
162. fra
163. whi
164. ken

Column 5

165. sep
33. Crd
166. shu
34. Dor
167. lib
168. lep
35. Wil
169. lin
170. fle
36. Nan
171. bel
37. Per
172. dom
38. Cel
173. epo
174. eli
175. mon
176. fas.
177. mar
178. ama
179. orn
180. ber
39. Pse
181. sup
40. Ery
182. fun
183. umb
184. min
185. ber
41. Ort
186. fer
42. Lad
187. dep
188. exu
189. jul
43. Lib
190. luc
191. sat
192. cro
193. aur
194. jes
195. com
196. cya
197. fla
198. sem
199. pul
200. for
201. qua
202. nod.

Column 6

203. com
204. inc
205. vib
206. axi
44. Pla
207. lyd
208. sub
45. Can
209. gra
46. Sym
210. cor
211. ill
212. mad
213. fur
214. amb
215. pal
216. obt
217. rub
218. ass
219. sem
220. vic
221. cos
222. dan
223. atr
47. Leu
224. hud
225. int
226. gla
227. fri
228. pro
229. bor
48. Pac
230. lon
49. Mes
231. sim
232. ple
50. Lep
233. ves
51. Dyt
234. vel
235. fug
52. Bre
236. men
53. Pal
237. lin
54. Pan
238. hym
239. fla
55. Mac

Column 7

240. bal
56. Tra
241. vir
242. lac
243. onu
244. car
245. abd
57. Agr
246. ang
247. ama
248. aeq
249. dim
250. api
251. mac
58. Het
252. sem
253. vul
254. ame
255. tri
256. tit
59. Arc
257. gra
258. cal
60. Les
259. ine
260. eur
261. con
262. ung
263. sig
264. vid
265. frc
266. dis
267. rec
268. unc
269. div
270. vig
271. ala
272. frf
61. Neo
273. aar
62. Hyp
274. lug
63. Arg
275. agr
276. alb
277. api
278. bip
279. emm
280. fum

Column 8

281. hin
282. imm
283. int
284. moe
285. rit
286. sed
287. sol
288. tib
289. ton
290. tra
291. vio
292. viv
64. Arl
293. min
65. Hcs
294. het
66. Amp
295. sau
67. Tlb
296. sal
68. Neh
297. pal
298. gra
299. int
300. ire
69. Chr
301. con
70. Tlg
302. dae
71. Coe
303. int
304. ang
305. res
72. Ena
306. div
307. hag
308. bor
309. cla
310. cya
311. pis
312. dur
313. min
314. gem
315. rec
316. lat
317. cul
318. lau
319. pol
320. sul

Column 9

321. sig
322. ves
323. dub
324. pic
325. con
326. ebr
327. exs
328. wee
329. pal
330. ant
331. car
332. dou
333. civ
334. clc
335. pra
336. ann
337. eis
338. bas
339. asp
340. sem
341. tra
342. coe
343. crd
73. Zon
344. exc
74. Isc
345. den
346. gem
347. pro
348. ram
349. pos
350. kel
351. dem
352. bar
353. uta
354. cre
355. per
356. err
357. ver
358. cer
359. dam
75. Ano
360. has

INDEX

Italics indicate illustrations

369

colubrinus, *70*
comanche, *220, 223*
common club-tail, 81
composita, 227
compositus, 80
concisum, *331*, 332
conditum, *308*, 309
confraternus, 92, *93*
confusa, 224
congener, 275, *276*
consanguis, 94
consobrinus, 90
constricta, *144*, 145
copulation, 18, 27, 255
copulatory organs, 18
Cordulegaster, 121, 152
  diadema, 155
  diastatops, *32*, 158
  darsalis, 45, 156
  erroneus, 155
  fasciatus, 158
  maculatus, 159
  obliquus, 158
  sayi, *15*, 155
CORDULEGASTERINAE, 152
Cordulia, 197
  shurtleffi, 43, 197, 199
CORDULINAE, 171
cornutus, *115*
corruptum, 232, *233*
Coryphaeschna, 131
  ingens, 23, 131
  virens, 132
costa, *15*
costalis, 222
costiferum, 239, *240*
coxa, 14
crassus, *91*, 92
credula, 353
crepuscular habits, 151
crest, 12, 20, 69
croceipennis, 222
cross veins, 17
cubitus, *15, 16*
culicinorum, 336, *337*
cultellatum, 327
cyanea, *220*, 223
cyathigerum, 324, *325*
Cyclophylla, 65
  protracta, *65*
cynosura, *178*, 180

daeckii, *310*
damula, 356, 357
danae, 239, *240*
Darners, 123
Davis, W. T., 55, 63, 66, 159, 178, 238, 255, 262, 358
defixa, 353
demorsa, *351*, 352
denticollis, 348, *349*
dentiferum, 329

deplanata, 217
depth of insertion, 43
descriptus, *43, 109*
designatus, *80*
devil's darning needles, 4
diadema, 155
diadophis, 79, *80*
diastatops, *32*, 158
Didymops, 169
  floridensis, 170
  transversa, 170
dilatatus, *96*, 97
dimidiatum, 261
Diplax, 231
discolor, 216, 304, 355
disjunctus, *278*
divagans, 322, *323*
Dog-tails, 178
domitia, 205
donneri, *93*, 94
Dorocordulia, 198
  lepida, *199*
  libera, 198, *199*
dorsalis, 45, 156
doubledayi, *335*
dragon, black, 66
drift, 24
Dromogomphus, *58*, 117
  armatus, 117
  spinosus, *118*
  spoliatus, 117, *118*
  dubium, 330, 331
  durum, *325*
  dusk flying, 151
Dythemis, *202*, 248
  fugax, 249
  velox, 249

ebrium, 332, *333*
egg parasites, 28
eggs, 8, 25, *43*
eiseni, *337*, 338
elegans, 260
elisa, *209*, 210
elongata, *192*, 193
emma, *294*
Enallagma, 311
  anna, *337*, 338
  antennatum, 334, *335*
  aspersum, *339*
  basidens, *339*
  boreale, *323*
  cardenium, *341*
  carunculatum, *335*
  civile, *335*, 336
  clausum, *323*, 324
  coecum, *341*
  concisum, *331*, 332
  culicinorum, 336, *337*
  cultellatum, 327
  cyatherigerum, 324, *325*
  divagans, 322, *323*

THIS BOOK

A HANDBOOK
OF THE DRAGONFLIES OF
NORTH AMERICA

was set, printed and bound by The Collegiate Press of Menasha, Wisconsin. The cover design is by The Decorative Designers of Chatham, New Jersey. The type face is 8A Modern. The type is set 10 on 12 point, Monotype. The type page is 26 x 43 picas. The end sheets and jackets are 65 pound Kiltie Green Bannockburn. The text paper is 28 x 42—74 pound Ambassador offset. The binding is Holliston extra colors book cloth, Vellum Finish 218.

With **THOMAS BOOKS** *careful attention is given to all details of manufacturing and design. It is the publisher's desire to present books that are satisfactory as to their physical qualities and artistic possibilities and appropriate for their particular use.* **THOMAS BOOKS** *will be true to those laws of quality that assure a good name and good will.*

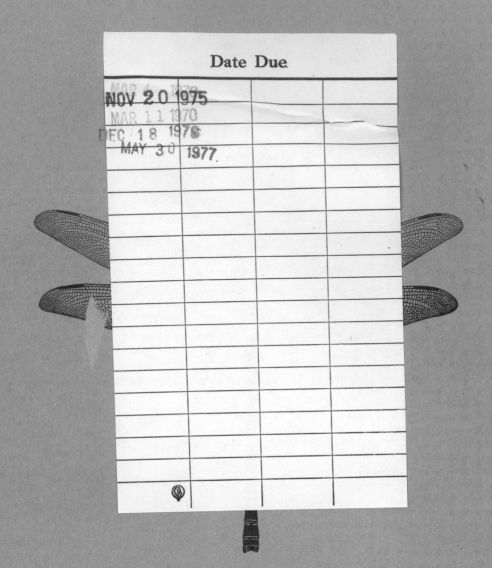

Date Due

NOV 20 1975			
MAR 11 1970			
DEC 18 1976			
MAY 30 1977			